W9-BDS-572

THEORY OF GENERALIZED SPECTRAL OPERATORS

Mathematics and Its Applications

A Series of Monographs and Texts Edited by
Jacob T. Schwartz, Courant Institute of Mathematical Sciences, New York University

Volume 1

Jacob T. Schwartz, LECTURES ON THE MATHEMATICAL METHOD IN ANALYTICAL ECONOMICS

Volume 2

O. A. Ladyzhenskaya, MATHEMATICAL THEORY OF VISCOUS INCOMPRESSIBLE FLOW

Volume 3

R. L. Stratonovich, TOPICS IN THE THEORY OF RANDOM NOISE *(in 2 volumes)*

Volume 4

S. Chowla, THE RIEMANN HYPOTHESIS AND HILBERT'S TENTH PROBLEM

Volume 5

Jacob T. Schwartz, THEORY OF MONEY

Volume 6

François Trèves, LINEAR PARTIAL DIFFERENTIAL EQUATIONS WITH CONSTANT COEFFICIENTS

Volume 7

G. E. Shilov, GENERALIZED FUNCTIONS AND PARTIAL DIFFERENTIAL EQUATIONS

Volume 8

I. I. Pyatetskii-Shapiro, AUTOMORPHIC FUNCTIONS AND THE GEOMETRY OF CLASSICAL DOMAINS

Volume 9

Ion Colojoară and Ciprian Foiaş, THEORY OF GENERALIZED SPECTRAL OPERATORS

Additional volumes in preparation

Theory of Generalized Spectral Operators

ION COLOJOARĂ and CIPRIAN FOIAŞ

Institute of Mathematics of the Academy of R.S.R.,
Bucharest, Rumania

GORDON AND BREACH
Science Publishers
New York • London • Paris

Copyright © 1968 Gordon and Breach, Science Publishers, Inc.
150 Fifth Avenue, New York, N. Y. 10011

Library of Congress Catalog Card Number: 68-24488

Editorial Office for Great Britain:

Gordon and Breach, Science Publishers, Ltd
8 Bloomsbury Way
London W.C.I

Editorial Office for France:

Gordon & Breach
7-9 rue Emile Dubois
Paris 14e

Distributed in France by:

Dunod Editeur
92 rue Bonaparte
Paris 6e

Distributed in Canada by:

The Ryerson Press
299 Queen Street West
Toronto 2B, Ontario

All rights reserved. No part of this book may be reproduced or utilized in any form or by any means, electronic or mechanical, including photocopying, recording, or by any information storage and retrieval system, without permission in writing from the publishers.

Printed in Germany

-MATH.
LIBRARY
QA
322
C71t
1168087

Contents

Introduction

The great development which the spectral theory, initiated by N. Dunford, has had in our time is well known. However, in the last six years, elements of a theory based not on spectral measures but on spectral spaces or spectral functional calculus began to be developed, parallel to the theory of scalar and spectral operators of Dunford.

The aim of this book is to give a systematic outline of these endeavors. We are mostly interested in presenting the new features which do not occur in connection with spectral measures (for instance in Chaps. II and IV the role played by the commutator, its quasinilpotent and nilpotent properties related to the spectral spaces, etc.) or the analogous form in these larger classes of known and useful properties of the scalar and spectral operators (Chaps. 3–4) as well as different classes of more or less concrete operators to which this enlarged theory applies, giving also a unitary explanation of their behaviour (Chaps. 5–6). We have restricted ourselves only to bounded operators in Banach space, since the generalization to unbounded operators or to locally convex spaces is straightforward or raises technical difficulties which would disturb the attention from the real new problems of this theory still in elaboration.

We have tried to make the book very comprehensible, the proofs being (with few exceptions in Chaps. 5 and 6) fastidiously detailed. The theorems used and not proved are taken only from well-known and widely quoted sources, like Dunford-Schwartz's treatise or Paley-Wiener's monograph, or from the well known article[27] by Dunford. However, the reader is supposed to have some acquaintance with the theory of operators.

The book is divided into six chapters, each of them supplemented by short comments, some of historical nature. Since the monograph is supposed to contain the first unified and general exposition of the subject, as well as a certain number of new results, we take the liberty to give a longer description of its contents.

In Chapter 1 three basic concepts are discussed. Namely in § 1 are given the elementary properties of the operators with the single-valued extension property [i.e., operators $T \in \mathbf{B}(\mathscr{X})$ such that if $(\lambda I - T)\, x(\lambda) \equiv 0$ for a certain $\mathscr{X}$-valued analytic function $x(\lambda)$, then $x(\lambda) \equiv 0$]. These operators have already been considered by N. Dunford[26] in 1952; however, our study of their behaviour with respect to the Dunford functional calculus[25,30] (i.e. Theorems 1.5–1.6) seems to be new. § 2 introduces the quasinilpotent equivalence $T_1 \overset{q}{\sim} T_2$ of two operators $T_1, T_2 \in \mathbf{B}(\mathscr{X})$ (= the set of all linear bounded operators on a Banach space $\mathscr{X}$), that is

$$\lim_{n\to\infty} \left\| \sum_{\nu=0}^{n} \binom{n}{\nu} (-1)^{\nu} T_1^{n-\nu} T_2^{\nu} \right\|^{1/n} = 0 = \lim_{n\to\infty} \left\| \sum_{\nu=0}^{n} \binom{n}{\nu} (-1)^{\nu} T_2^{n-\nu} T_1^{\nu} \right\|^{1/n}.$$

This equivalence was introduced by the authors[19] as the extension in the noncommutative case of the fact that for two commuting operators T_1 and T_2, $T_1 - T_2$ is quasinilpotent. It is shown that the spectrum, the single-valued extension property as well as the spectrum of an element $x \in \mathscr{X}$ with respect to an operator with the single-valued extension property, are invariant with regard to the quasinilpotent equivalence. Finally in § 3 are studied the elementary properties of the spectral maximal spaces of an operator T, that is of the maximal invariant subspaces $\mathscr{Y}$ of T, such that the spectrum of the restriction of T to $\mathscr{Y}$ be contained in a certain closed set.

Chapter 2 is devoted to the study of a large class of operators, called decomposable operators (since they admit spectral decompositions), a class in which many features of Dunford's theory are still valid.

In § 1 it is first shown that decomposable operators have the single-valued extension property; using this fact the structure of the spectral maximal spaces of such operators is determined [namely the spectral maximal space corresponding to the closed set F is $\mathscr{X}_T(F) = \{x \in \mathscr{X} \mid \sigma_T(x) \subset F\}$], as well as the behaviour of decomposability with respect to Dunford's functional calculus.

§ 2 shows the behaviour of decomposable operators with respect to quasinilpotent equivalence. Thus if T_1 is decomposable and $T_2 \overset{q}{\sim} T_1$, then T_2 is also decomposable and the maximal spectral spaces $\mathscr{X}_{T_1}(F)$, $\mathscr{X}_{T_2}(F)$ of T_1 and T_2, corresponding to any closed set F, coincide. Moreover, if T_1 and T_2 are decomposable and this last coincidence property is true, then $T_1 \overset{q}{\sim} T_2$. These results, due to the authors,[19] constitute a generalization (with a slight improvement since the noncommutative case is also included) of the canonical decomposition of Dunford's spectral operators.

In § 3 a new property is established concerning commutators of decomposable operators. Let S and T be two decomposable operators, then for any operator A we have $A\mathscr{X}_S(F) \subset \mathscr{X}_T(F)$ for all closed sets F if and only if

$$\|C(T, S)^n A\|^{1/n} \to 0, \quad \text{where} \quad C(T, S): X \to TX - XS.$$

In particular, for an operator A, the maximal spectral spaces of a decomposable operator T are invariant if and only if

$$\|C(T, T)^n A\|^{1/n} \to 0, \quad \text{where} \quad C(T, T): X \to TX - XT.$$

§ 4 shows that in the case of a certain weak similarity, which does not conserve neither the spectral properties of an operator nor its decomposability, certain invariant subspaces are nevertheless conserved.

Chapter 3 begins with the introduction of the following basic notions: admissible algebra $\mathfrak{A}$ of functions, $\mathfrak{A}$-spectral function, and $\mathfrak{A}$-scalar operator. These definitions are, at least for bounded operators in a Banach space, the most general up to date, essentially because of the avoidance of any topological structure on $\mathfrak{A}$. It is worth mentioning that an operator T is $\mathfrak{A}$-scalar if there exists an $\mathfrak{A}$-scalar function $\mathbf{U}$ [i.e. an algebraic homomorphism $\mathbf{U}: f \to \mathbf{U}_f$ of $\mathfrak{A}$ into the Banach algebra $\mathbf{B}(\mathscr{X})$ verifying some algebraic and analytical properties] such that $\mathbf{U}_\lambda = T$ (here λ is the identical function $\lambda \to \lambda$ on C).

In § 2 "uniqueness" property is proved, namely that if $\mathfrak{A}$ is an inverse-closed (i.e. if $f \in \mathfrak{A}, f \neq 0$, then $1/f \in \mathfrak{A}$) algebra of continuous functions, then the $\mathfrak{A}$-spectral functions corresponding to a same $\mathfrak{A}$-scalar operator T are unique in the following sense: If $\mathbf{U}$ and $\mathbf{V}$ are $\mathfrak{A}$-spectral functions and $\mathbf{U}_\lambda = T = \mathbf{V}_\lambda$, then $\mathbf{U}_f \overset{q}{\sim} \mathbf{V}_f$ for all $f \in \mathfrak{A}$.

In § 3 $\mathfrak{A}$-decomposable and $\mathfrak{A}$-spectral operators are introduced, characterized, and studied (elementary properties).

§ 4 is inspired by the paper of Ringrose.[98] It contains a study of the totally ordered families (nests) of certain invariant subspaces for an $\mathfrak{A}$-decomposable operator. Since compact operators are also $\mathfrak{A}$-scalar operators for a suitable choice of the admissible algebra $\mathfrak{A}$, this study can be considered as an extension of that of Ringrose, which was especially concerned with compact operators.

Chapter 4 is devoted to the more particular but interesting case when $\mathfrak{A} = C^\infty(R^2) = C^\infty$ and the $\mathfrak{A}$-spectral functions are supposed to be distributions. Such $\mathfrak{A}$-scalar or $\mathfrak{A}$-spectral operators, called generalized scalar or generalized spectral operators, were introduced by the authors separately (for the scalar case see Ref. 39 and for the spectral case see Ref. 15 and also Ref. 81). These classes of operators, although they are the first natural extension of the class of scalar and spectral operators of Dunford, still present many unsolved problems, some of them of very great interest because of their novelty, as the question of regularity (see Definition IV.1.7). The research in this direction is to be found in §§ 1, 2, and 4. Thus the best result is the following: If $\mathbf{U}$ and $\mathbf{V}$ are two spectral distributions of the same generalized scalar operator then $(\mathbf{U}_f - \mathbf{V}_f)^{[n]} = 0$ for all $f \in C^\infty$. However, if T is an operator with spectral multiplicity 1, we have unicity! Finally if T, S are two generalized scalar operators such that $T \overset{q}{\sim} S$, then for a certain n we had before $(T - S)^{[n]} = 0 = (S - T)^{[n]}$. (For the definition of $(T - S)^{[n]}$ see Chap. 1. § 2.)

The first result was already obtained in Ref. 39, while the other two are new.

In § 3 it is shown that the sum and product of two commuting regular (respectively, completely regular), generalized scalar (respectively, spectral) operators are generalized scalar (respectively, spectral) operators: from which it results that the sum and product of two commuting scalar or spectral operators are generalized scalar or spectral operators.

In §§ 5, 6, 7 are given extensions (due to the first author[15,17,18]) to generalized scalar and spectral operators of certain results of Foguel,[36] Stampfli,[117] and Kurepa[67] concerning scalar and spectral operators. Thus (in § 6) it is shown that if $T = S + Q$ is the canonical decomposition of a generalized spectral operator in its generalized scalar part and its quasinilpotent part Q, then if T belongs to a closed left ideal of operators, there exists an integer $p \geqslant 0$ such that S^{p+1} and Q^{p+1} belong also to this ideal, or (in § 7) that if T^n or e^T are generalized scalar or spectral then, if $\sigma(T)$ does not separate 0 and ∞, T is itself a generalized scalar or spectral operator.

Chapter 5 deals especially with operators having their spectrum on the unit circle or the real line.

§ 1 gives precise delineations of the generalized spectral operators, whose spectrum lies on the unit circle. It is shown (Proposition 1.2) that these operators coincide with Fr. Wolf's operators[130] so that the following characterisations coincide with those of Wolf. As applications we give a theorem on the existence of invariant subspaces generalizing a theorem by Sz.-Nagy and the second author[119], as well as a multiplication theorem for the spectrum of automorphisms of Banach algebras.

§ 2 is devoted to the study of an important algebra of functions, namely the algebra $\mathfrak{A}[\varrho]$ of functions $f(e^{it}) = \sum_{n=-\infty}^{\infty} a_n e^{int}$ for which $\|f\| = \sum_{n=-\infty}^{\infty} |a_n| \varrho_n < \infty$, $\varrho = \{\varrho_n\}$ being a fixed sequence of numbers $\geqslant 1$ verifying $\varrho_{n+m} \leqslant \varrho_n \varrho_m$ $(n, m \in Z)$ and $\sqrt[n]{\varrho_n} \to 1$ as $|n| \to \infty$. The main result (Theorem 2.7) is that $\mathfrak{A}[\varrho]$ is an admissible algebra if and only if it is a regular Banach algebra. A criterion for this regularity, due to A. Beurling, is proved in Theorem 2.12. This proof, inspired by the paper[128] of J. Wermer, is self-contained using only a classical theorem by Paley-Wiener.[94] In virtue of these results, operators T such that $\sigma(T)$ is contained in the unit circle C_1 are decomposable (precisely $\mathfrak{A}$-scalar) if $\{\|T^n\|\}_{n\in Z}$ satisfies the Beurling condition, i.e.

$$\sum_{n\in Z} \frac{\log \|T^n\|}{1+n^2} < \infty.$$

In § 3 it is shown that if $\sigma(T) \subset C_1$ and

$$\|(\lambda I - T)^{-1}\| \leqslant M \exp(k\big||\lambda| - 1\big|^{-\beta}), \qquad (|\lambda| \neq 1, |\lambda| \to 1)$$

for a certain $\beta > 0$, then T verifies the above conditions. Applying, in § 4, this remark to operators T whose spectrum is on the real line, we obtain that if

$$\|(\lambda I - T)^{-1}\| \leqslant M \exp(k\, |\mathrm{Im}\, \lambda|^{-\beta}), \qquad (\mathrm{Im}\, \lambda \neq 0, \mathrm{Im}\, \lambda \to 0),$$

then T is decomposable (even an $\mathfrak{A}$-scalar operator for a suitable admissible algebra $\mathfrak{A}$).

§ 4 ends (Theorem 4.5) with precise delineations of the generalized scalar operators with real spectra. These operators coincide with operators investigated by Tillmann[121,122] and Kantorovitz[55] whose characterization can, of course, be found here.

In § 5 we consider operators T in Hilbert space, whose spectra are contained on the unit circle or on the real line, such that $I - T^*T$ in the first case and $T^* - T$ in the second belong to a Schatten ideal of compact operators. We show, following the method devised by J. Schwartz,[112] that the resolvents of such operators satisfy the growth conditions stated before. In this way it is obtained that such operators are $\mathfrak{A}$-scalar operators for suitable choices of the admissible algebras $\mathfrak{A}$. Finally, in § 6 we study the triangular model, given by Sahnovič,[104] of operators possessing adequate invariant subspaces. There are other more precise models, but we have chosen Sahnovič's model on account of its simplicity. Let us mention that here one can also find, together with its proof, a recent result on invariant subspaces (see Theorem 6.13 of this chapter) by J. Feldman.

Chapter 6, the last of our monograph, deals with more concrete examples of decomposable operators. In § 1 we study the operators of multiplication by a fixed regular function in spaces of differentiable functions. These operators are certainly the most concrete examples of generalized scalar operators. In spite of this we haven't succeeded in showing that they are regular, although in various particular cases they are (see Corollary 1.16). Let us remark that, among other things, our study shows that two multiplication operators T and S are quasinilpotent equivalent if and only if $T = S$. (Theorem 1.7.)

§§ 2–3 deal with convolution operators. In § 2 it is shown in particular that every convolution operator $g \to g * f$ in $L^1(G)$ for a fixed $f \in L^1(G)$ (where G is a locally compact Abelian group) is a decomposable operator, and that there exist, for any admissible algebra $\mathfrak{A}$, convolution operators which are not $\mathfrak{A}$-scalar regular operators. In § 3 some results of Krabbe concerning convolution operators in $L^p(-\infty, \infty)$, are introduced in a self-contained way which is naturally inserted in the content of this book. In § 4 our only aim is to make clear that these operators seem to occur also in the study of a new class of operators considered recently by N. Dunford.[29]

We finish with a list of some open questions related to the topics presented in this book.

The quoting of the propositions, theorems, remarks, etc. is done as usual, namely we quote the chapter, the paragraph, and the section, omitting the chapter if it concerns the same one, etc. Not all the titles in the "Bibliography" are used in the text. Those which are used are indicated in the "Notes and Remarks" at the end of every chapter. Many of results given in this monograph are published here for the first time; some have been known to us for some time, others have been obtained in the process of writing this book.

One of the shortcomings of this monograph, of which the authors are fully aware, is the absence of applications to the resolvants of ordinary differential operators with a singular boundary problem. In this respect we recommend the papers of Ljance.

This monograph was written at the suggestion and with the encouragement of Prof. J. Schwartz; we take this opportunity to express our gratitude to him. We also want to thank our colleagues C. Apostol and F. Vasilescu who read the manuscript and made some useful remarks. Finally we should like to particularly thank Mrs. A. Wick who in fact rewrote our manuscript in real English.

Bucharest, July 1966 The Authors

Appendix to the Introduction

Before starting with our exposition we wish to recall some definitions and features of Dunford's theory (see Refs. 27 and 28).

Let $\mathscr{X}$ be a Banach space, $\mathbf{B}(\mathscr{X})$ the Banach algebra of the linear bounded operators of $\mathscr{X}$, $\mathscr{P}_{\mathscr{X}}$ the set of the projectors of $\mathscr{X}$, and $\mathscr{B}$ the family of the Borelian sets of the complex plane C. A mapping $\mathbf{E}\colon \mathscr{B} \to \mathscr{P}_{\mathscr{X}}$ is called a *spectral measure* if

$$\mathbf{E}(B_1 \cap B_2) = \mathbf{E}(B_1)\,\mathbf{E}(B_2), \quad (B_1, B_2 \in \mathscr{B}) \tag{1}$$

$$\mathbf{E}\left(\bigcup_{n=1}^{\infty} B_n\right) x = \sum_{n=1}^{\infty} \mathbf{E}(B_n)\, x, \quad (B_n \in \mathscr{B}, B_n \cap B_m = \varnothing \text{ if } n \neq m,\ x \in \mathscr{X}) \tag{2}$$

$$\mathbf{E}(C) = I. \tag{3}$$

An operator $T \in B(\mathscr{X})$ is called *spectral* if there exists a spectral measure $\mathbf{E}$ such that

$$T\mathbf{E}(B) = \mathbf{E}(B)\, T, \quad (B \in \mathscr{B}), \tag{i}$$

$$\sigma(T\,|\mathbf{E}(B)\,\mathscr{X}) \subset \bar{B}, \quad (B \in \mathscr{B}). \tag{ii}$$

The spectral measure $\mathbf{E}$ verifying (i) and (ii) is uniquely determined by T. It is called the spectral measure of T. A spectral operator S is said to be of scalar type (or simply scalar) if it has the form

$$S = \int_C \lambda \, d\mathbf{E}_\lambda,$$

where $\mathbf{E}$ is its spectral measure.

An operator $Q \in \mathbf{B}(\mathscr{X})$ is called quasinilpotent if $\lim_{n\to\infty} \|Q^n\|^{1/n} = 0$, or equivalently, if $\sigma(Q) = \{0\}$. Dunford has shown [27,28] that an operator T is spectral if and only if it has the form $T = S + Q$, where S is a scalar operator and Q a quasinilpotent operator, which commutes with S. Furthermore, this decomposition, called canonical, is unique. S is said to be the scalar part of T and Q its radical part.

Finally, let us recall also that if $F \subset C$ is closed and if $\mathscr{X}_T(F)$ is defined as in Definition I.1.1., then $\mathbf{E}(F)\mathscr{X} = \mathscr{X}_T(F)$, $\mathbf{E}$ being the spectral measure of T.

Chapter 1

Preliminaries

1. Operators with the Single-valued Extension Property

Let $\mathscr{X}$ be a complex Banach space, $\mathbf{B}(\mathscr{X})$ the algebra of the linear bounded operators on $\mathscr{X}$, and C the field of complex numbers.

1.1. DEFINITION. An operator $T \in \mathbf{B}(\mathscr{X})$ is said to have the *single-valued extension property* if for any analytic function $f: D_f \to \mathscr{X}$, $D_f \subset C$ open, with $(\lambda I - T) f(\lambda) \equiv 0$, it results $f(\lambda) \equiv 0$.

For an operator $T \in \mathbf{B}(\mathscr{H})$ having the single-valued extension property and for $x \in \mathscr{X}$ we can consider the set $\varrho_T(x)$ of elements $\lambda_0 \in C$ such that there exists an analytic function $\lambda \to x(\lambda)$ defined in a neighborhood of λ_0, with values in $\mathscr{X}$, which verifies $(\lambda I - T)\, x(\lambda) \equiv x$.

According to Definition 1.1, $x(\lambda)$ is unique. Evidently $\varrho_T(x)$ is open and $\varrho(T) \subset \varrho_T(x)$. Take $\sigma_T(x) = \complement \varrho_T(x)$ and

$$\mathscr{X}_T(F) = \{x \in \mathscr{X} \mid \sigma_T(x) \subset F\},$$

where $F \subset C$. Obviously $\mathscr{X}_T(F) = \mathscr{X}_T(F \cap \sigma(T))$.

1.2. PROPOSITION. *Let $T \in \mathbf{B}(\mathscr{X})$ be an operator having the single-valued extension property. Then*

(i) $F_1 \subset F_2$ *implies* $\mathscr{X}_T(F_1) \subset \mathscr{X}_T(F_2)$;

(ii) $\mathscr{X}_T(F)$ *is a linear subspace (not necessarily closed) of* $\mathscr{X}$;

(iii) $\sigma_T(x) = \varnothing$ *if and only if* $x = 0$;

(iv) $\sigma_T(Ax) \subset \sigma_T(x)$ *for every* $A \in \mathbf{B}(\mathscr{X})$ *with* $AT = TA$;

(v) $\sigma_T(x(\lambda)) = \sigma_T(x)$ *for every* $x \in \mathscr{X}$ *and* $\lambda \in \varrho_T(x)$.

PROOF:

(i) Trivial.

(ii) Consider $x, y \in \mathscr{X}$ and $\alpha, \beta \in C$. Let $\lambda \to x(\lambda)$ [respectively, $\lambda \to y(\lambda)$] be the analytic function defined on $\varrho_T(x)$ [respectively, $\varrho_T(y)$] which verifies $(\lambda I - T)\,x(\lambda) \equiv x$ [respectively, $(\lambda I - T)\,y(\lambda) \equiv y$]. Then $z(\lambda) = \alpha x(\lambda) + \beta y(\lambda)$ verifies $(\lambda I - T)\,z(\lambda) \equiv \alpha x + \beta y$ on $\varrho_T(x) \cap \varrho_T(y)$, hence $\varrho_T(x) \cap \varrho_T(y) \subset \varrho_T(\alpha x + \beta y)$, i.e. $\sigma_T(\alpha x + \beta y) \subset \sigma_T(x) \cup \sigma_T(y)$.

Now, if $x, y \in \mathscr{X}_T(F)$, then $\sigma_T(x), \sigma_T(y) \subset F$, therefore $\sigma_T(\alpha x + \beta y) \subset F$, i.e.

$$\alpha x + \beta y \in \mathscr{X}_T(F).$$

(iii) If $\sigma_T(x) = \emptyset$, then $x(\lambda)$ is an entire function. Since it satisfies $(\lambda I - T)\,x(\lambda) \equiv x$ for $|\lambda| > \|T\|$ we have

$$x(\lambda) \equiv R(\lambda, T)\,x \to 0, \qquad (|\lambda| \to \infty), \tag{1}$$

therefore by Liouville's theorem (Ref. 47 or 30),

$$x(\lambda) \equiv 0. \tag{2}$$

From (1) and (2) it follows that

$$x = \frac{1}{2\pi i} \int_{|\lambda| = \|T\| + 1} x(\lambda)\,d\lambda = 0.$$

Conversely, it is evident that $x = 0$ implies $\sigma_T(x) = \emptyset$.

(iv) T and A being commuting operators, we have for every $\lambda \in \varrho_T(x)$

$$(\lambda I - T)\,(Ax(\lambda)) = A\,(\lambda I - T)\,x(\lambda) \equiv Ax,$$

therefore

$$\varrho_T(x) \subset \varrho_T(Ax), \text{ i.e. } \sigma_T(Ax) \subset \sigma_T(x).$$

(v) Consider $\lambda \in \varrho_T(x)$ and $\mu \to (x(\lambda))\,(\mu)$, the analytic function for which we have $(\mu I - T)\,(x(\lambda))\,(\mu) \equiv x(\lambda)$ on $\varrho_T(x(\lambda))$, consequently

$$\begin{aligned}(\mu I - T)\,&(\lambda I - T)\,(x(\lambda))\,(\mu)\\ &= (\lambda I - T)\,(\mu I - T)\,(x(\lambda))\,(\mu) = (\lambda I - T)\,x(\lambda) = x,\end{aligned}$$

for every $\mu \in \varrho_T(x(\lambda))$, therefore $\sigma_T(x) \subset \sigma_T(x(\lambda))$.

In order to establish the opposite inclusion, we remark that for a fixed $\lambda \in \varrho_T(x)$ the function $g_\lambda : \varrho_T(x) \to \mathscr{X}$ defined by

$$g_\lambda(\mu) = \begin{cases} -\dfrac{x(\mu) - x(\lambda)}{\mu - \lambda}, & \mu \neq \lambda, \\ -x'(\lambda), & \mu = \lambda, \end{cases}$$

is analytic in $\varrho_T(x)$ and

$$(\mu I - T)\, g_\lambda(\mu) = -(\mu I - T)\left(\frac{x(\mu) - x(\lambda)}{\mu - \lambda}\right)$$

$$= -\frac{1}{\mu - \lambda}\,[(\mu I - T)\,x(\mu) - (\lambda I - T)\,x(\lambda)$$

$$- (\mu - \lambda)\,x(\lambda)]$$

$$= -\frac{1}{\mu - \lambda}\,[x - x - (\mu - \lambda)\,x(\lambda)] = x(\lambda) \quad \text{for} \quad \mu \neq \lambda.$$

If we make $\mu \to \lambda$ we obtain that the equality between the extreme terms of the above sequence of equalities holds also for $\mu = \lambda$. Therefore $\varrho_T(x) \subset \varrho_T(x(\lambda))$, i.e. $\sigma_T(x(\lambda)) \subset \sigma_T(x)$.

1.3. PROPOSITION. *Let $T_\alpha \in \mathbf{B}(\mathcal{X}_\alpha)$ $(\alpha = 1, 2)$. Then $T_1 \oplus T_2 \in \mathbf{B}(\mathcal{X}_1 \oplus \mathcal{X}_2)$ has the single-valued extension property if and only if both T_1 and T_2 have this property. Moreover*

$$\sigma_{T_1 \oplus T_2}(x_1 \oplus x_2) = \sigma_{T_1}(x_1) \cup \sigma_{T_2}(x_2).$$

Proof. Let us suppose that T_1 and T_2 have the single-valued extension property, and let $f = f_1 \oplus f_2$ be an analytic $\mathcal{X}_1 \oplus \mathcal{X}_2$-valued function defined on an open set G, where $f_1 : G \to \mathcal{X}_1$ and $f_2 : G \to \mathcal{X}_2$ are analytic functions. Now if

$$(\lambda I_1 - T_1) f_1(\lambda) \oplus (\lambda I_2 - T_2) f_2(\lambda) = [\lambda\,(I_1 \oplus I_2) - (T_1 \oplus T_2)]\, f(x) \equiv \mathbf{0},$$

then

$$(\lambda I_1 - T_1) f_1(\lambda) \equiv 0 \quad \text{and} \quad (\lambda I_2 - T_2) f_2(\lambda) \equiv 0,$$

hence

$$f_1(\lambda) \equiv 0 \equiv f_2(x),$$

i.e. $f(\lambda) \equiv 0$. So $T_1 \oplus T_2$ has the single-valued extension property.

Conversely, let us suppose that $T_1 \oplus T_2$ has the single-valued extension property, and let $f_\alpha : G \to \mathcal{X}_\alpha$ $(G \subset C$ open; $\alpha = 1, 2)$ be analytic functions such that

$$(\lambda I_\alpha - T_\alpha) f_\alpha(\lambda) \equiv 0, \quad (\alpha\ 1, =2),$$

then

$$[\lambda (I_1 \oplus I_2) - (T_1 \oplus T_2)] (f_1(\lambda) \oplus f_2(\lambda))$$
$$= (\lambda I_1 - T_1) f_1(\lambda) \oplus (\lambda I_2 - T_2) f_2(\lambda) \equiv 0,$$

therefore

$$f_1(\lambda) \oplus f_2(\lambda) \equiv 0,$$

hence

$$f_1(\lambda) \equiv 0 \equiv f_2(\lambda);$$

this shows that T_α ($\alpha = 1, 2$) has the single-valued extension property.

Now let $\lambda_0 \in \varrho_{T_1 \oplus T_2}(x_1 \oplus x_2)$, then there exists a neighborhood D of λ_0 and an analytic function $f = f_1 \oplus f_2 : D \to \mathscr{X}_1 \oplus \mathscr{X}_2$ (with f_1, f_2 analytic functions) such that

$$(\lambda I_1 - T_1) f_1(\lambda) \oplus (\lambda I_2 - T_2) f_2(\lambda) = [\lambda (I_1 \oplus I_2) - (T_1 \oplus T_2)] f(\lambda)$$
$$\equiv x_1 \oplus x_2,$$

hence

$$(\lambda I_1 - T_1) f_1(\lambda) \equiv x_1 \quad \text{and} \quad (\lambda I_2 - T_2) f_2(\lambda) \equiv x_2,$$

therefore

$$\lambda_0 \in \varrho_{T_1}(x_1) \cap \varrho_{T_2}(x_2).$$

In the same way one can prove also the other inclusion.

1.4. PROPOSITION. *In the hypothesis of the preceding lemma, we have*

$$\mathscr{X}_{1_{T_1}}(F_1) \oplus \mathscr{X}_{2_{T_2}}(F_2) \subset (\mathscr{X}_1 \oplus \mathscr{X}_2)_{T_1 \oplus T_2}(F_1 \cup F_2) \tag{1}$$

($F_1, F_2 \subset C$). Moreover, for any set $F \subset C$, we have

$$\mathscr{X}_{1_{T_1}}(F) \oplus \mathscr{X}_{2_{T_2}}(F) = (\mathscr{X}_1 \oplus \mathscr{X}_2)_{T_1 \oplus T_2}(F). \tag{2}$$

Proof. Let $x_\alpha \in \mathscr{X}_{\alpha_{T_\alpha}}(F_\alpha)$ ($\alpha = 1, 2$), i.e. $\sigma_{T_\alpha}(x_\alpha) \subset F_\alpha$, then on account of the preceding lemma, we have

$$\sigma_{T_1 \oplus T_2}(x_1 \oplus x_2) = \sigma_{T_1}(x_1) \cup \sigma_{T_2}(x_2) \subset F_1 \cup F_2,$$

i.e.

$$x_1 \oplus x_2 \in (\mathscr{X}_1 \oplus \mathscr{X}_2)_{T_1 \oplus T_2}(F_1 \cup F_2).$$

Let now

$$x_1 \oplus x_2 \in (\mathscr{X}_1 \oplus \mathscr{X}_2)_{T_1 \otimes T_2}(F),$$
$$\sigma_{T_1}(x_1) \cup \sigma_{T_2}(x_2) = \sigma_{T_1 \oplus T_2}(x_1 \oplus x_2) \subset F,$$

whence

$$\sigma_{T_\alpha}(x_\alpha) \subset F, \quad (\alpha = 1, 2),$$

i.e.

$$x_\alpha \in \mathscr{X}_{\alpha T_\alpha}(F), \quad (\alpha = 1, 2),$$

therefore

$$x_1 \oplus x_2 \in \mathscr{X}_{1_{T_1}}(F) \oplus \mathscr{X}_{2_{T_2}}(F).$$

1.5. THEOREM. *Let $T \in \mathbf{B}(\mathscr{X})$, and let $f: G \to C$ [G open $\supset \sigma(T)$] be an analytic function nonconstant on every component of G. Then $f(T)$ has the single-valued extension property if and only if T has this property.*

Proof. Let us suppose that T has the single-valued extension property and $f(T)$ has not this property. Then there exists an analytic function $h: D \to \mathscr{X}$ (where D is a disk) such that

$$[\mu I - f(T)]\, h(\mu) = 0 \quad \text{and} \quad h(\mu) \not\equiv 0. \tag{1}$$

From (1) it results that $D \subset \sigma(f(T)) = f(\sigma(T))$. Hence, for a fixed $\mu \in D$ the equation

$$\mu - f(\lambda) = 0 \tag{2}$$

has only a finite number of solutions in $\sigma(T)$ [because f is analytic in G and $\sigma(T)$ is compact]. The solution of Eq. (2) which are of order > 1, are also solutions of the equation

$$f'(\lambda) = 0. \tag{3}$$

But Eq. (3) has also only a finite number of solutions in $\sigma(T)$. Let $\lambda_1^0, \ldots, \lambda_k^0$ be these solutions. If we consider a disk $D_1 \subset D \setminus \{f(\lambda_1^0), \ldots, f(\lambda_k^0)\}$, Eq. (2) has, for every $\mu \in D_1$ only solutions of order $= 1$. Let $\lambda_1(\mu), \ldots, \lambda_n(\mu)$ be these solutions.

By Rouché's theorem there exists a disk $D_2 \subset D_1$ such that Eq. (2) has the same number n of solutions $\lambda_1(\mu), \ldots, \lambda_n(\mu)$ in G_0 for every $\mu \in D_2$, where $G_0 \subset G$ is a suitable neighborhood of $\sigma(T)$. These functions are analytic in $\mu \in D_2$. We can write

$$\mu - f(\lambda) = [\lambda - \lambda_1(\mu)]\, [\lambda - \lambda_2(\mu)] \cdots [\lambda - \lambda_m(\mu)]\, g_\mu(\lambda),$$

$$[\lambda \in G_0,\ \mu \in D_2], \tag{4}$$

where g_μ is an analytic function in λ (and μ) such that $g_\mu(\lambda) \neq 0$ [$\lambda \in G_0$; $\mu \in D_2$].

Therefore $g_\mu(T)$ makes sense and

$$\sigma(g_\mu(T)) = g_\mu(\sigma(T)) \not\ni 0,$$

hence $g_\mu(T)^{-1}$ exists and belongs to $\mathbf{B}(\mathscr{X})$.

From (4) it follows by Dunford's functional calculus

$$\mu I - f(T) = [T - \lambda_1(\mu)\, I]\, [T - \lambda_2(\mu)\, I] \cdots [T - \lambda_n(\mu)\, I]\, g_\mu(T),$$

hence

$$[T - \lambda_1(\mu)\, I]\, [T - \lambda_2(\mu)\, I] \cdots [T - \lambda_n(\mu)\, I]\, h(\mu)$$
$$= g_\mu(T)^{-1}\, [\mu I - f(T)]\, h(\mu) \equiv 0. \tag{5}$$

We observe that all the solutions $\lambda_1(\mu), \ldots, \lambda_n(\mu)$ are nonconstant. Indeed, if there did exist a $\lambda_{i_0}(\mu) \equiv \lambda_{i_0}$, then we should have

$$\mu = f(\lambda_{i_0}(\mu)) \equiv f(\lambda_{i_0}),$$

which is not possible (μ being arbitrary in D_2).

The function λ_1 being nonconstant, there exists a $\mu_1^0 \in D$ such that $\lambda_1'(\mu_1^0) \neq 0$. Therefore there is a disk $D_1^0 = \{\lambda \in C \,|\, |\lambda - \lambda_1(\mu_1^0)| < r_1\}$ in which λ_1^{-1} exists. We have

$$(T - \lambda I)\, \{[T - \lambda_2\, (\lambda_1^{-1}(\lambda))I] \cdots [T - \lambda_n\, (\lambda_1^{-1}(\lambda))\, I]\, h\, (\lambda_1^{-1}(\lambda))\} \equiv 0, \text{ on } D_1^0,$$

hence

$$[T - \lambda_2\, (\lambda_1^{-1}(\lambda))\, I] \cdots [T - \lambda_n\, (\lambda_1^{-1}(\lambda))\, I]\, h\, (\lambda_1^{-1}(\lambda)) \equiv 0, \tag{6}$$

since T has the single-valued extension property and the function $\lambda \to [T_2 - \lambda_2\, (\lambda_1^{-1}(\lambda))\, I] \cdots [T - \lambda_n\, (\lambda_1^{-1}(\lambda))\, I]\, h\, (\lambda_1^{-1}(\lambda))$ $(D_1^0 \to \mathscr{X})$ is analytic.

We observe that the identity (6) is of the same kind as (5), except for the first factor. Applying to $\lambda_2 \circ \lambda_1^{-1}$ the above argument, we obtain

$$[T - \lambda_3\, (\lambda_2^{-1}(\lambda))\, I] \cdots [T - \lambda_n\, (\lambda_2^{-1}(\lambda))\, I]\, h\, (\lambda_2^{-1}(\lambda)) \equiv 0$$

on a disk $D_2^0 \supset D$.

If we repeat this procedure we come to the identity

$$h\, (\lambda_n^{-1}\, (\lambda)) \equiv 0$$

on a disk D_n^0, hence $h(\mu) = 0$ on the domain $\lambda_n^{-1}\, (D_n^0)$, therefore $h(\mu) \equiv 0$ on D, which is impossible.

Conversely, suppose that $f(T)$ has the single-valued extension property and T has not this property. Then there exists an analytic $\mathscr{X}$-valued function $x(\lambda)$ defined on a disk D such that

$$(\lambda I - T)\, x(\lambda) \equiv 0 \quad \text{and} \quad x(\lambda) \not\equiv 0. \tag{7}$$

From (7) it follows that $D \subset \sigma(T)$, hence $D \subset G$; thus f is analytic on D. We have

$$f(\lambda) - f(\xi) = (\lambda - \xi)\, g_\lambda(\xi) \quad \text{for} \quad \lambda \in D, \quad \xi \in G,$$

where g_λ is also analytic in G.

By Dunford's functional calculus we obtain

$$f(\lambda)\, I - f(T) = (\lambda I - T)\, g_\mu(T). \tag{8}$$

From (7) and (8) one obtains that

$$[f(\lambda)\, I - f(T)]\, x(\lambda) \equiv 0.$$

Since f is not constant on D, we can choose a $\lambda_0 \in D$ such that $f'(\lambda_0) \neq 0$. Then for $D_0 = \{\lambda \in C \,|\, |\lambda - \lambda_0| < r\}$ with r small enough f^{-1} exists on $f(D_0)$. So, if we put $y(\mu) = x(f^{-1}(\mu))$ on $f(D_0)$ we obtain

$$[\mu I - f(T)]\, y(\mu) \equiv 0,$$

hence [since $f(T)$ has the single-valued extension property] $y(\mu) \equiv 0$. From this identity it follows that $x(\lambda) \equiv 0$ on D_0, hence also on D.

1.6. THEOREM. *Let $T \in \mathbf{B}(\mathscr{X})$ be an operator with the single-valued extension property, and let $f: G \to G$ [G open $\supset \sigma(T)$] be an analytic function. If f is nonconstant on every component of G then $f(T)$ has the single-valued extension property and*

$$\mathscr{X}_{f(T)}(F) = \mathscr{X}_T(f^{-1}(F))$$

for every closed set $F \subset \sigma(f(T)) = f(\sigma(T))$.

Proof. Let $x \in \mathscr{X}_{f(T)}(F)$, then there exists an analytic function $\tilde{x}$: $\complement F \to \mathscr{X}$ such that

$$[\mu I - f(T)]\, \tilde{x}(\mu) \equiv x.$$

We observe that $\tilde{x}\,(f(\lambda))$ makes sense for every $\lambda \in \complement f^{-1}(F) = f^{-1}(\complement F)$, hence

$$[f(\lambda)\, I - f(T)]\, \tilde{x}\,(f(\lambda)) \equiv x, \quad \text{on} \quad \complement f^{-1}(F). \tag{1}$$

We may write

$$f(\lambda) - f(\xi) = (\lambda - \xi)\, g_\lambda(\xi), \quad (\lambda, \xi \in G),$$

where $g_\lambda(\xi)$ is an analytic function in λ and ξ, hence

$$f(\lambda)\, I - f(T) = (\lambda I - T)\, g_\lambda(T). \tag{2}$$

From (1) and (2) it follows that

$$(\lambda I - T)\big(g_\lambda(T)\, \tilde{x}\,(f(\lambda))\big) \equiv x,$$

where $\lambda \to g_\lambda(T)\, \tilde{x}\,(f(\lambda))\,(: \complement f^{-1}(F) \cap G \to \mathscr{X})$ is an analytic function since $\lambda \to g_\lambda(T)$ is analytic (see Ref. 30, VII, 3.14) and so is $\lambda \to \tilde{x}\,(f(\lambda))$, therefore $\complement f^{-1}(F) \cap G \subset \varrho_T(x)$. As $\complement G \subset \varrho(T) \subset \varrho_T(x)$, it follows $\complement f^{-1}(F) \subset \varrho_T(x)$, i.e. $\sigma_T(x) \subset f^{-1}(F)$, hence $x \in \mathscr{X}_T\,(f^{-1}(F))$.

Let now $x \in \mathscr{X}_T\,(f^{-1}(F))$. There exists an $\mathscr{X}$-valued analytic function $x(\lambda)$ defined on $\varrho_T(x) \supset \complement f^{-1}(F)$ such that

$$(\lambda I - T)\, x(\lambda) \equiv x. \tag{3}$$

If we put $F_0 = f^{-1}(F) \cap \sigma(T)$, then $f(F_0) \subset F$, i.e.

$$\complement F \subset \complement f(F_0). \tag{4}$$

Let now $\mu_0 \in \complement F$, then from (4) it follows that $\mu_0 - f(\lambda) \neq 0$, for every $\lambda \in F_0$. We may surround F_0 by a system of curves $\Gamma_0 \subset G$ such that $\mu_0 \notin f(H \cup \Gamma_0)$ (where H is the set whose boundary is Γ_0). Then there exists a disk $D_0 = D\,(\mu_0, r) \subset \complement F$ such that

$$D_0 \cap f(H \cup \Gamma_0) = \varnothing,$$

hence

$$\mu - f(\lambda) \neq 0 \quad \text{for every } \mu \in D_0 \quad \text{and} \quad \lambda \in \Gamma_0.$$

So the function $g\colon D_0 \to \mathscr{X}$ defined by

$$g(\mu) = \frac{1}{2\pi i} \int_{\Gamma_0} \frac{x(\lambda)}{\mu - f(\lambda)}\, d\lambda \tag{5}$$

is analytic.

Let Γ be another system of curves contained in G surrounding $\sigma(T)$, and also Γ_0. We have for $\lambda \in \Gamma_0$

$$[\mu I - f(T)]\, x(\lambda) = \frac{1}{2\pi i} \int_{\Gamma} [\mu - f(\xi)]\, R(\xi, T)\, x(\lambda)\, d\xi$$

$$\left\{ = \frac{1}{2\pi i} \int_{\Gamma} [\mu - f(\xi)]\, R(\xi, T)\, R(\lambda, T)\, x\, d\xi \right.$$

$$\left. = \frac{1}{2\pi i} \int_{\Gamma} [\mu - f(\xi)]\, \frac{[R(\xi, T) - R(\lambda, T)]\, x}{\lambda - \xi}\, d\xi \right\}$$

$$= \frac{1}{2\pi i} \int_{\Gamma} \frac{\mu - f(\xi)}{\lambda - \xi} [R(\xi, T)\, x - x(\lambda)]\, d\xi$$

$$= \frac{1}{2\pi i} \int_{\Gamma} \frac{\mu - f(\xi)}{\lambda - \xi} R(\xi, T)\, x\, d\xi$$

$$+ \left(\mu \frac{1}{2\pi i} \int_{\Gamma} \frac{d\xi}{\xi - \lambda} - \frac{1}{2\pi i} \int_{\Gamma} \frac{f(\xi)}{\xi - \lambda}\, d\xi \right) x(\lambda),$$

hence

$$[\mu I - f(T)]\, x(\lambda) = \frac{1}{2\pi i} \int_{\Gamma} \frac{\mu - f(\xi)}{\lambda - \xi} R(\xi, T)\, x\, d\xi + [\mu - f(\lambda)]\, x(\lambda). \tag{6}$$

From (5) and (6), for $\mu \in D_0$, it follows

$$[\mu I - f(T)]\, g(\mu) = \frac{1}{2\pi i} \int_{\Gamma_0} \frac{1}{\mu - f(\lambda)} [\mu I - f(T)]\, x(\lambda)\, d\lambda$$

$$= - \frac{1}{4\pi^2} \int_{\Gamma_0} \int_{\Gamma} \frac{[\mu - f(\xi)]\, R(\xi, T)\, x}{[\mu - f(\lambda)]\, (\lambda - \xi)}\, d\xi\, d\lambda$$

$$+ \frac{1}{2\pi i} \int_{\Gamma_0} x(\lambda)\, d\lambda$$

$$= \frac{1}{2\pi i} \int_{|\lambda| = \|T\| + 1} x(\lambda)\, d\lambda$$

$$- \frac{1}{4\pi^2} \int_{\Gamma} \left(\int_{\Gamma_0} \frac{d\lambda}{[\mu - f(\lambda)]\, (\lambda - \xi)} \right) [\mu - f(\xi)]\, R(\xi, T)\, x\, d\xi$$

$$= \frac{1}{2\pi i} \int_{|\lambda| = \|T\| + 1} x(\lambda)\, d\lambda$$

$$= \frac{1}{2\pi i} \int_{|\lambda| = \|T\| + 1} R(\lambda, T)\, x\, d\lambda = x,$$

(since the function $1/[\mu - f(\lambda)](\lambda - \xi)$ is analytic in λ on H). We have seen that, for every $\mu_0 \in \complement F$ there exists a disk $D_0 \ni \mu_0$, and an analytic function $g: D_0 \to \mathscr{X}$ such that $[\mu I - f(T)]g(\mu) \equiv x$, hence $\complement F \subset \varrho_{f(T)}(x)$, i.e. $x \in \mathscr{X}_{f(T)}(F)$. So $\mathscr{X}_T(f^{-1}(F)) \subset \mathscr{X}_{f(T)}(F)$.

1.7. EXAMPLE. *Let H be a Hilbert space and $T \in \mathbf{B}(\mathscr{H})$ an isometric non-unitary operator. Then T^* (the adjoint of T) has not the single-valued extension property.*

Indeed, in this case $T^*T = I$ and $TT^* = P \neq I$, where P is an orthogonal projection.

For $|\lambda| < 1$ and $x \in \mathscr{H}$, we have

$$\left\|\sum_{n=k}^{n+p} \lambda^k T^k x\right\| \leqslant \sum_{k=n}^{n+p} |\lambda|^k \|T_x^k\| = \|x\| \sum_{k=n}^{n+p} |\lambda|^k \leqslant \|x\| \frac{|\lambda|^n}{1 - |\lambda|} \xrightarrow[n\to\infty]{} 0.$$

Therefore $\tilde{x}: D(0, 1) \to \mathscr{X}$ $[D(0, 1) = \{\lambda \in C \,|\, |\lambda| < 1\}]$ defined by

$$\tilde{x}(\lambda) = \sum_{n=0}^{\infty} \lambda^n T^n x$$

is an analytic function.

We observe that if $Px = 0$, then $T^*x = 0$ so that

$$T^*\tilde{x}(\lambda) = \sum_{n=0}^{\infty} \lambda^n T^* T^n x = \sum_{n=1}^{\infty} \lambda^n (T^*T) T^{n-1} x = \sum_{n=1}^{\infty} \lambda^n T^{n-1} x$$

$$= \lambda \sum_{n=1}^{\infty} \lambda^{n-1} T^{n-1} x = \lambda \tilde{x}(\lambda),$$

for every $\lambda \in D(0, 1)$, hence

$$(\lambda I - T^*)\tilde{x}(\lambda) \equiv 0 \quad \text{on} \quad D(0, 1).$$

On the other hand $\tilde{x}(\lambda) \not\equiv 0$ for $x \neq 0$, and since $P \neq I$, there are $x \neq 0$ with $Px = 0$; so that the operator T^* has not the single-valued extension property.

2. Quasi-nilpotent Equivalent Operators

For $T_1, T_2 \in \mathbf{B}(\mathscr{X})$ not necessarily permutable we use the notation

$$(T_1 - T_2)^{[n]} = \sum_{k=0}^{n} (-1)^{n-k} \binom{n}{k} T_1^k T_2^{n-k}.\dagger \tag{1}$$

†) Obviously the notation is abusive since $(T_1 - T_2)^{[n]}$ is not function of $T_1 - T_2$, but it is suggestive since $(T_1 - T_2)^{[n]} = (T_1 - T_2)^n$ if T_1 and T_2 commute.

2.1. Definition. We say that $T_1, T_2 \in \mathbf{B}(\mathscr{X})$ are *quasinilpotent equivalent*, and write $T_1 \overset{q}{\sim} T_2$, if

$$\lim_{n\to\infty} \|(T_1 - T_2)^{[n]}\|^{1/n} = 0 \quad \text{and} \quad \lim_{n\to\infty} \|(T_2 - T_1)^{[n]}\|^{1/n} = 0.$$

It is evident that this relation is reflexive and symmetric. Let us show that it is also transitive. In order to do this, let $\alpha, \beta, \gamma \in C$, then

$$\begin{aligned}
&\sum_{k=0}^{n} \binom{n}{k} \alpha^k \gamma^{n-k} \\
&= (\alpha - \gamma)^n = [(\alpha - \beta) + (\beta - \gamma)]^n \\
&= \sum_{k=0}^{n} \binom{n}{k} (\alpha - \beta)^k (\beta - \gamma)^{n-k} \\
&= \sum_{k=0}^{n} \sum_{j=0}^{k} \sum_{i=0}^{n-k} (-1)^{n-(i+j)} \binom{n}{k}\binom{k}{j}\binom{n-k}{i} \alpha^j \beta^{k+i-j} \gamma^{n-(k+i)} \\
&= \sum_{j=0}^{n} \sum_{p\geq j}^{n} C_{j,p} \alpha^j \beta^{p-j} \gamma^{n-p}.
\end{aligned}$$

Since this equality holds for every $\alpha, \beta, \gamma \in C$ the coefficients $C_{j,p}$ are equal to zero when $p - j \neq 0$, and equal to $(-1)^{n-j}\binom{n}{j}$ when $p = j$. Using this remark we have

$$\begin{aligned}
&\sum_{k}^{n} \binom{n}{k} (T_1 - T_2)^{[k]} (T_2 - T_3)^{[n-k]} \\
&= \sum_{k=0}^{n} \sum_{j=0}^{k} \sum_{i=0}^{n-k} (-1)^{n-(j+i)} \binom{n}{k}\binom{k}{j}\binom{n-k}{i} T_1^j T_2^{k+i-j} T_3^{n-(k+i)} \\
&= \sum_{j=0}^{n} \sum_{n\geq p}^{n} C_{j,p} T_1^j T_2^{p-j} T^{n-p} = \sum_{j=0}^{n} (-1)^{n-j} \binom{n}{j} T_1^j T_3^{n-j},
\end{aligned}$$

from which, according to Definition 2.1, we therefore have

$$(T_1 - T_3)^{[n]} = \sum_{k=0}^{n} \binom{n}{k} (T_1 - T_2)^{[k]} (T_2 - T_3)^{[n-k]}. \tag{2}$$

Let $T_i \in B(\mathscr{X})$ $(i = 1, 2, 3)$ be such that $T_1 \overset{q}{\sim} T_2$ and $T_2 \overset{q}{\sim} T_3$. Then, for any $\varepsilon > 0$ there exists a n_ε such that

$$\|(T_1 - T_2)^{[k]}\| < \varepsilon^k \quad \text{and} \quad \|(T_2 - T_3)^{[k]}\| < \varepsilon^k,$$

for every $k \geqslant n_\varepsilon$. If $\|(T_1 - T_2)^{[k]}\| \geqslant \varepsilon^k$ and $\|(T_2 - T_3)^{[k]}\| \geqslant \varepsilon^k$ for some $0 \leqslant k < n_\varepsilon$, taking

$$M'_{\varepsilon,k} > \frac{\|(T_1 - T_2)^{[k]}\|}{\varepsilon^k} (\geqslant 1) \quad \text{and} \quad M''_{\varepsilon,k} > \frac{\|(T_2 - T_3)^{[k]}\|}{\varepsilon^k} (\geqslant 1)$$

it follows that $\|(T_1 - T_2)^{[k]}\| < M'_{\varepsilon,k}\varepsilon^k$ and $\|(T_2 - T_3)^{[k]}\| < M''_{\varepsilon,k}\varepsilon^k$ $(0 \leqslant k < n_\varepsilon)$. If we put $M_\varepsilon = \max\limits_{0 \leqq k \leqq n_\varepsilon} (M'_{\varepsilon,k}, M''_{\varepsilon,k})$ $(\geqslant 1)$, we have thus

$$\|(T_1 - T_2)^{[k]}\| < \varepsilon^k M_\varepsilon \quad \text{and} \quad \|(T_2 - T_3)^{[k]}\| < \varepsilon^k M_\varepsilon \tag{3}$$

for any $k \geqslant 0$.

From (2) and (3) it follows

$$\|(T_1 - T_3)^{[n]}\| \leqslant \sum_{k=0}^{n} \binom{n}{k} \|(T_1 - T_2)^{[k]}\| \cdot \|(T_2 - T_3)^{[n-k]}\|$$

$$< \sum_{k=0}^{n} \binom{n}{k} \varepsilon^k \varepsilon^{n-k} M_\varepsilon^2 = (2\varepsilon)^n M_\varepsilon^2,$$

i.e.

$$\|(T_1 - T_3)^{[n]}\|^{1/n} < 2\varepsilon M_\varepsilon^{2/n},$$

whence

$$\overline{\lim_{n\to\infty}} \|(T_1 - T_3)^{[n]}\|^{1/n} \leqslant 2\varepsilon \lim_{n\to\infty} M_\varepsilon^{2/n} = 2\varepsilon,$$

therefore ($\varepsilon > 0$ being arbitrary) $\lim\limits_{n\to\infty} \|(T_1 - T_3)^{[n]}\|^{1/n} = 0$. Analogously, one can proved that $\lim\limits_{n\to\infty} \|(T_3 - T_1)^{[n]}\|^{1/n} = 0$.

2.2. THEOREM. *Consider $T_1, T_2 \in \mathbf{B}(\mathscr{X})$. If $T_1 \overset{q}{\sim} T_2$, then $\sigma(T_1) = \sigma(T_2)$.*

Proof. We first observe that if $A, B \in \mathbf{B}(\mathscr{X})$ and $n \geqslant 0$, then

$$A(A - B)^{[n]} - (A - B)^{[n]} B$$

$$= \sum_{i=0}^{n} (-1)^{n-i} \binom{n}{i} A^{i+1} B^{n-i} - \sum_{j=0}^{n} (-1)^{n-j} \binom{n}{j} A^j B^{n+1-j}$$

$$= A^{n+1} + \sum_{k=1}^{n} (-1)^{n+1-k} \left[\binom{n}{k} + \binom{n}{k-1}\right] A^k B^{n+1-k} + (-1)^{n+1} B^{n+1}$$

$$= A^{n+1} + \sum_{k=1}^{n} (-1)^{n+1-k} \binom{n+1}{k} A^k B^{n+1-k} + (-1)^{n+1} B^{n+1}$$

$$= (A - B)^{[n+1]},$$

hence

$$A(A - B)^{[n]} = (A - B)^{[n+1]} + (A - B)^{[n]}B. \tag{1}$$

Consider now $D_1 = \{\lambda \in C \mid |\lambda - \lambda_0| \leqslant r_1\} \subset \varrho(T_1)$, and

$$D_0 = \{\lambda \in C \mid |\lambda - \lambda_0| \leqslant r_0\} \text{ with } r_1 > r_0 .$$

Let $R(\mu, T) = \sum_{n=0}^{\infty} R_n(\lambda)(\mu - \lambda)^n$ be the Taylor expansion of the resolvent around each point λ of D_0. Using the formula

$$R_n(\lambda) = \frac{1}{n!}\frac{d^n}{d\lambda^n} R(\lambda, T_1) = \frac{1}{2\pi i}\int_{|\xi - \lambda_0| = r_1} \frac{R(\xi, T_1)}{(\xi - \lambda)^{n+1}}\, d\xi$$

and denoting with M_1 the maximum of $\|R(\xi, T_1)\|$ on D_1, we obtain

$$\|R_n(\lambda)\| \leqslant r_1 M_1/(r_1 - r_0)^{n+1}, \quad (n \geqslant 0).$$

This inequality shows that the series

$$R(\lambda) = \sum_{n=0}^{\infty} (-1)^n (T_2 - T_1)^{[n]} R_n(\lambda) \tag{3}$$

converges uniformly in D_0. In this way formula (3) gives an analytic function in $\varrho(T_1)$.

By differentiating n times the equality

$$(\lambda I - T_1) R(\lambda, T_1) = R(\lambda, T_1)(\lambda I - T_1) = I, \tag{4}$$

we obtain

$$(\lambda I - T_1)\frac{d^n}{d\lambda^n} R(\lambda, T_1) = \left(\frac{d^n}{d\lambda^n} R(\lambda, T_1)\right)(\lambda I - T_1)$$

$$= -n\frac{d^{n-1}}{d\lambda^{n-1}} R(\lambda, T_1). \tag{5}$$

In view of (3), (1), (2), (4), and (5) we obtain for every $\lambda \in D_0$

$$(\lambda I - T_2) R(\lambda) = \sum_{n=0}^{\infty} (-1)^n (\lambda I - T_2)(T_2 - T_1)^{[n]} R_n(\lambda)$$

$$= \sum_{n=0}^{\infty} (\lambda I - T_2)[(\lambda I - T_2) - (\lambda I - T_1)]^{[n]} R_n(\lambda)$$

$$= \sum_{n=0}^{\infty} \{[(\lambda I - T_2) - (\lambda I - T_1)]^{[n+1]} + [(\lambda I - T_2) - (\lambda I - T_1)]^{[n]} (\lambda I - T_1)\} R_n(\lambda)$$

$$= \sum_{n=0}^{\infty} (-1)^{n+1} (T_2 - T_1)^{[n+1]} R_n(\lambda) + (\lambda I - T_1) R_0(\lambda) + \sum_{n=1}^{\infty} (-1)^n (T_2 - T_1)^{[n]} (\lambda I - T_1) \frac{d^n}{d\lambda^n} R(\lambda, T_1) \frac{1}{n!}$$

$$= (\lambda I - T_1) R(\lambda, T_1) + \sum_{n=0}^{\infty} (-1)^{n+1} (T_2 - T_1)^{[n+1]} R_n(\lambda) + \sum_{n=1}^{\infty} (-1)^n (T_2 - T_1)^{[n]} \left[-\frac{d^{n-1}}{d\lambda^{n-1}} R(\lambda, T_1) \right] \frac{1}{(n-1)!}$$

$$= I + \sum_{n=0}^{\infty} (-1)^{n+1} (T_2 - T_1)^{[n+1]} R_n(\lambda) - \sum_{n=1}^{\infty} (-1)^n (T_2 - T_1)^{[n]} R_{n-1}(\lambda) = I,$$

and analogously

$$R(\lambda)(\lambda I - T_2) = I,$$

therefore $\lambda \in \varrho(T_2)$. Consequently $\varrho(T_1) \subset \varrho(T_2)$, i.e. $\sigma(T_2) \subset \sigma(T_1)$. Similarly one can show that $\sigma(T_1) \subset \sigma(T_2)$.

2.3. THEOREM. *Let $T_1, T_2 \in \mathbf{B}(\mathscr{X})$. If T_1 has the single-valued extension property and $T_1 \overset{q}{\sim} T_2$, then T_2 also has the single-valued extension property.*

Proof. Let $f: D_f \to \mathscr{X}$ (D_f open) be analytic verifying the property

$$(\lambda I - T_2) f(\lambda) \equiv 0. \tag{1}$$

Writing $(T_1 - T_2)^{[n]}$ explicitly, in view of (1) we deduce

$$(T_1 - T_2)^{[n]} f(\lambda) = (T_1 - \lambda I)^n f(\lambda). \tag{2}$$

From

$$\lim_{n\to\infty} \left(\frac{\|(T_1 - T_2)^{[n]}\|}{|\mu - \lambda|^{n+1}} \right)^{1/n} = \frac{\lim_{n\to\infty} \|(T_1 - T_2)^{[n]}\|^{1/n}}{\lim_{n\to\infty} |\mu - \lambda|^{(n+1)/n}} = \frac{0}{|\mu - \lambda|} = 0$$

by the root test the series

$$\sum_{n=0}^{\infty} \frac{(T_1 - T_2)^{[n]}}{(\mu - \lambda)^{n+1}}$$

is absolutely convergent in the uniform topology of $\mathbf{B}(\mathscr{X})$ for every $\mu \neq \lambda$. It is known (Ref. 47, relation 5.2.3) that

$$R(\mu, T_1) = \sum_{n=0}^{\infty} \frac{(T_1 - \lambda I)^n}{(\mu - \lambda)^{n+1}} \tag{3}$$

for every μ such that $|\mu - \lambda| > \|T_1 - \lambda I\|$.

In view of (2) and (3) we may write

$$\begin{aligned}(\mu I - T_1)&\left(\sum_{n=0}^{\infty} \frac{(T_1 - T_2)^{[n]}}{(\mu - \lambda)^{n+1}}\right) f(\lambda)\\ &= (\mu I - T_1)\left(\sum_{n=0}^{\infty} \frac{(T_1 - \lambda I)^n}{(\mu - \lambda)^{n+1}}\right) f(\lambda)\\ &= (\mu I - T_1)\, R(\mu, T_1) f(\lambda) = f(\lambda),\end{aligned}$$

for $|\mu - \lambda| > \|T_1 - \lambda I\|$, therefore the analytic function on $\mathbf{C}\{\lambda\}$

$$g_\lambda(\mu) = \sum_{n=0}^{\infty} \frac{(T_1 - T_2)^{[n]}}{(\mu - \lambda)^{n+1}} f(\lambda)$$

verifies the relation

$$(\mu I - T_1)\, g_\lambda(\mu) = f(\lambda) \tag{4}$$

on an open set of $\mathbf{C}\{x\}$, namely on $\{\mu \in C \,|\, |\mu - \lambda| > \|T_1 - \lambda I\|\}$; it follows, by analytic extension, that g_λ verifies the relation (4) for every $\mu \neq \lambda$. Thus $\mathbf{C}\{\lambda\} \subset \varrho_{T_1}(f(\lambda))$ i.e.

$$\sigma_{T_1}(f(\lambda)) \subset \{\lambda\}. \tag{5}$$

Let $\lambda_0 \in D_f$, $D_0 = \{\lambda \in C \,|\, |\lambda - \lambda_0| \leqslant r_0\} \subset D_f$, and $\lambda, \mu \in \operatorname{Int} D_0$. Then integrating (4) we get

$$(\mu I - T_1) \frac{1}{2\pi i} \int_{|\xi - \lambda_0| = r_0} \frac{g_\xi(\mu)\, d\xi}{\xi - \lambda} = \frac{1}{2\pi i} \int_{|\xi - \lambda_0| = r_0} \frac{f(\xi)\, d\xi}{\xi - \lambda} = f(\lambda).$$

Now for λ fixed

$$\frac{1}{2\pi i} \int_{|\xi - \lambda_0| = r_0} \frac{g_\xi(\mu)\, d\xi}{\xi - \lambda}$$

is an analytic function in μ for all $|\mu - \lambda_0| < r_0$. Accordingly for $|\lambda - \lambda_0| < r_0$, $\operatorname{Int} D_0 = \{\mu \in C \mid |\mu - \lambda_0| < r_0\} \subset \varrho_{T_1}(f(\lambda))$, hence $\lambda \in \varrho_{T_1}(f(\lambda))$ On account of (5) it results

$$\sigma_{T_1}(f(\lambda)) = \varnothing,$$

for all $\lambda \in \operatorname{Int} D_0$, therefore, according to Proposition 1.2 (iii), $f(\lambda) = 0$. In view of the fact that $\lambda_0 \in D_f$ is arbitrarily chosen, it follows that $f(\lambda) \equiv 0$ on D_f.

2.4. THEOREM. *Let $T_1, T_2 \in \mathbf{B}(\mathscr{X})$. If T_1 has the single-valued extension property and $T_1 \overset{q}{\sim} T_2$, then $\sigma_{T_1}(x) = \sigma_{T_2}(x)$ for every $x \in \mathscr{X}$.*

Remark. We observe that $\sigma_{T_2}(x)$ makes sense because, according to Theorem 2.3, T_2 has the single extension property.

Proof. Let $x_1(\lambda)$ be the analytic function on $\varrho_{T_1}(x)$ which verifies

$$(\lambda I - T_1)\, x_1(\lambda) \equiv x. \tag{1}$$

We consider $D_0 = \{\lambda \mid |\lambda - \lambda_0| \leqslant r_0\} \subset \varrho_{T_1}(x)$ and $r_1 > r_0$ such that $D_1 = \{\lambda \mid |\lambda - \lambda_0| \leqslant r_1\} \subset \varrho_{T_1}(x)$. Let M_1 be the maximum of $\|x_1(\lambda)\|$ on D_1.

For $\lambda \in D_0$ we then have

$$\left\| \frac{x_1^{(n)}(\lambda)}{n!} \right\| = \left\| \frac{1}{2\pi i} \int_{|\xi - \lambda_0| = r_1} \frac{x_1(\xi)}{(\xi - \lambda)^{n+1}}\, d\xi \right\| \leqslant \frac{M_1 r_1}{(r_1 - r_0)^{n+1}}. \tag{2}$$

Because $T_1 \overset{q}{\sim} T_2$, it follows [see 2.1(3)] that for every $\varepsilon > 0$ there exists a $M_\varepsilon > 0$ such that

$$\|(T_2 - T_1)^{[n]}\| < \varepsilon^n M_\varepsilon \quad \text{for every} \quad n \geqslant 0. \tag{3}$$

From (2) and (3) it follows

$$\begin{aligned} \left\| (T_2 - T_1)^{[n]} \frac{x_1^{(n)}(\lambda)}{n!} \right\| &\leqslant \|(T_2 - T_1)^{[n]}\| \cdot \left\| \frac{x_1^{(n)}(\lambda)}{n!} \right\| \\ &< \frac{M_\varepsilon M_1 r_1}{r_1 - r_0} \left(\frac{\varepsilon}{r_1 - r_0} \right)^n, \end{aligned}$$

from which, by taking $\varepsilon = (r_1 - r_0)/2$, we obtain

$$\left\| (T_2 - T_1)^{[n]} \frac{x_1^{(n)}(\lambda)}{n!} \right\| < \frac{M}{2^n} \quad \text{for every} \quad n \geqslant 0, \tag{4}$$

where M does not depend on $\lambda \in D_0$.

Relation (4) shows that the series

$$\sum_{n=0}^{\infty} (-1)^n (T_2 - T_1)^{[n]} \frac{x_1^{(n)}(\lambda)}{n!}$$

converges absolutely and uniformly in D_0; therefore $D_0 \subset \varrho_{T_1}(x)$ being arbitrary, it converges absolutely and uniformly in every compact $K \subset \varrho_{T_1}(x)$. It follows that

$$x_2(\lambda) = \sum_{n=0}^{\infty} (-1)^n (T_2 - T_1{}^{[n]}) \frac{x_1^{(n)}(\lambda)}{n!} \tag{5}$$

is analytic on $\varrho_{T_1}(x)$. In addition we will show that

$$(\lambda I - T_2)\, x_2(\lambda) \equiv x. \tag{6}$$

If we take n times the derivative of the identity (1), we have

$$(\lambda I - T_1)\, x_1^{(n)}(\lambda) \equiv -n x_1^{(n-1)}(\lambda). \tag{7}$$

In view of (5), 2.2.(1), (7) and (1), we obtain

$$\begin{aligned}
(\lambda I - T_2)\, x_2(\lambda) &= \sum_{n=0}^{\infty} (-1)^n (\lambda I - T_2)(T_2 - T_1)^{[n]} \frac{x_1^{(n)}(\lambda)}{n!} \\
&= \sum_{n=0}^{\infty} (\lambda I - T_2)\,[(\lambda I - T_2) - (\lambda I - T_1)]^{[n]} \frac{x_1^{(n)}(\lambda)}{n!} \\
&= \sum_{n=0}^{\infty} \{[(\lambda I - T_2) - (\lambda I - T_1)]^{[n+1]} \\
&\quad + [(\lambda I - T_2) - (\lambda I - T_1)]^{[n]} (\lambda I - T_1)\} \frac{x_1^{(n)}(\lambda)}{n!} \\
&= \sum_{n=0}^{\infty} (-1)^{n+1} (T_2 - T_1)^{[n+1]} \frac{x_1^{(n)}(\lambda)}{n!} \\
&\quad + \sum_{n=0}^{\infty} (-1)^n (T_2 - T_1)^{[n]} (\lambda I - T_1) \frac{x_1^{(n)}(\lambda)}{n!} \\
&= \sum_{n=0}^{\infty} (-1)^{n+1} (T_2 - T_1)^{[n+1]} \frac{x_1^{(n)}(\lambda)}{n!} + (\lambda I - T_1)\, x_1(\lambda) \\
&\quad - \sum_{n=1}^{\infty} (-1)^n (T_2 - T_1)^{[n]} \frac{x_1^{(n-1)}(\lambda)}{(n-1)!} \\
&= (\lambda I - T_1)\, x_1(\lambda) \equiv x \quad \text{on} \quad \varrho_{T_1}(x).
\end{aligned}$$

Therefore, the identity (6) is verified and from this follows $\varrho_{T_1}(x) \subset \varrho_{T_2}(x)$, i.e. $\sigma_{T_2}(x) \subset \sigma_{T_1}(x)$. Analogously one can show that $\sigma_{T_1}(x) \subset \sigma_{T_2}(x)$.

3. Spectral Maximal Spaces

3.1. Definition. Let $\mathscr{X}$ be a Banach space and $T \in \mathbf{B}(\mathscr{X})$. A closed linear subspace $\mathscr{Y}$ of $\mathscr{X}$ is called *spectral maximal space* of T, if

(i) $\mathscr{Y}$ is invariant to T;

(ii) if $\mathscr{Z}$ is another closed linear subspace of $\mathscr{X}$, invariant to T, such that $\sigma(T|\mathscr{Z}) \subset \sigma(T|\mathscr{Y})$, then $\mathscr{Z} \subset \mathscr{Y}$.

3.2. Proposition. *A spectral maximal space of $T \in \mathbf{B}(\mathscr{X})$ is ultra-invariant to T i.e. invariant to any operator A commuting with T.*

Proof. Let $\mathscr{Y}$ be a spectral maximal space of T, and for a fixed $\lambda \in \varrho(A)$, let us put $\mathscr{Y}_\lambda = R(\lambda, A)\mathscr{Y}$. Obviously $\mathscr{Y}_\lambda$ is a closed linear subspace of $\mathscr{X}$. As T commutes with $R(\lambda, A)$, since $TA = AT$, and $T\mathscr{Y} \subset \mathscr{Y}$, it follows that $T\mathscr{Y}_\lambda \subset \mathscr{Y}_\lambda$.

We remark also that

$$T|\mathscr{Y}_\lambda = R(\lambda, A)(T|\mathscr{Y})(\lambda I - A)\mathscr{Y}_\lambda = [(\lambda I - A)|Y_\lambda]^{-1}(T|\mathscr{Y})(\lambda I - A)\mathscr{Y}_\lambda,$$

hence

$$\sigma(T|\mathscr{Y}_\lambda) = \sigma(T|\mathscr{Y}). \tag{1}$$

$\mathscr{Y}$ being a spectral maximal space of T, we have $\mathscr{Y}_\lambda \subset \mathscr{Y}$, so that

$$R(\lambda, A)x \in \mathscr{Y} \quad \text{for every} \quad x \in \mathscr{Y}.$$

By Dunford's functional calculus [see Ref. 30, VII.3, Theorem 10(c)] we have

$$A = \frac{1}{2\pi i}\int_\Gamma \lambda R(\lambda, A)\, d\lambda,$$

where Γ is a system of closed rectifiable Jordan curves surrounding $\sigma(A)$, hence

$$Ax = \frac{1}{2\pi i}\int_\Gamma \lambda R(\lambda, A)x\, d\lambda, \quad (x \in \mathscr{Y}).$$

Thus, Ax being the limit of sums of the form

$$\frac{1}{2\pi i} \sum_{k=1}^{n} \lambda_k (\lambda_{k+1} - \lambda_k) R(\lambda_k, A) x,$$

and $\mathcal{Y}$ being a closed linear subspace, it follows that $Ax \in \mathcal{Y}$.

3.3. Corollary. *For all spectral maximal spaces $\mathcal{Y}$ of T, we have*

$$\sigma(T|\mathcal{Y}) \subset \sigma(T).$$

Proof. Using the same argument (for $A = T$) as in the preceding proof, we obtain $R(\lambda, T)\mathcal{Y} \subset \mathcal{Y}$, for $\lambda \in \varrho(T)$; consequently $R(\lambda, T|\mathcal{Y}) = R(\lambda, T)|\mathcal{Y}$ exists for every $\lambda \in \varrho(T)$, therefore $\varrho(T) \subset \varrho(T|\mathcal{Y})$.

3.4. Corollary. *Let $\mathcal{Y}_1$ and $\mathcal{Y}_2$ be two spectral maximal spaces of T. Then the following two assertions are equivalent:*

$$\mathcal{Y}_1 \subset \mathcal{Y}_2; \tag{i}$$

$$\sigma(T|\mathcal{Y}_1) \subset \sigma(T|\mathcal{Y}_2). \tag{ii}$$

Proof

(i) $\Rightarrow$ (ii). The proof is analogous to that of the previous corollary.

(ii) $\Rightarrow$ (i). If $\sigma(T|\mathcal{Y}_1) \subset \sigma(T|\mathcal{Y}_2)$, taking in Definition 3.1 $\mathcal{Y} = \mathcal{Y}_2$ and $\mathcal{Z} = \mathcal{Y}_1$, one obtains that $\mathcal{Y}_1 \subset \mathcal{Y}_2$.

3.5. Proposition. *Let T have the single-valued extension property. If $\mathcal{Y}$ is a spectral maximal space of T, then*

$$\mathcal{O}_T(x) \subset \mathcal{Y} \quad \textit{for every} \quad x \in \mathcal{Y},$$

where $\mathcal{O}_T(x)$ is the linear closed subspace generated by all the values $x(\lambda)$ with $\lambda \in \varrho_T(x)$.

Proof. It suffices to prove that $x(\lambda) \in \mathcal{Y}$, for every $\lambda \in \varrho_T(x)$. For $\lambda \in \varrho(T|\mathcal{Y})$, we have $x(\lambda) = R(\lambda, T|\mathcal{Y})x$, so that it remains to consider the case $\lambda \in \sigma(T|\mathcal{Y})$.

Let us suppose that there exists a $\lambda_0 \in \varrho_T(x) \cap \sigma(T|\mathcal{Y})$ such that $x(\lambda_0) \notin \mathcal{Y}$, and let

$$\mathcal{Z} = \{z = y + \alpha x(\lambda_0) |\, y \in \mathcal{Y}, \alpha \in C\}.$$

$\mathscr{Z}$ is a closed linear subspace of $\mathscr{X}$. On account of $(\lambda_0 I - T)\, x(\lambda_0) = x$, we have

$$Tz = Ty + \alpha Tx\,(\lambda_0) = T\,(y - \alpha x) + \alpha\lambda_0 x\,(\lambda_0) \in \mathscr{Z};$$

therefore

$$T\mathscr{Z} \subset \mathscr{Z}. \tag{1}$$

We shall show that

$$\sigma\,(T|\mathscr{Z}) \subset \sigma\,(T|\mathscr{Y}). \tag{2}$$

With this aim, let us take a $\lambda \in \varrho\,(T|\mathscr{Y})$. If

$$0 = (\lambda I - T)\, z = (\lambda I - T)\,[y + \alpha x\,(\lambda_0)]$$

$$= (\lambda I - T)\, y + \alpha x + (\lambda - \lambda_0)\, \alpha x\,(\lambda_0)$$

then $\alpha = 0$, since $\lambda \neq \lambda_0$ [because $\lambda_0 \in \sigma\,(T|\mathscr{Y})$ and $\lambda \in \varrho\,(T|\mathscr{Y})$], $x(\lambda_0) \neq 0$ [because $x(\lambda_0) \notin \mathscr{Y} \ni 0$], and $(\lambda I - T)\, y = 0$. From $\lambda \in \varrho\,(T|\mathscr{Y})$, $y \in \mathscr{Y}$, and $(\lambda I - T)\, y = 0$ it follows that $y = 0$ and consequently $z = 0$. Therefore $(\lambda I - T)|\mathscr{Z}$ is injective.

Let $z = y + \alpha x\,(\lambda_0) \in \mathscr{Z}$ be arbitrary; then $z_0 = y_0 + \alpha_0 x\,(\lambda_0)$, where

$$\begin{cases} y_0 = R\,(\lambda, T|\mathscr{Y}) \left(y - \dfrac{\alpha}{\lambda - \lambda_0}\, x \right) \in \mathscr{Y} \\[2ex] \alpha_0 = \dfrac{\alpha}{\lambda - \lambda_0} \in C \end{cases}$$

satisfies

$$(\lambda I - T)\, z_0 = (\lambda I - T) \left[R\,(\lambda, T|\mathscr{Y}) \left(y - \frac{\alpha}{\lambda - \lambda_0}\, x \right) + \frac{\alpha}{\lambda - \lambda_0}\, x(\lambda_0) \right]$$

$$= y - \frac{\alpha}{\lambda - \lambda_0}\, x + \frac{\alpha}{\lambda - \lambda_0}\, x + (\lambda - \lambda_0) \frac{\alpha}{\lambda - \lambda_0}\, x(\lambda_0)$$

$$= y + \alpha x\,(\lambda_0) = z.$$

The linear continuous mapping $(\lambda I - T)|\mathscr{Z}$, being bijective, is, by the theorem of Banach (Ref. 30, II.2.2) bicontinuous, therefore $\lambda \in \varrho\,(T|\mathscr{Z})$.

Since $\mathscr{Y}$ is a spectral maximal space of T, from (1), (2) it follows that $\mathscr{Z} \subset \mathscr{Y}$ in contradiction with the assumption $x(\lambda_0) \notin \mathscr{Y}$.

3.6. Proposition. *If $\mathscr{Y}$ is a spectral maximal space of T and D is a domain such that there is an analytic $\mathscr{X}$-valued function $f(\lambda) \not\equiv 0$ defined on D verifying*

$$(\lambda I - T) f(\lambda) \equiv 0 \quad on \quad D, \tag{1}$$

then

$$D \cap \sigma(T|\mathscr{Y}) = \varnothing \quad or \quad D \subset \sigma_p(T|\mathscr{Y}),$$

where $\sigma_P(T|\mathscr{Y})$ is the point spectrum of $T|\mathscr{Y}$.

Proof. Let us suppose that $D \cap \sigma(T|\mathscr{Y}) \neq \varnothing$ and let $\lambda_0 \in D \cap \sigma(T|\mathscr{Y})$. By differentiating n times the identity (1), we obtain

$$Tf^{(n)}(\lambda) = \lambda f^{(n)}(\lambda) + nf^{(n-1)}(\lambda), \quad (n = 0, 1, \ldots; \lambda \in D). \tag{2}$$

Denote by $\mathscr{X}$ the linear subspace generated by $f(\lambda_0), f'(\lambda_0), \ldots, f^{(n)}(\lambda_0)$. $\mathscr{X}_n$ being of finite dimension, is closed.

Let

$$x = \sum_{k=0}^{n} \alpha_k f^{(k)}(\lambda_0) \in \mathscr{X}_n.$$

Then

$$Tx = \sum_{k=0}^{n} \alpha_k Tf^{(k)}(\lambda_0) = \sum_{k=0}^{n} \alpha_k [\lambda_0 f^{(k)}(\lambda_0) + kf^{(k-1)}(\lambda_0)] \in \mathscr{X}_n,$$

hence

$$T\mathscr{X}_n \subset \mathscr{X}_n.$$

We observe that the matrix of the operator $(\lambda I - T)|\mathscr{X}_n$ is

$$\begin{pmatrix} \lambda - \lambda_0 & -1 & 0 & \cdots\cdots\cdots 0 \\ 0 & \lambda - \lambda_0 & -2 & \cdots\cdots\cdots 0 \\ 0 & 0 & \lambda - \lambda_0 & \cdots\cdots\cdots 0 \\ \cdots & \cdots & \cdots & \cdots\cdots\cdots \\ 0 & 0 & 0 & \cdots\cdots \lambda - \lambda_0 \end{pmatrix}$$

so that

$$\det [(\lambda I - T)|\mathscr{X}_n] = (\lambda - \lambda_0)^{n+1};$$

whence $R(\lambda, T|\mathscr{X}_n)$ exists for any $\lambda \neq \lambda_0$, therefore $\mathbf{C}\{\lambda_0\} \subset \varrho(T|\mathscr{X}_n)$, i.e.

$$\sigma(T|\mathscr{X}_n) \subset \{\lambda_0\}, \quad (n = 0, 1, \ldots). \tag{3}$$

$\mathscr{Y}$ being a spectral maximal space of T, from (3) and $\lambda_0 \in \sigma(T|\mathscr{Y})$ we deduce

$$\mathscr{X}_n \subset \mathscr{Y}, \quad (n = 0, 1 \ldots). \tag{4}$$

From (4) it follows that $f^{(n)}(\lambda_0) \in \mathscr{Y}$ $(n = 0, 1, \ldots)$, hence

$$f(\lambda) = \sum_{n=0}^{\infty} \frac{(\lambda - \lambda_0)^n}{n!} f^n(\lambda_0) \in \mathscr{Y},$$

for λ belonging to a neighborhood of λ_0, and by analytic extension

$$f(\lambda) \in \mathscr{Y}, \quad \text{for every} \quad \lambda \in D. \tag{5}$$

For any $\lambda \in D$ there exists a $0 \leqslant n < \infty$ such that $f^{(n)}(\lambda) \neq 0$, since otherwise $f(\mu) = 0$, for any $\mu \in D$. Let

$$n_\lambda = \min \{n | f^{(n)}(\lambda) \neq 0\}.$$

Then $f^{(n_\lambda - 1)}(\lambda) = 0, f^{(n_\lambda)}(\lambda) \neq 0$ so that from (2) it follows

$$Tf^{(n_\lambda)}(\lambda) = \lambda f^{(n_\lambda)}(\lambda). \tag{6}$$

By (5) we have also $f^{(n)}(\lambda) \in \mathscr{Y}$,, for any $0 \leqslant n < \infty$ and $\lambda \in D$, hence (6) implies that $\lambda \in \sigma_p(T|\mathscr{Y})$. This completes our proof.

Let $\sigma_l(T)$ be the limit spectrum of T, i.e.

$$\sigma_l(T) = \{\lambda \in C | \exists (x_n)_{n \in N} \subset \mathscr{X} \quad \text{with} \quad \|x_n\| = 1$$
$$\text{and} \quad \lim_{n \to \infty} (\lambda I - T) x_n = 0\};$$

$\sigma_c(T)$ its continuous spectrum, i.e.

$\sigma_c(T) = \{\lambda \in C |\, \lambda I - T$ is injective, nonsurjective, $\overline{(\lambda I - T) \mathscr{X}} = \mathscr{X}\}$;

and $\sigma_r(T)$ its residual spectrum, i.e.

$\sigma_r(T) = \{\lambda \in C | \lambda I - T$ is injective, $\overline{(\lambda I - T) \mathscr{X}} \neq \mathscr{X}\}$.

Denote by $\sigma_p^0(T)$ the set of $\lambda \in C$ such that there exists a neighborhood V of λ and a $\mathscr{X}$-valued analytic function $f(\xi) \not\equiv 0$ on V verifying $(\xi I - T) f(\xi) \equiv 0$, and by $\sigma_r^0(T)$ the set of $\lambda \in C$ such that $\lambda I - T$ is injective nonsurjective, and $(\lambda I - T)^{-1}$ is bounded.

Evidently $\sigma_r^0(T) = \sigma(T) \setminus \sigma_l(T)$ is open, $\sigma_r^0(T) \subset \sigma_r(T)$, and $\sigma_p^0(T) \subset \sigma_p(T)$ (this last inclusion can be obtained by an argument used in the proof of the preceding proposition). By definition $\sigma_p^0(T)$ is also open.

3.7. PROPOSITION. *Let $\mathscr{Y}$ be a spectral maximal space of T. Then if D is a connected component of $\sigma_p^0(T)$ or $\sigma_r^0(T)$, we have*

$$D \cap \sigma(T|\mathscr{Y}) = \emptyset \quad or \quad D \subset \sigma(T|\mathscr{Y}).$$

Proof. For $D \subset \sigma_p^0(T)$, the proposition is an easy consequence of Proposition 3.5. For $D \subset \sigma_r^0(T)$ let us suppose that $D \cap \sigma(T|\mathscr{Y}) \neq 0$ and $D \not\subset \sigma(T|\mathscr{Y})$; then there exists a $\lambda_0 \in D$ such that

$$\lambda_0 \in \partial\sigma(T|\mathscr{Y}) \quad [\text{the boundary of } \sigma(T|\mathscr{Y})]. \tag{1}$$

Now, for every operator T, we have

$$\partial\sigma(T) \subset \sigma_l(T) \tag{2}$$

[since otherwise for $\lambda_n \to \lambda_0 \in \partial\sigma(T)$ we should have that $R(\lambda_n, T)$ is bounded, so that by the first resolvent equation

$$R(\lambda_n, T) - R(\lambda_m, T) = (\lambda_m - \lambda_n) R(\lambda_n, T) R(\lambda_m, T)$$

the $\lim_{n\to\infty} R(\lambda_m, T) = R_0 \in \mathbf{B}(\mathscr{X})$ would exist; by continuity $(\lambda I - T) R_0 = R_0(\lambda I - T) = I$, hence $\lambda \notin \sigma(T)$], so that by (1) and (2) we have

$$\lambda_0 \in \sigma_l(T|\mathscr{Y}). \tag{3}$$

But evidently

$$\sigma_l(T|\mathscr{Y}) \subset \sigma_l(T),$$

hence $\lambda_0 \in \sigma_l(T)$, in contradiction with $\lambda_0 \in D \subset \sigma_r^0(T)$.

3.8. PROPOSITION. *Consider $T \in \mathbf{B}(\mathscr{X})$ with the single-valued extension property. If $\mathscr{X}_T(F)$ (see 1.1) is closed, then $\mathscr{X}_T(F)$ is a spectral maximal space of T and*

$$\sigma(T|\mathscr{X}_T(F)) \subset \sigma(T) \cap F.$$

Proof. Let us first show that $\sigma(T|\mathscr{X}_T(F)) \subset F$. Let $\lambda_0 \in \complement F$. For every $x \in \mathscr{X}_T(F)$ we have $\sigma_T(x) \subset F$, i.e. $\complement F \subset \varrho_T(x)$. Therefore $x(\lambda_0)$ makes sense and from the equality $\varrho_T(x(\lambda_0)) = \varrho_T(x)$ [Proposition 1.2(v)] it follows $x(\lambda_0) \in \mathscr{X}_T(F)$.

Let $A: \mathscr{X}_T(F) \to \mathscr{X}_T(F)$ be defined by $Ax = x(\lambda_0)$. It is evident that A is linear. We will show that A is closed. Let $\{x_n\}_{n\in N} \subset \mathscr{H}_T(F)$ with $\lim_{n\to\infty} x_n$

$= x$ and $\lim_{n\to\infty} Ax_n = y$. From the fact that $\mathscr{X}_T(F)$ is closed it results that $x \in \mathscr{X}_T(F)$ and $y = \lim_{n\to\infty} Ax_n = \lim_{n\to\infty} x_n(\lambda_0) \in \mathscr{X}_T(F)$. We have

$$(\lambda_0 I - T)\, Ax_n = (\lambda_0 I - T)\, x_n(\lambda_0) = x_n,$$

from which follows $(\lambda_0 I - T)\, y = x$. On the other hand $(\lambda_0 I - T)\, x(\lambda_0) = x$, therefore $(\lambda_0 I - T)\, [y - x(\lambda_0)] = 0$. Let us note $z = y - x(\lambda_0)$. Having $y, x(\lambda_0) \in \mathscr{X}_T(F)$, it results that $z \in \mathscr{X}_T(F)$ [Proposition 1.2(ii)], therefore

$$\sigma_T(z) \subset F. \tag{1}$$

Let $f: \complement\{\lambda_0\} \to \mathscr{H}$ be defined by $f(\lambda) = z/(\lambda - \lambda_0)$. Then

$$(\lambda I - T) f(\lambda) = \frac{1}{\lambda - \lambda_0} (\lambda I - T)\, z = \frac{1}{\lambda - \lambda_0} [(\lambda_0 I - T)\, z + (\lambda - \lambda_0)\, z]$$

$$= \frac{\lambda - \lambda_0}{\lambda - \lambda_0} z = z,$$

shows that

$$\sigma_T(z) \subset \{\lambda_0\}. \tag{2}$$

From (1) and (2) it follows that $\sigma_T(z) \subset F \cap \{\lambda_0\} = \varnothing$. From this and as a consequence of Proposition 1.2(iii), we have $z = 0$, therefore $y = x(\lambda_0) = Ax$. It follows that the operator A is closed and, therefore, according to Banach's theorem (see Ref. 30), $A \in \mathbf{B}\,(\mathscr{X}_T(F))$.

We observe that $(\lambda_0 I - T)\, Ax = (\lambda_0 - T)\, x(\lambda) = x$, for every $x \in \mathscr{X}_T(F)$, therefore

$$(\lambda I|\mathscr{X}_T(F) - T|\mathscr{X}_T(F))\, A = I|\mathscr{X}_T(F). \tag{3}$$

On the other hand for every $x \in \mathscr{X}_T(F)$ we have $((\lambda_0 I - T)\, x)\, (\lambda_0) = (\lambda_0 I - T)\, x(\lambda_0)$, from which, according to the definition of A, follows

$$A\, (\lambda_0 I - T)\, x = ((\lambda_0 I - T)\, x)\, (\lambda_0) = (\lambda_0 I - T)\, x(\lambda_0) = x,$$

therefore

$$A\, (\lambda_0 I|\mathscr{X}_T(F) - T|\mathscr{X}_T(F)) = I|\mathscr{X}_T(F). \tag{4}$$

From (3) and (4) follows that $A = (\lambda_0 I|\mathscr{X}_T(F) - T|\mathscr{X}_T(F))^{-1}$, therefore $\lambda_0 \in \varrho\, (T|\mathscr{X}_T(F))$. Consequently $\complement F \subset \varrho\, (T|\mathscr{X}_T(F))$, i.e. $\sigma\, (T|\mathscr{X}_T(F)) \subset F$.

Let $\mathscr{Y}$ be a closed vector subspace of $\mathscr{X}$, such that $T\mathscr{Y} \subset \mathscr{Y}$ and $\sigma(T|\mathscr{Y}) \subset \sigma(T|\mathscr{X}_T(F))$. Then, for any $x \in \mathscr{Y}$ we have

$$\sigma_T(x) = \sigma_{T|\mathscr{Y}}(x) \subset \sigma(T|\mathscr{Y}) \subset \sigma(T|\mathscr{Y}_T(F)) \subset F,$$

hence $x \in \mathscr{X}_T(F)$. Thus $\mathscr{Y} \subset \mathscr{X}_T(F)$, and $\mathscr{X}_T(F)$ is spectral maximal of T. If we apply Corollary 3.3 it results that $\sigma(T|\mathscr{X}_T(F)) \subset \sigma(T)$, therefore

$$\sigma(T|\mathscr{X}_T(F)) \subset \sigma(T) \cap F.$$

3.9. Examples. Let us show that the single-valued extension property does not imply that the spaces $\mathscr{X}_T(F)$ (F closed $\subset C$) are closed.

Let $\mathscr{X} = \bigoplus_{n=2}^{\infty} C^n$ (the direct sum of spaces C^n), and let $T = \bigoplus_{n=2}^{\infty} Q_n$ where Q_n is the operator defined by the Jordan matrix

$$\begin{pmatrix} 0 & 1 & 0 & 0 \ldots\ldots 0 \\ 0 & 0 & 1 & 0 \ldots\ldots 0 \\ \ldots & \ldots & \ldots & \ldots \\ 0 & 0 & 0 & 0 \ldots\ldots 1 \\ 0 & 0 & 0 & 0 \ldots\ldots 0 \end{pmatrix}.$$

We have

$$\|Q_n\| = \|(Q_n)^{n-1}\| = 1, \tag{1}$$

and

$$(Q_n)^n = 0, \tag{2}$$

hence

$$\|T\| = \sup_{2 \leq n} \|Q_n\| = 1. \tag{3}$$

Let G be an open set in G and let $f = \bigoplus_{n=2}^{\infty} f_n : G \to \mathscr{X}$ be an analytic function (hence every component f_n: $G \to C^n$ is analytic) such that $(\lambda I - T) \times$ $\times f(\lambda) \equiv 0$, i.e.

$$(\lambda I_n - Q_n) f_n(\lambda) \equiv 0 \quad \text{for every } n \geqslant 2. \tag{4}$$

From (2) and (4) it results that $0 = (Q_n)^n f_n(\lambda) = \lambda^n f_n(\lambda)$, therefore $f_n(\lambda)$ $\equiv 0$ ($n = 2, 3, \ldots$), hence $f(\lambda) \equiv 0$. So that T has the single-valued extension property.

From (3) it follows that $\|T^p\| \leqslant \|T\|^p = 1$. On the other hand $\|T^p\| = \sup_{n \geqslant 2} \|(Q_n)^p\| \geqslant \|(Q_{p+1})^p\| = 1$ [by (1)], hence $\|T^p\| = 1$, therefore

$$\lim_{p \to \infty} \|T^p\|^{1/p} = 1.$$

This implies that $\sigma(T) \cap \{\lambda \in C \mid |\lambda| = 1\} \neq \emptyset$, hence $\sigma(T) \neq \{0\}$.

It is evident that $\mathscr{Y}_m = \bigoplus_{n=2}^{m} C^n$ $(m = 2, 3, \ldots)$ is included in $\mathscr{X}_T(\{0\})$. This results from the fact that $T^m y = 0$ for all $y \in \mathscr{Y}_m$, hence $y(\lambda) = \sum_{k=0}^{m-1} T^k y/\lambda^{k+1}$ is defined for all $\lambda \neq 0$.

Now *let us suppose that* $\mathscr{X}_T(\{0\})$ *is closed*, then

$$\mathscr{X}_T(\{0\}) \supset \overline{\bigcup_{m=2}^{\infty} \mathscr{Y}_m}.$$

But the last space is just $\mathscr{X}$. In this manner $\mathscr{X}_T(\{0\}) = \mathscr{X}$. Using now Proposition 3.8 we have

$$\sigma(T) = \sigma(T|\mathscr{X}_T(\{0\})) \subset \sigma(T) \cap \{0\} \subset \{0\},$$

hence $\sigma(T) = \{0\}$. This is impossible since we have already remarked that $\sigma(T) \neq \{0\}$.

We conclude that for our operator T the space $\mathscr{X}_T(\{0\})$ is not closed, though T has the single-valued extension property.

3.10. PROPOSITION. *Let $T \in \mathbf{B}(\mathscr{X})$ and let σ be a separate part of $\sigma(T)$. Let*

$$\mathbf{E}(\sigma, T) = \frac{1}{2\pi i} \int_{\Gamma} R(\lambda, T)\, d\lambda$$

[where Γ is a system of curves situated in $\varrho(T)$ and surrounding σ] be the spectral projection corresponding to σ (Ref. 30, VII, § 3). *Then $\mathbf{E}(\sigma, T)\mathscr{X}$ is a spectral maximal space of T and*

$$\sigma(T|\mathbf{E}(\sigma, T)\mathscr{X}) = \sigma. \tag{1}$$

Proof. Formula (1) is proved in Ref. 30 (VII, § 3, Theorem 20), hence it rests only to prove that $\mathbf{E}(\sigma, T)\mathscr{X}$ is a spectral maximal space of T. For this let $\mathscr{Y} \subset \mathscr{X}$ be a closed linear subspace invariant to T such that

$\sigma(T|\mathscr{Y}) \subset \sigma$. Then $(\lambda I|\mathscr{Y} - T|\mathscr{Y})^{-1}$ exists for all $\lambda \notin \sigma$. In this manner if $y \in \mathscr{Y}$, we have

$$\mathbf{E}(\sigma, T)\, y = \frac{1}{2\pi i}\int_{\Gamma} R(\lambda, T)\, y\, d\lambda = \frac{1}{2\pi i}\int_{\Gamma} R(\lambda, T|\mathscr{Y})\, y\, d\lambda$$

$$= \frac{1}{2\pi i}\int_{|\lambda| = \|T\| + 1} R(\lambda, T|\mathscr{Y})\, y\, d\lambda$$

$$= \frac{1}{2\pi i}\int_{|\lambda| = \|T\| + 1} R(\lambda, T)\, y\, d\lambda = y,$$

so that $y \in \mathbf{E}(\sigma, T)\,\mathscr{X}$, hence $\mathscr{Y} \subset \mathbf{E}(\sigma|T)\,\mathscr{X}$.

Notes and Remarks

The concept of an operator with the single-valued extension property was introduced by N. Dunford in Refs. 26 and 27. We remark that his definition requires both the unicity and the analytic extendibility of $(\lambda I - T)^{-1} x$ defined on $\varrho(T)$ (where $x \in \mathscr{X}$). The form of our definition of the single-valued extension property seems to occur for the first time in Ref. 39.

The second assertion in Proposition 1.2 is in fact Lemma 1.6 of Ref. 26, while the third is Lemma 1.12 of the same paper. The latter result has been obtained in the hypothesis that "$\mathscr{X}_T(F)$ is closed for every closed set $F \subset C$." The same result has been obtained without this hypothesis in Refs. 27 and 28. It seems that the point (v) of Proposition 1.2 appears for the first time explicitly in Ref. 19.

In Lemma 1.39 of Ref. 26 it is shown that if T is a spectral operator on a Banach space $\mathscr{X}$, $\mathbf{E}$ its resolution of identity, and σ a closed set $\subset C$, then $\mathbf{E}(\sigma)\, x = x$ if and only if $\sigma_T(x) \subset \sigma$ which is equivalent to $\mathbf{E}(\sigma)\,\mathscr{X} = \mathscr{X}_T(\sigma)$.

It seems that Proposition 1.3–1.4 and Theorems 1.5–1.6 are new. However, the relation

$$\mathscr{X}_{f(T)}(F) = \mathscr{X}_T\left(f^{-1}(F)\right)$$

has been obtained earlier by Maeda (Ref. 83, Proposition 1) for functions of m-times continuous differentiable with compact support and for scalar generalized operators T.

The first example of an operator without the single-valued extension property is due to S. Kakutani.[53] Example 1.7 given here is in fact an abstract form of Kakutani's result.

Sufficient conditions that an operator be without the single-valued extension property were given by G. M. Kesel'man in Ref. 58.

The notion of quasinilpotent equivalence was introduced in Ref. 19; it was suggested by a result from Ref. 39 (Proposition 4). This equivalence could be called *uniform*. In an evident manner one can introduce the notion *strong* or *weak* quasinilpotent equivalence. However these quasi-nilpotent equivalences are all equivalent. Indeed, evidently "uniform" ⇒ "strong" ⇒ "weak". The implication "weak" ⇒ "uniform" follows from the following.

LEMMA. *Let $\mathscr{X}$ be a Banach space and $A_n \in \mathbf{B}(\mathscr{X})$ $(n \in N)$. If*

$$\lim_{n\to\infty} |\langle A_n x, x^* \rangle|^{1/n} = 0 \quad \textit{for every} \quad x \in \mathscr{X} \quad \textit{and } x^* \in \mathscr{X}^*$$

then

$$\lim_{n\to\infty} \|A_n\|^{1/n} = 0.$$

Proof. Let $\varepsilon > 0$ and $x \in \mathscr{X}$, $x^* \in \mathscr{X}^*$, then there exists a $M(x, x^*) \geqslant 0$ such that

$$|\langle A_n x, x^* \rangle| \leqslant M(x, x^*)\, \varepsilon^n \quad \text{for all} \quad n \in N.$$

Putting $B_n = A_n/\varepsilon^n$, we get

$$|\langle B_n x, x^* \rangle| \leqslant M(x, x^*), \quad (n \in N)$$

hence by the Banach-Steinhaus' theorem (Ref. 30, II, § 3, No. 21) there exists a constant $M \geqslant 0$ such that

$$\|B_n\| \leqslant M, \quad (n \in N)$$

i.e. $\|A_n\| \leqslant M\varepsilon^n$, hence

$$\overline{\lim_{n\to\infty}} \|A_n\|^{1/n} \leqslant \varepsilon.$$

$\varepsilon > 0$ being arbitrary chosen, we get $\lim_{n\to\infty} \|A_n\|^{1/n} = 0$.

Let us mention also another type of equivalence introduced by C. Apostol in a forthcoming paper.[1] By Ref. 1 two operators $A, B \in \mathbf{B}(\mathscr{X})$ are *asymptotically equivalent* if

$$\lim_{n\to\infty} \|A^n - B^n\|^{1/n} = 0.$$

Apostol showed that the asymptotic equivalence implies the quasinilpotent equivalence; moreover, in certain cases, that $A = B$.

Theorems 2.2–2.4 appear for the first time in Ref. 19.

The concept of spectral *maximal* space seems to have been explicitly formulated for the first time in Ref. 41.

Let us mention a paper of Bishop[11] where related questions can be found. For instance Bishop introduced the space $M(F, T) = \overline{\mathscr{X}_T(F)}$, and the set $N(F, T)$ of all vectors $x \in \mathscr{X}$ which have the property that for each $\varepsilon > 0$ there exists an $\mathscr{X}$-valued analytic function on $\complement F$ such that

$$\|(\lambda I - T) f(\lambda) - x\| < \varepsilon \quad \text{for all} \quad \lambda \in \complement F.$$

It is clear from the definition that $N(F, T)$ is closed and that $M(F, T)$ is a subspace (in general proper) of $N(F, T)$.

Let us remark that from our results it follows that if T has the single-valued extension property and $\mathscr{X}_T(F)$ is closed, then

$$N(F, T) = \mathscr{X}_T(F).$$

The results from 3.2–3.7 were obtained in Ref. 41. Proposition 3.8 was published in Ref. 19.

Chapter 2

Decomposable Operators

1. The Structure of Spectral Maximal Spaces of Decomposable Operators

1.1. Definition. An operator $T \in \mathbf{B}(\mathscr{X})$ is called *decomposable* if for every finite open covering $\{G_i\}_{1 \leqslant i \leqslant n}$ of $\sigma(T)$ there exists a system $\{\mathscr{Y}_i\}_{1 \leqslant i \leqslant n}$ of spectral maximal spaces of T such that

$$\sigma(T|\mathscr{Y}_i) \subset G_i \text{ for every } 1 \leqslant i \leqslant n; \tag{i}$$

$$\mathscr{X} = \sum_{i=1}^{n} \mathscr{Y}_i. \tag{ii}$$

1.2. Lemma. *If T is decomposable and if there is no spectral maximal space $\mathscr{Y} \neq \{0\}$ of T such that $\sigma(T|\mathscr{Y}) \subset G$, where G is an open fixed set, then*

$$G \cap \sigma(T) = \varnothing.$$

Proof. Let $G_1 = G$, and G_2 be arbitrary under the condition $\sigma(T) \subset G_1 \cup G_2$. Let $\{\mathscr{Y}_i\}_{i=1,2}$ be a corresponding system of spectral maximal spaces. From $\sigma(T|\mathscr{Y}_1) \subset G_1 = G$ we have necessarily $\mathscr{Y}_1 = \{0\}$, hence $\mathscr{X} = \mathscr{Y}_2$ and consequently $\sigma(T) = \sigma(T|\mathscr{Y}_2) \subset G_2$. This shows that $\sigma(T)$ is included in every open set G_2 such that $G \cup G_2 \supset \sigma(T)$. Now, if $\lambda_0 \in G$, then we can take $G_2 = \{\lambda \in C \,|\, |\lambda| < \|T\| + 1, |\lambda - \lambda_0| > r$ for r sufficiently small. But $\sigma(T) \subset G_2$, hence $\lambda_0 \notin \sigma(T)$.

1.3. Theorem. *If T is decomposable then*

$$\sigma_p^0(T) = \sigma_r^0(T) = \varnothing.$$

Proof. Suppose the contrary. For instance let G be a component of $\sigma_p^0(T)$. Then by Proposition 1.3.7 there is no spectral maximal space $\mathscr{Y} \neq \{0\}$ of T such that $\sigma(T|\mathscr{Y}) \subset G$, so that by Lemma 1.2, $G \cap \sigma(T) = \varnothing$, hence $G \cap \sigma_p^0(T) = \varnothing$, which is impossible [since $G \subset \sigma_p^0(T)$]. Analogously for $\sigma_r^0(T)$.

1.4. COROLLARY. *If T is decomposable, then*

(i) *T has the single-valued extension property;*
(ii) $\sigma(T) = \sigma_l(T)$.

This corollary permits to consider for any $x \in \mathscr{X}$ the sets $\varrho_T(x)$ and $\sigma_T(x)$, and the $\mathscr{X}$-valued analytic function $x(\lambda)$ (see Definition 1.1.1).

1.5. THEOREM. *Let T be decomposable. Then for all $F \subset \sigma(T)$, F closed, $\mathscr{X}_T(F)$ (see* 1.1.1) *is a spectral maximal space of T, and $\sigma(T|\mathscr{X}_T(F)) \subset F$. Conversely, if $\mathscr{Y}$ is a spectral maximal space of T, then*

$$\mathscr{Y} = \mathscr{X}_T\big(\sigma(T|\mathscr{Y})\big).$$

Proof. Let $F \subset \sigma(T)$ be closed and fixed, and let G be an open set arbitrary under the condition $G \supset F$. Choose another open set H such that $F \cap \bar{H} = \emptyset$ and $G \cup H \supset \sigma(T)$, and put $G_1 = G, G_2 = H$. Let $\{\mathscr{Y}_i\}_{i=1,2}$ be a corresponding system of spectral maximal spaces of T, and let $x \in \mathscr{X}_T(F)$; then

$$\sigma(T|\mathscr{Y}_i) \subset G_i, \quad (i = 1, 2),$$

$$x = y_1 + y_2, \quad \text{with} \quad y_i \in \mathscr{Y}_i, \quad (i = 1, 2).$$

Now for $\lambda \in \complement F \cap \varrho(T|\mathscr{Y}_2)$ we have

$$(\lambda I - T)\,[(\lambda I|\mathscr{Y}_2 - T|\mathscr{Y}_2)^{-1} y_2 - x(\lambda)] = y_2 - x = -y_1, \tag{1}$$

hence

$$\complement F \cap \varrho(T|\mathscr{Y}_2) \subset \varrho_T(-y_1) = \varrho_T(y_1),$$

i.e.

$$\sigma_T(y_1) \subset F \cup \sigma(T|\mathscr{Y}_2) \subset F \cup \bar{G}_2.$$

Let now Γ be a finite system of curves surrounding F and contained in $\complement\bar{H} \cap \complement F$.

By (1), for $\lambda \in \Gamma$ we have

$$y_1(\lambda) = -(\lambda I|\mathscr{Y}_2 - T|\mathscr{Y}_2)^{-1} y_2 + x(\lambda),$$

hence

$$\frac{1}{2\pi i}\int_\Gamma y_1(\lambda)\,d\lambda = -\frac{1}{2\pi i}\int_\Gamma R(\lambda, T|\mathscr{Y}_2)\,y_2\,d\lambda + \frac{1}{2\pi i}\int_\Gamma x(\lambda)\,d\lambda. \tag{2}$$

But the first member of (2) belongs to $\mathcal{O}_T(y_1) \subset \mathscr{Y}_1$, in virtue of Proposition 1.3.5, and the first term of the second member is null [because

$\sigma(T|\mathscr{Y}_2)$ is "outside" of Γ]. Accordingly

$$x = \frac{1}{2\pi i}\int_{|\lambda|=\|T\|+1} R(\lambda, T)\, x\, d\lambda = \frac{1}{2\pi i}\int_\Gamma x(\lambda)\, d\lambda$$

$$= \frac{1}{2\pi i}\int_\Gamma y_1(\lambda)\, d\lambda \in \mathscr{Y}_1,$$

so that $\mathscr{X}_T(F) \subset \mathscr{Y}_1$. In other words

$$\mathscr{X}_T(F) \subset \bigcap_{G_1=G\supset F} \mathscr{Y}_1 = \mathscr{Z},$$

where $\{\mathscr{Y}_i\}_{i=1,2}$ is a system corresponding to the covering $\{G_i\}_{i=1,2}$ o $\sigma(T)$ with $G_1 = G$ open $\supset F$ and $G_2 = H$ open, $F \cap \bar{H} = \varnothing$, G, H arbitrary. On the other hand, if $z \in \mathscr{Z}$, then from $\sigma_T(z) = \sigma_{T|\mathscr{Y}_1}(z) \subset \sigma(T|\mathscr{Y}_1) \subset G$ it follows that

$$\sigma_T(z) = \bigcap_{G\supset F} G = F,$$

i.e. $z \in \mathscr{X}_T(F)$, so that $\mathscr{Z} \subset \mathscr{X}_T(F)$, hence

$$\mathscr{X}_T(F) = \bigcap_{G_1=G\supset F} \mathscr{Y}_1 .$$

Accordingly $\mathscr{X}_T(F)$ is a closed linear subspace of $\mathscr{X}$ (being a certain intersection of closed linear subspaces). Then, by Proposition 1.3.8, $\mathscr{X}_T(F)$ is a spectral maximal space of T, and $\sigma(T|\mathscr{X}_T(F)) \subset F$.

Now if $\mathscr{Y}$ is a spectral maximal space of T, from

$$\sigma\big(T|\mathscr{X}_T(\sigma(T|\mathscr{Y}))\big) \subset \sigma(T|\mathscr{Y})$$

(by the first part of the theorem) and Corollary 1.3.4 it follows that

$$\mathscr{X}_T(\sigma(T|\mathscr{Y})) \subset \mathscr{Y}.$$

Conversely, if $x \in \mathscr{Y}$, then

$$\sigma_T(x) = \sigma_{T|\mathscr{Y}}(x) \subset \sigma(T|\mathscr{Y}),$$

hence $x \in \mathscr{X}_T(\sigma(T|\mathscr{Y}))$.

1.6. Examples. We shall indicate two classes of linear operators, whose study can be considered in many ways accomplished today, and which are decomposable operators.

(i) *Compact operators are decomposable*

To this end let T be a compact operator in $\mathscr{X}$ and let $\{G_i\}_{1 \leqslant i \leqslant m}$ be a finite open covering of $\sigma(T)$. On account of the particular form of $\sigma(T)$ (see Ref. 30, VII, § 4, Theorem 5) we can choose separate parts σ_i of $\sigma(T)$ such that $\sigma_i \subset G_i$. Then

$$\mathscr{X} = \sum_{i=1}^{n} \mathbf{E}(\sigma_i, T)\,\mathscr{X},$$

and applying 1.3.10 we have that each $\mathscr{Y}_i = \mathbf{E}(\sigma_i, T)\,\mathscr{X}$ is a spectral maximal space such that $\sigma(T|\mathscr{Y}) = \sigma_i \subset G_i$. This shows that T is decomposable.

(ii) *Spectral operators* (in Dunford's sense[26,27]) *are decomposable.*

First, if T is a spectral operator it has the single-valued extension property (see Ref. 27, Theorem 2). On the other hand if $\sigma \to \mathbf{E}(\sigma)$ (σ Borel set $\subset C$) is the spectral measure of T, then on account of Dunford's formula (see Ref. 27, Theorem 4)

$$\mathscr{X}_T(F) = \mathbf{E}(F)\,\mathscr{X}, \quad (F \text{ closed} \subset C)$$

is closed, hence, by Proposition 1.3.8, a spectral maximal space. Let $\{G_i\}_{1 \leqslant i \leqslant n}$ be a finite open covering of $\sigma(T)$, and let $\{\varphi_i\}_{1 \leqslant i \leqslant n}$ be a system of continuous functions such that

$$\sum_{i=1}^{n} \varphi_i = 1 \quad \text{for any} \quad \lambda \in \sigma(T)$$

and

$$\sigma_i = \operatorname{supp}(\varphi_i) \subset G_i, \quad (1 \leqslant i \leqslant n).$$

Then, for any $x \in \mathscr{X}$, we have

$$x = \sum_{i=1}^{n} x_i, \quad \text{where} \quad x_i = U_{\varphi_i} x = \int \varphi_i(\lambda)\, d\mathbf{E}(\lambda)\, x \in \mathbf{E}(\sigma_i)\,\mathscr{X}.$$

Putting $\mathscr{Y}_i = \mathbf{E}(\sigma_i)\,\mathscr{X}$ we have the desired system of spectral maximal spaces for T.

1.7. It is evident that if $T_\alpha \in \mathbf{B}(\mathscr{X}_\alpha)$ ($\alpha = 1, 2$) and if $\mathscr{Y}_\alpha$ is a closed linear subspace of $\mathscr{X}_\alpha$ invariant to T_α, then

$$\sigma(T_1 \oplus T_2 | \mathscr{Y}_1 \oplus \mathscr{Y}_2) = \sigma(T_1 | \mathscr{Y}_1) \cup \sigma(T_2 | \mathscr{Y}_2),$$

where $\mathscr{Y}_1 \oplus \mathscr{Y}_2$ is considered as subspace of

$$\mathscr{X}_1 \oplus \mathscr{X}_2 = \{x_1 \oplus x_2 = (x_1, x_2) | x_\alpha \in \mathscr{X}_\alpha, \quad \alpha = 1, 2\}$$

and $\|x_1 \oplus x_2\| = (\|x_1\|^2 + \|x_2\|^2)^{1/2}$.

1.8. PROPOSITION. *If $T_\alpha \in \mathbf{B}(\mathscr{X}_\alpha)$ $(\alpha = 1, 2)$ are decomposable operators, then $T_1 \oplus T_2 \in \mathbf{B}(\mathscr{X}_1 \oplus \mathscr{X}_2)$ is also decomposable.*

Proof. Let $\{G_i\}_{1 \leqslant i \leqslant n}$ be a finite open covering of $\sigma(T_1 \oplus T_2) = \sigma(T_1) \cup \sigma(T_2)$. T_α $(\alpha = 1, 2)$ being decomposable there exists a system $\{\mathscr{Y}_i^\alpha\}_{1 \leqslant i \leqslant n}$ of spectral maximal spaces of T_α such that

$$\sigma(T_\alpha|\mathscr{Y}_i^\alpha) \subset G_i, \quad (1 \leqslant i \leqslant n; \alpha = 1, 2) \tag{1}$$

and

$$\mathscr{X}_\alpha = \sum_{i=1}^{n} \mathscr{Y}_i^\alpha. \tag{2}$$

We put

$$\mathscr{Y}_i = \mathscr{Y}_i^1 \oplus \mathscr{Y}_i^2, \quad (1 \leqslant i \leqslant n). \tag{3}$$

$\mathscr{Y}_i$ is a closed linear subspace of $\mathscr{X}_1 \oplus \mathscr{X}_2$, since $\mathscr{Y}_1$ and $\mathscr{Y}_2$ are closed linear subspaces of $\mathscr{X}_1$ and $\mathscr{X}_2$ respectively.

We have (see Theorem 1.5)

$$\mathscr{Y}_i^\alpha = \mathscr{X}_{\alpha T_\alpha}\big(\sigma(T|\mathscr{Y}_i^\alpha)\big). \tag{4}$$

From (3), (4), and Proposition 1.1.4 it results

$$\begin{aligned}
\mathscr{Y}_i &= \mathscr{X}_{1_{T_1}}\big(\sigma(T_1|\mathscr{Y}_i^1)\big) \oplus \mathscr{X}_{2_{T_2}}\big(\sigma(T_2|\mathscr{Y}_i^2)\big) \\
&\subset (\mathscr{X}_1 \oplus \mathscr{X}_2)_{T_1 \oplus T_2}\big(\sigma(T_1|\mathscr{Y}_i^1) \cup \sigma(T_2|\mathscr{Y}_i^2)\big) \\
&= (\mathscr{X}_1 \oplus \mathscr{X}_2)_{T_1 \oplus T_2}\big(\sigma(T_1 \oplus T_2|\mathscr{Y}_i^1 \oplus \mathscr{Y}_i^2)\big) \\
&= (\mathscr{X}_1 \oplus \mathscr{X}_2)_{T_1 \oplus T_2}\big(\sigma(T_1 \oplus T_2|\mathscr{Y}_i)\big) = \mathscr{Z}_i,
\end{aligned}$$

hence, by Propositions 1.1.4 and 1.3.7, the closed linear subspace

$$\mathscr{Z}_i = (\mathscr{X}_1 \oplus \mathscr{X}_2)_{T_1 \oplus T_2}\big(\sigma(T_1 \oplus T_2|\mathscr{Y}_i)\big)$$

is a spectral maximal space of $T_1 \oplus T_2$.

We have [on account of Proposition 1.3.7 and 1.7, and the inclusion (1)]

$$\sigma(T_1 \oplus T_2|\mathscr{Z}_i) \subset \sigma(T_1 \oplus T_2|\mathscr{Y}_i) = \sigma(T_1|\mathscr{Y}_i^1) \cup \sigma(T_2|\mathscr{Y}_i^2) \subset G_i.$$

On the other hand, from (2) and (3), we deduce

$$\begin{aligned}
\mathscr{X}_1 \oplus \mathscr{X}_2 &= \left(\sum_{i=1}^{n} \mathscr{Y}_i^1\right) \oplus \left(\sum_{i=1}^{n} \mathscr{Y}_i^2\right) \\
&= \sum_{i=1}^{n} (\mathscr{Y}_i^1 \oplus \mathscr{Y}_i^2) \subset \sum_{i=1}^{n} \mathscr{Z}_i \subset \mathscr{X}_1 \oplus \mathscr{X}_2.
\end{aligned}$$

1.9. PROPOSITION. *Let $T \in \mathbf{B}(\mathscr{X})$, and let σ be a separate part of $\sigma(T)$. If T is decomposable, then $T|\mathbf{E}(\sigma, T)\mathscr{X}$ is also decomposable, where*

$$\mathbf{E}(\sigma, T) = \frac{1}{2\pi i} \int_\Gamma R(\lambda, T)\, d\lambda$$

[Γ being a system of closed Jordan curves surrounding σ and separating the sets σ and $\sigma' = \sigma(T) \setminus \sigma$].

Proof. Let $\{G_i\}_{1 \leqslant i \leqslant n}$ be an open finite covering of $\sigma(T|\mathbf{E}(\sigma, T)\mathscr{X}) = \sigma$. Let U be an open neighborhood of σ such that $\bar{U}$ (the closure of U) belongs to the "interior" of Γ. We put $U_i = U \cap G_i$.

Let now U_0 be an open neighborhood of σ' such that $\bar{U}_0$ is on the "outside" of Γ. $\{U_i\}_{0 \leqslant i \leqslant n}$ is an open covering of $\sigma(T)$.

T being decomposable, there exists a system $\{\mathscr{Y}_i\}_{0 \leqslant i \leqslant n}$ of spectral maximal spaces of T such that

$$\sigma(T|\mathscr{Y}_i) \subset U_i, \quad (0 \leqslant i \leqslant n) \tag{1}$$

and

$$\mathscr{X} = \sum_{i=0}^{n} \mathscr{Y}_i. \tag{2}$$

For any $x \in \mathscr{Y}_i$ $(1 \leqslant i \leqslant n)$ we have

$$\sigma_T(x) = \sigma_{T|\mathscr{Y}_i}(x) \subset \sigma(T|\mathscr{Y}_i) \subset U_i,$$

hence $\complement U_i \subset \varrho_T(x)$, therefore $\Gamma \subset \varrho_T(x)$ so that

$$x = \frac{1}{2\pi i} \int_\Gamma x(\lambda)\, d\lambda = \frac{1}{2\pi i} \int_{|\lambda| = \|T\| + 1} x(\lambda)\, d\lambda$$

$$= \frac{1}{2\pi i} \int_{|\lambda| = \|T\| + 1} R(\lambda, T)\, x\, d\lambda = \mathbf{E}(\sigma, T)\, x \in \mathbf{E}(\sigma, T)\mathscr{X}.$$

Thus

$$\mathscr{Y}_i \subset \mathbf{E}(\sigma, T)\mathscr{X}, \quad (1 \leqslant i \leqslant n). \tag{3}$$

Analogously $\mathscr{Y}_0 \subset \mathbf{E}(\sigma', T)\mathscr{X}$, therefore

$$\mathbf{E}(\sigma, T)\mathscr{Y}_0 = \{0\}. \tag{4}$$

We will show that

$$\mathscr{X}^\sigma_{T|\mathscr{X}^\sigma}(F) = \mathscr{X}_T(F), \quad (F \text{ closed} \subset \sigma) \tag{5}$$

where we have put $\mathscr{X}^\sigma = \mathbf{E}(\sigma, T)\mathscr{X}$.

Indeed, if $x \in \mathscr{X}_{T|\mathscr{X}^\sigma}(F)$, then $\sigma_{T|\mathscr{X}^\sigma}(x) \subset F \subset \sigma$, but $\sigma_T(x) = \sigma_{T|\mathscr{X}^\sigma}(x)$ (because $\mathscr{X}^\sigma$ is invariant to T), hence $\sigma_T(x) \subset F$ i.e. $x \in \mathscr{X}_T(F)$.

$\mathscr{X}^\sigma$ being a spectral maximal space of T (by Proposition 1.3.10), we have

$$\mathscr{X}^\sigma = \mathscr{X}_T\left(\sigma\left(T|\mathscr{X}^\sigma\right)\right) = \mathscr{X}_T(\sigma).$$

Now if $x \in \mathscr{X}_T(F)$, then $\sigma_T(x) \subset F \subset \sigma$, i.e. $x \in \mathscr{X}_T(\sigma) = \mathscr{X}^\sigma$, so that we have $x \in \mathscr{X}^\sigma$, and $\sigma_{T|\mathscr{X}^\sigma}(x) = \sigma_T(x) \subset F$, hence $x \in \mathscr{X}^\sigma_{T|\mathscr{X}^\sigma}(F)$.

From the fact that $\mathscr{Y}_i$ is a spectral maximal space of T and from (5), it follows

$$\mathscr{Y}_i = \mathscr{X}_T\left(\sigma\left(T|\mathscr{Y}_i\right)\right) = \mathscr{X}^\sigma_{T|\mathscr{X}^\sigma}\left(\sigma\left(T|\mathscr{Y}_i\right)\right) = \mathscr{X}^\sigma_{T|\mathscr{X}^\sigma}\left(\sigma\left(\left(T|\mathscr{X}^\sigma\right)|\,\mathscr{Y}_i\right)\right),$$

hence $\mathscr{Y}_i$ is a spectral maximal space of $T|\mathscr{X}^\sigma$.

On account of (2), (4), and (3), we obtain

$$\mathscr{X}^\sigma = \mathbf{E}(\sigma, T)\,\mathscr{X} = \sum_{i=0}^{n} \mathbf{E}(\sigma, T)\,\mathscr{Y}_i = \sum_{i=1}^{n} \mathbf{E}(\sigma, T)\,\mathscr{Y}_i = \sum_{i=1}^{n} \mathscr{Y}_i \subset \mathscr{X}^\sigma,$$

i.e.

$$\mathscr{X}^\sigma = \sum_{i=1}^{n} \mathscr{Y}_i.$$

We have

$$\sigma\left(\left(T|\mathscr{X}^\sigma\right)|\mathscr{Y}_i\right) = \sigma\left(T|\mathscr{Y}_i\right) \subset U_i \subset G_i, \quad (1 \leqslant i \leqslant n).$$

1.10. THEOREM. *Let $T \in \mathbf{B}(\mathscr{X})$ be decomposable, and let $f: G \to C$ [$G \supset \sigma(T)$, G open connected] be an analytic function. Then $f(T)$ is also decomposable.*

Proof. If f is constant, evidently $f(T)$ is decomposable. Henceforth we shall suppose that is not constant. Let $F \subset \sigma(T)$ be a closed set; then $f(F)$ is closed (being compact) and $f(F) \subset f(\sigma(T)) = \sigma\left(f(T)\right)$.

From Theorem 1.1.6 and Proposition 1.1.2 it follows that

$$\mathscr{X}_{f(T)}\left(f(F)\right) = \mathscr{X}_T\left(f^{-1}\left(f(F)\right)\right) \supset \mathscr{X}_T(F). \tag{1}$$

The operator T being decomposable, $\mathscr{X}_T\left(f^{-1}\left(f(F)\right)\right)$ is closed, hence $\mathscr{X}_{f(T)}\left(f(F)\right)$ is closed, therefore (Proposition 1.3.8) $\mathscr{X}_{f(T)}\left(f(F)\right)$ is a spectral maximal space of $f(T)$ and

$$\sigma\left(f(T)|\mathscr{X}_{f(T)}\left(f(F)\right)\right) \subset \sigma\left(f(T)\right) \cap f(F). \tag{2}$$

Let $\{G_i\}_{1 \leqslant i \leqslant n}$ be a finite, open covering of $\sigma\left(f(T)\right) = f(\sigma(T))$. Then

$$\bigcup_{i=1}^{n} f^{-1}(G_i) = f^{-1}\left(\bigcup_{i=1}^{n} G_i\right) \supset f^{-1}\left(f(\sigma(T))\right) \supset \sigma(T).$$

T being decomposable, there exists a system $\{\mathcal{Y}_i\}_{1 \leqslant i \leqslant n}$ of spectral maximal spaces of T such that

$$\sigma(T|\mathcal{Y}_i) \subset f^{-1}(G_i), \quad (1 \leqslant i \leqslant n) \tag{3}$$

and

$$\mathcal{X} = \sum_{i=1}^{n} \mathcal{Y}_i. \tag{4}$$

$\mathcal{Y}_i$ being a spectral maximal space of T, and $f(T)\,T = Tf(T)$, it follows that $f(T)\,\mathcal{Y}_i \subset \mathcal{Y}_i$, hence $f(T)|\mathcal{Y}_i = f(T|\mathcal{Y}_i)$, therefore

$$\sigma(f(T)|\mathcal{Y}_i) = \sigma(f(T|\mathcal{Y}_i)) = f(\sigma(T|\mathcal{Y}_i)). \tag{5}$$

We put

$$\mathcal{X}_i = \mathcal{H}_{f(T)}(\dot{\sigma}(f(T)|\mathcal{Y}_i)).$$

$\mathcal{X}_i$ is a spectral maximal space of $f(T)$ in virtue of Proposition 1.3.8.

From (5), (1) and Theorem 1.5, we obtain

$$\mathcal{X}_i = \mathcal{X}_{f(T)}(\sigma(f(T)|\mathcal{Y}_i)) = \mathcal{X}_{f(T)}(f(\sigma(T)|\mathcal{Y}_i)) \supset \mathcal{X}_T(\sigma(T|\mathcal{Y}_i)) = \mathcal{Y}_i.$$

From this inclusion and (4) it results that

$$\mathcal{X} = \sum_{i=1}^{n} \mathcal{X}_i.$$

On account of (2), (5), and (3), we have finally

$$\sigma(f(T)|\mathcal{X}_i) = \sigma\big(f(T)|\mathcal{X}_{f(T)}(\sigma(f(T)|\mathcal{Y}_i))\big) \subset \sigma(f(T)|\mathcal{Y}_i)$$
$$= f(\sigma(T|\mathcal{Y}_i)) \subset f(f^{-1}(G_i)) \subset G_i.$$

So that $f(T)$ is decomposable.

1.11. Corollary. *Let $T \in \mathbf{B}(\mathcal{X})$ be decomposable and let $f: G \to C$ [$G \supset \sigma(T)$, G arbitrary open set] be an analytic function. Then $f(T)$ is also decomposable.*

Proof. $\sigma(T)$ being compact there is only a finite number of connected components of G which intersect $\sigma(T)$. Let these be $G_1, \ldots, G_n$ and let $f_i = f|G_i$. The sets $\sigma_i = G_i \cap \sigma(T)$ are separate parts of $\sigma(T)$. Having $\sigma(T) = \bigcup_{i=1}^{n} \sigma_i$, it results that

$$\mathcal{X} = \bigoplus_{i=1}^{n} \mathbf{E}(\sigma_i, T)\,\mathcal{X}$$

and

$$T = \bigoplus_{i=1}^{n} (T|\mathbf{E}(\sigma_i, T)\mathscr{X}).$$

$T|\mathbf{E}(\sigma_i, T)\mathscr{X}$ $(1 \leqslant i \leqslant n)$ is decomposable, by Proposition 1.9. The function f being analytic on the domain G_i, it follows from the preceding theorem that

$$f(T)|\mathbf{E}(\sigma_i, T)\mathscr{X} = f(T|\mathbf{E}_i(\sigma_i, T)\mathscr{X}) = f_i(T|\mathbf{E}(\sigma_i, T)\mathscr{X})$$

is decomposable. Therefore, by Proposition 1.8

$$f(T) = \bigoplus_{i=1}^{n} (f(T)|\mathbf{E}(\sigma_i, T)\mathscr{X})$$

is a decomposable operator.

It is evident that without some assumptions on f we cannot obtain the converse property to the preceding corollary. Such an additional condition is given in the following.

1.12. Proposition. *Let $T \in \mathbf{B}(\mathscr{X})$ and let $f: G \to C$ $[G \supset \sigma(T), G$ open$]$ be an analytic function such that $f(\lambda_1) \neq f(\lambda_2)$, if $\lambda_1 \neq \lambda_2$, $\lambda_1, \lambda_2 \in \sigma(T)$. Then if $f(T)$ is decomposable, T is also decomposable.*

Proof. Let F be a closed subset of $\sigma(T)$. Then $f(F) = F'$ is a closed set of $f(\sigma(T)) = \sigma(f(T))$, and $f^{-1}(F') \cap \sigma(T) = F$. In virtue of Theorem 1.1.6 we have

$$\mathscr{X}_{f(T)}(F') = \mathscr{X}_T(f^{-1}(F')) = \mathscr{X}_T(f^{-1}(F') \cap \sigma(T)) = \mathscr{X}_T(F),$$

hence $\mathscr{X}_T(F)$ is closed, so that, by Proposition 1.3.8, it is a spectral maximal space of T. Let now $\{G_i\}_{1 \leqslant i \leqslant n}$ be a finite open covering of $\sigma(T)$. We may suppose that $G_i \subset G$. f, being analytic, is an open mapping, thus $H_i = f(G_i)$ are open, so that $\{H_i\}_{1 \leqslant i \leqslant n}$ is an open finite covering of $\sigma(f(T))$. $f(T)$ being decomposable, there exists a system $\{\mathscr{Y}_i\}_{1 \leqslant i \leqslant n}$ of spectral maximal spaces of $f(T)$ such that

$$F'_i = \sigma(T|\mathscr{Y}_i) \subset H_i, \tag{1}$$

$$\mathscr{X} = \sum_{i=1}^{n} \mathscr{Y}_i. \tag{2}$$

But by Theorem 1.5 we have

$$\mathscr{Y}_i = \mathscr{X}_{f(T)}(F_i'),$$

so that

$$\mathscr{Y}_i = \mathscr{X}_T(f^{-1}(F_i)) = \mathscr{X}_T(F_i), \quad \text{where} \quad F_i = f^{-1}(F_i') \cap \sigma(T).$$

In virtue of the remark at the beginning of the proof, $\mathscr{Y}_i$ is a spectral maximal space of T. Moreover, using once more Theorem 1.5 we obtain

$$\sigma(T|\mathscr{Y}_i) \subset F_i \subset f^{-1}(H_i) \cap \sigma(T) = G_i \cap \sigma(T) \subset G_i.$$

These inclusions, valid for $i = 1, 2, \dots n$, together with (2) show that T is decomposable.

As an immediate consequence of Corollary 1.11 and Proposition 1.12 one obtains

1.13. Corollary. *Let $T \in \mathbf{B}(\mathscr{X})$ and let $\sigma(T)$ be contained in an angle [closed] $< 2\pi/k$ with vertex in the origin, where k is an integer > 0. Then T is decomposable if and only if T^k is decomposable.*

1.14. *Remark.* Let us notice that Proposition 1.12 is not a corollary of Proposition 1.10 applied to $f(T)$. To see this, let $\mathscr{X}$ be the space of the square integrable functions on the unit disk and let

$$Tu(s,t) = (s^2 + t^2)^{1/5} e^{2i/5 \operatorname{Arg}(s+it)} u(s,t), \quad (u \in \mathscr{X}),$$

where the Arg is taken with values in $[0, 2\pi)$. It is evident that

$$\sigma(T) = \left\{\lambda \in C \mid |\lambda| \leqslant 1, \quad 0 \leqslant \operatorname{Arg} \lambda \leqslant \frac{4\pi}{5}\right\},$$

$$\sigma(T^2) = \left\{\lambda \in C \mid |\lambda| \leqslant 1, \quad 0 \leqslant \operatorname{Arg} \lambda \leqslant \frac{8\pi}{5}\right\}. \tag{1}$$

In this way there are operators which verify (1). On the other hand, Proposition 1.12 can be always used when T verifies (1), and $f(\lambda) = \lambda^2$. But there is no analytic function $f_1 : G_i \to C$ [$G_1 \supset \sigma(T)$ open], with $T_1 = T^2$ such that $f_1(T_1) = T$ (so that corollary 1.11 may be applied). Indeed if such a function did exist then $f_1(\lambda^2) = \lambda$ in a neighborhood of $\sigma(T)$. In particular $f_1'(\lambda^2)\, 2\lambda|_{\lambda=0} = 1$: contradiction.

2. Quasinilpotent Equivalence of Decomposable Operators

2.1. THEOREM. *Let $T_1, T_2 \in \mathbf{B}(\mathscr{X})$. If T_1 is decomposable and $T_1 \overset{q}{\sim} T_2$, then T_2 is also decomposable and*

$$\mathscr{X}_{T_1}(F) = \mathscr{X}_{T_2}(F),$$

for every closed $F \subset C$.

Proof. We first observe that every spectral maximal space of T_1 is spectral maximal also of T_2. Indeed, let $\mathscr{Y} \subset \mathscr{X}$ be a spectral maximal space for T_1, then, by Theorem 1.5, it has the form

$$\mathscr{Y} = \mathscr{X}_{T_1}(\sigma(T_1|\mathscr{Y})). \tag{1}$$

But

$$\begin{aligned} \mathscr{X}_{T_2}(\sigma(T_1|\mathscr{Y})) &= \{x \in \mathscr{X} \mid \sigma_{T_2}(x) \subset \sigma(T_1|\mathscr{Y})\} \\ &= \{x \in \mathscr{X} \mid \sigma_{T_1}(x) \subset \sigma(T_1|\mathscr{Y})\} = \mathscr{X}_{T_1}(\sigma(T_1|\mathscr{Y})) \end{aligned} \tag{2}$$

(according to Theorem 1.2.4), therefore $\mathscr{X}_{T_2}(\sigma(T_1|\mathscr{Y}))$ is closed [because $\mathscr{X}_{T_1}(\sigma(T_1|\mathscr{Y}))$ is closed], so that, in view of Proposition 1.3.8 $\mathscr{X}_{T_2}(\sigma(T_1|\mathscr{Y}))$ is spectral maximal space of T_2.

Let $\{G_i\}_{1 \leqslant i \leqslant n}$ be a finite open covering of $\sigma(T_2)$ which, according to Theorem 1.2.2, is also a covering of $\sigma(T_1)$.

T_1 being decomposable, there exists a system $\{\mathscr{Y}_i\}_{1 \leqslant i \leqslant n}$ of spectral maximal spaces of T_1 (therefore, on the basis of the above remark, also of T_2) such that

$$\sigma(T_1|\mathscr{Y}_i) \subset G_i, \quad (1 \leqslant i \leqslant n) \tag{3}$$

and every $x \in \mathscr{X}$ can be written under the form

$$x = \sum_{i=1}^{n} y_i \quad \text{with} \quad y_i \in \mathscr{Y}_i \quad (1 \leqslant i \leqslant n). \tag{4}$$

From (1) and (2) we obtain

$$\mathscr{Y}_i = \mathscr{X}_{T_1}(\sigma(T_1|\mathscr{Y}_i)) = \mathscr{X}_{T_2}(\sigma(T_1|\mathscr{Y}_i))$$

from which, according to Corollary 1.3.4 it results

$$\sigma(T_1|\mathscr{Y}_i) \subset \sigma(T_2|\mathscr{X}_{T_2}(\sigma(T_1|\mathscr{Y}_i))),$$

but on account of Proposition 1.3.8

$$\sigma(T_2|\mathscr{X}_{T_2}(\sigma(T_1|\mathscr{Y}_i))) \subset \sigma(T_1|\mathscr{Y}_i) \cap \sigma(T_2) \subset G_i,$$

therefore

$$\sigma(T_2|\mathscr{Y}_i) \subset G_i. \tag{5}$$

Relations (4) and (5) show that T_2 is decomposable. From Theorem 1.2.4 it follows that $\mathscr{X}_{T_1}(F) = \mathscr{X}_{T_2}(F)$ for every closed $F \subset C$.

Remark. By using Uryshon's lemma (Ref. 13, § 4, Theorem 1) it is possible to prove the above theorem without using Theorem 1.2.4.

2.2. THEOREM. *If $T_1, T_2 \in \mathbf{B}(\mathscr{X})$ are decomposable operators such that*

$$\mathscr{X}_{T_1}(F) = \mathscr{X}_{T_2}(F), \quad \textit{for every closed set } F \subset C, \tag{1}$$

then $T_1 \overset{q}{\sim} T_2$.

Proof. Let $\varepsilon > 0$ and let $\{G_i\}_{1 \leqslant i \leqslant n}$ be a finite, open covering of $\sigma(T_1)$ with $d(G_i) < \varepsilon$ $\left[d(G_i) = \sup\limits_{\lambda, \mu \in G_i} |\lambda - \mu|\right]$. The operator T_1 being decomposable, there exists a system $\{\mathscr{Y}_i\}_{1 \leqslant i \leqslant n}$ of spectral maximal spaces of T_1, such that

$$\sigma(T|\mathscr{Y}_i) \subset G_i, \quad (1 \leqslant i \leqslant n) \tag{2}$$

and every $x \in \mathscr{X}$ is of the form $x = \sum\limits_{i=1}^{n_\varepsilon} y_i$ with $y_i \in \mathscr{Y}_i$.

From Theorem 1.5 and from relation (1) we obtain

$$\mathscr{Y}_i = \mathscr{X}_{T_1}(\sigma(T_1|\mathscr{Y}_i)) = \mathscr{X}_{T_2}(\sigma(T_1|\mathscr{Y}_i)),$$

therefore, in view of the same theorem, $\mathscr{Y}_i$ is a spectral maximal space also of T_2.

If we note

$$X_{\alpha,i} = (T_\alpha - \lambda_i I)|\mathscr{Y}_i, \quad (\alpha = 1, 2; 1 \leqslant i \leqslant n_\varepsilon) \tag{3}$$

(where $\lambda_i \in G_i$), applying the "mapping spectral theorem" (Ref. 30, VII, § 3, Theorem 11) and having in view (2), we obtain

$$\begin{aligned} \sigma(X_{\alpha,i}) &= (id - \lambda_i)[\sigma(T_\alpha|\mathscr{Y}_i)] = \{\lambda - \lambda_i \,|\, \lambda \in \sigma(T_\alpha|\mathscr{Y}_i)\} \\ &\subset \{\lambda - \lambda_i | \lambda \in G_i\} \subset \{\mu \,|\, |\mu| < \varepsilon\}. \end{aligned} \tag{4}$$

From the equality $\lim\limits_{n\to\infty} \|T^n\|^{1/n} = \sup\limits_{\lambda \in \sigma(T)} |\lambda|$, which holds for every $T \in \mathbf{B}(\mathscr{X})$ (Ref. 30, VII, § 3, Lemma 4), and from (4) we obtain

$$\lim_{n\to\infty} \|X_{\alpha,i}^n\|^{1/n} = \sup_{\lambda \in \sigma(X_{\alpha,i})} |\lambda| \leqslant \varepsilon,$$

whence it follows [using the same argument as in the proof of relation (3) from 1.2.1] the existence of a constant $M_\varepsilon > 0$ such that

$$\|X^n_{\alpha,i}\| < \varepsilon^n M_\varepsilon \quad \text{for every} \quad n \geqslant 0 \quad \text{and} \quad 1 \leqslant i \leqslant n_\varepsilon. \tag{5}$$

We obtain from (5)

$$\|(X_{1,i} - X_{2,i})^{[n]}\| = \|\sum_{k=0}^{n} (-1)^{n-k} \binom{n}{k} X^k_{1,i} X^{n-k}_{2,i}\| \leqslant \sum_{k=0}^{n} \binom{n}{k} \|X^k_{1,i}\| \times$$

$$\times \|X^{n-k}_{2,i}\| \leqslant M^2_\varepsilon \sum_{k=0}^{n} \binom{n}{k} \varepsilon^k \varepsilon^{n-k} = M^2_\varepsilon (2\varepsilon)^n. \tag{6}$$

Let $\mathscr{Y} = \mathscr{Y}_1 \oplus \cdots \oplus \mathscr{Y}_n$. The linear mapping $y_1 \oplus \cdots \oplus y_{n_\varepsilon} \to y_1 + \cdots + y_{n_\varepsilon}$ from $\mathscr{Y}$ to $\mathscr{X}$ being continuous and surjective, it follows from the theorem of closed graph (Ref. 47, Theorem 2.12.1) that there exists a constant $M \geqslant 0$ such that, for every $x \in \mathscr{X}$ there is a $y_1 \oplus \cdots \oplus y_{n_\varepsilon}$ with $x = y_1 + \cdots + y_{n_\varepsilon}$ and

$$\|y_1\| + \cdots + \|y_{n_\varepsilon}\| \leqslant M \|x\|. \tag{7}$$

From (3), (6), and (7) follows, for every $x \in \mathscr{X}$,

$$\|(T_1 - T_2)^{[n]} x\| = \|\sum_{i=1}^{n_\varepsilon} (T_1 - T_2)^{[n]} y_i\| \leqslant \sum_{i=1}^{n_\varepsilon} \|(T_1 - T_2)^{[n]} y_i\|$$

$$= \sum_{i=1}^{n_\varepsilon} \|(X_{1,i} - X_{2,i})^{[n]} y_i\| \leqslant \sum_{j=1}^{n_\varepsilon} \|(X_{1,i} - X_{2,i})^{[n]}\| \cdot \|y_i\|$$

$$\leqslant M^2_\varepsilon (2\varepsilon)^n \sum_{i=1}^{n_\varepsilon} \|y_i\| \leqslant M M^2_\varepsilon (2\varepsilon)^n \|x\|,$$

whence

$$\|(T_1 - T_2)^{[n]}\| \leqslant M M^2_\varepsilon (2\varepsilon)^n,$$

therefore

$$\overline{\lim_{n\to\infty}} \|(T_1 - T_2)^{[n]}\|^{1/n} \leqslant 2\varepsilon \lim_{n\to\infty} (M M^2_\varepsilon)^{1/n} = 2\varepsilon.$$

$\varepsilon > 0$ being arbitrary, we have $\lim_{n\to\infty} \|(T_1 - T_2)^{[n]}\|^{1/n} = 0$. Analogously one can show that $\lim_{n\to\infty} \|(T_2 - T_1)^{[n]}\|^{1/n} = 0$.

2.3. Corollary. *If $T_1, T_2 \in \mathbf{B}(\mathscr{X})$ are decomposable, then $T_1 \overset{q}{\sim} T_2$ if and only if $\mathscr{X}_{T_1}(F) = \mathscr{X}_{T_2}(F)$, for every closed $F \subset C$.*

2.4. COROLLARY. *If $T_1, T_2 \in \mathbf{B}(\mathscr{X})$ are spectral operators and $\mathbf{E}_1, \mathbf{E}_2$ their spectral measures, then $T_1 \overset{a}{\sim} T_2$ if and only if $\mathbf{E}_1 = \mathbf{E}_2$.*

Proof. Let us suppose that $\mathbf{E}_1 = \mathbf{E}_2$, then in view of one of Dunford's results (Ref. 27, Theorem 4) we have

$$\mathscr{X}_{T_1}(F) = \{x \in \mathscr{X} | \sigma_{T_1}(x) \subset F\} = \mathbf{E}_1(F)\,\mathscr{X} = \mathbf{E}_2(F)\,\mathscr{X}$$
$$= \{x \in \mathscr{X} | \sigma_{T_2}(x) \subset F\} = \mathscr{X}_{T_2}(F),$$

for every closed $F \subset C$. Therefore, according to Theorem 2.2, $T_1 \overset{a}{\sim} T_2$.

Conversely, let us suppose that $T_1 \overset{a}{\sim} T_2$. Then, applying Theorem 2.1, it results

$$\mathbf{E}_1(F)\,\mathscr{X} = \mathscr{X}_{T_1}(F) = \mathscr{X}_{T_2}(F) = \mathbf{E}_2(F)\,\mathscr{X}, \quad (F \subset C \text{ closed})$$

therefore (Ref. 30, IX, § 9, exercise 23)

$$\mathbf{E}_2(F)\,\mathbf{E}_1(F) = \mathbf{E}_1(F). \tag{1}$$

It is known that in a metric space every open set G is of type F_σ; more precisely $G = \bigcup_{n=1}^{\infty} F_n$ with $F_n \subset F_{n+1}$ closed. Therefore if $G \subset C$ is open, then

$$\mathbf{E}_2(G)\,\mathbf{E}_1(G) = \mathbf{E}_2\,(\lim_{n\to\infty} F_n)\,\mathbf{E}_1\,(\lim_{n\to\infty} F_n) = \lim_{n\to\infty} \mathbf{E}_2(F_n)\,\mathbf{E}_1(F_n)$$
$$= \lim_{n\to\infty} \mathbf{E}_1(F_n) = \mathbf{E}_1(G),$$

where the convergences take place in the strong-operator topology. As $G = \complement F$ with F closed, it follows that

$$I - \mathbf{E}_2(F) - \mathbf{E}_1(F) + \mathbf{E}_2(F)\,\mathbf{E}_1(F) = [I - \mathbf{E}_2(F)]\,[I - \mathbf{E}_1(F)]$$
$$= \mathbf{E}_2\,(\complement F)\,\mathbf{E}_1\,(\complement F) = \mathbf{E}_1\,(\complement F)$$
$$= I - \mathbf{E}_1(F),$$

hence

$$\mathbf{E}_2(F)\,\mathbf{E}_1(F) = \mathbf{E}_2(F). \tag{2}$$

From (1) and (2) follows

$$\mathbf{E}_1(F) = \mathbf{E}_2(F) \quad \text{for every closed set} \quad F \subset C, \tag{3}$$

therefore also

$$\mathbf{E}_1(G) = \mathbf{E}_2(G) \quad \text{for every open set} \quad G \subset C. \tag{4}$$

For every $x \in \mathscr{X}$ and $x^* \in \mathscr{X}^* = \mathbf{B}(X, C)$ the measures $\langle \mathbf{E}_1(\cdot)\, x, x^* \rangle$ and $\langle \mathbf{E}_2(\cdot)\, x, x^* \rangle$ being regular, from (3) or (4) it follows

$$\langle \mathbf{E}_1(B)\, x, x^* \rangle = \langle \mathbf{E}_2(B)\, x, x^* \rangle,$$

hence

$$\mathbf{E}_1(B) = \mathbf{E}_2(B) \quad \text{for every Borelian set} \quad B \subset C.$$

2.5. Corollary. *Let $T_1, T_2 \in \mathbf{B}(\mathscr{H})$. If T_1 is spectral and $T_1 \overset{a}{\sim} T_2$, then also T_2 is spectral.*

Proof. Let $\mathbf{E}$ be the spectral measure of T_1. We will show that T_2 is spectral with the spectral measure $\mathbf{E}$.

Because $T_1 \overset{a}{\sim} T_2$, in view of Theorem 2.1 it results that $\mathscr{X}_{T_1}(F) = \mathscr{X}_{T_2}(F)$ for every $F \subset C$ closed. But

$$\mathscr{X}_{T_1}(F) = \{x \in \mathscr{X} \mid \sigma_{T_1}(F) \subset F\} = \mathbf{E}(F)\mathscr{X}$$

(Ref. 27, Theorem 4), therefore $\mathbf{E}(F)\mathscr{X}$ is a spectral maximal space of T_2, hence invariant to T_2. From $T_2\mathbf{E}(F)\mathscr{X} \subset \mathbf{E}(F)\mathscr{X}$ it follows that

$$\mathbf{E}(F)\, T_2\mathbf{E}(F) = T_2\mathbf{E}(F) \quad \text{for every} \quad F \subset C \text{ closed.} \tag{1}$$

Reasoning as in the case of the preceding corollary, we obtain

$$\mathbf{E}(G)\, T_2\mathbf{E}(G) = T_2\mathbf{E}(G) \quad \text{for every} \quad G \subset C \text{ open.} \tag{2}$$

If we write $G = \complement F$, with F closed, it results from (2) that $T_2 - \mathbf{E}(F)\, T_2 - T_2\mathbf{E}(F) + \mathbf{E}(F)\, T_2\mathbf{E}(T) = [I - \mathbf{E}(F)]\, T_2\, [I - \mathbf{E}(F)] = T_2\, [I - \mathbf{E}(F)] = T_2 - T_2\mathbf{E}(F)$, hence

$$\mathbf{E}(F)\, T_2\mathbf{E}(F) = \mathbf{E}(F)\, T_2. \tag{3}$$

From (1) and (3) follows

$$T_2\mathbf{E}(F) = \mathbf{E}(F)\, T_2 \quad \text{for every} \quad F \subset C \text{ closed.}$$

Still reasoning as in the case of the preceding corollary, we obtain

$$T_2\mathbf{E}(B) = \mathbf{E}(B)\, T_2 \quad \text{for every Borelian set} \quad B \subset C. \tag{4}$$

Let us observe that if $\mathscr{Y}$ is a closed linear subspace of $\mathscr{X}$ invariant to an operator $A \in \mathbf{B}(\mathscr{X})$, then $\|A|\mathscr{Y}\| \leqslant \|A\|$, therefore

$$\left\| [T_1|\mathbf{E}(B)\mathscr{X} - T_2|\mathbf{E}(B)\mathscr{X}]^{[n]} \right\|^{1/n} \leqslant \left\| (T_1 - T_2)^{[n]} \right\|^{1/n}$$

for every Borelian set $B \subset C$ and $n \in N$.

From this inequality and from the fact that $T_1 \overset{q}{\sim} T_2$ it follows $T_1|\mathbf{E}(B)\mathscr{X} \overset{q}{\sim} T_2\mathbf{E}(B)\mathscr{X}$, whence, in view of Theorem 1.2.2, we obtain

$$\sigma(T_1|\mathbf{E}(B)\mathscr{X}) = \sigma(T_2|\mathbf{E}(B)\mathscr{X}).$$

T_1 being spectral, we have $\sigma(T_1|\mathbf{E}(B)\mathscr{X}) \subset \bar{B}$, therefore

$$\sigma(T_2|\mathbf{E}(B)\mathscr{X}) \subset \bar{B} \quad \text{for every Borelian set} \quad B \subset C. \tag{5}$$

Relations (4) and (5) show that T_2 is spectral.

2.6. THEOREM. *If $T \in \mathbf{B}(\mathscr{X})$ is decomposable and if $A \in \mathbf{B}(\mathscr{X})$ verifies the following two conditions*

(i) *$A\mathscr{X}_T(F) \subset \mathscr{X}_T(F)$, for every closed set $F \subset C$;*

(ii) *$\sigma(A|\mathscr{X}_T(F)) \subset F$, for every closed set $F \subset C$,*

then A is decomposable, and

$$\mathscr{X}_A(F) = \mathscr{X}_T(F), \quad \textit{for every closed set} \quad F \subset C.$$

Proof. We observe that the proof is analogous to the proof of Theorem 2.2.

Let $\varepsilon > 0$ and let $\{G_i\}_{1 \leqslant i \leqslant n_\varepsilon}$ be a finite, open covering of $\sigma(T)$ with $d(G_i) < \varepsilon$ $[d(G_i) = \sup_{\lambda,\mu \in G_i} |\lambda - \mu|]$. The operator T being decomposable, there exists a system $\{\mathscr{Y}_i\}_{1 \leqslant i \leqslant n_\varepsilon}$ of spectral maximal spaces of T, such that

$$\sigma(T|\mathscr{Y}_i) \subset G_i, \quad (1 \leqslant i \leqslant n_\varepsilon)$$

and every $x \in \mathscr{X}$ is of the form $x = \sum_{i=1}^{n_\varepsilon} y_i$, with $y_i \in \mathscr{Y}_i$.

For $\lambda_i \in G_i$ arbitrary we put $T_i = (T - \lambda_i I)|\mathscr{Y}_i$ and $A_i = (A - \lambda_i I)|\mathscr{Y}_i$. By Theorem 1.6 and hypothesis (i), we have

$$A_i = (A - \lambda_i I)|\mathscr{Y}_i = (A - \lambda_i I)|\mathscr{X}_T(\sigma(T|\mathscr{Y}_i)) \in B(\mathscr{Y}_i). \tag{1}$$

Applying the "mapping spectral theorem" (Ref. 30, VII, § 3, Theorem 11) we obtain

$$\sigma(T_i) = \{\lambda - \lambda_i | \lambda \in \sigma(T|\mathscr{Y}_i)\} \subset \{\lambda - \lambda_i | \lambda \in G_i\} \subset \{\lambda | \, |\lambda| < \varepsilon\}. \tag{2}$$

We have

$$\lim_{n \to \infty} \|T_i^n\|^{1/n} = \sup_{\lambda \in \sigma(T_i)} |\lambda| \leqslant \varepsilon, \quad (1 \leqslant i \leqslant n_\varepsilon),$$

whence it follows the existence of a constant $M_\varepsilon > 0$ such that

$$\|T_i^n\| \leqslant \varepsilon^n M_\varepsilon \quad \text{for every} \quad n \geqslant 0 \quad \text{and} \quad 1 \leqslant i \leqslant n_\varepsilon. \tag{3}$$

From Theorem 1.5, and from hypothesis (ii), it follows that

$$\sigma(A|\mathscr{Y}_i) = \sigma\big(A|\mathscr{X}_T(\sigma(T|\mathscr{Y}_i))\big) \subset \sigma(T|\mathscr{Y}_i),$$

whence

$$\sigma(A_i) = \{\lambda - \lambda_i|\lambda \in \sigma(A|\mathscr{Y}_i)\} \subset \{\lambda - \lambda_i|\lambda \in \sigma(T|\mathscr{Y}_i)\} \subset \{\lambda||\lambda| < \varepsilon\}.$$

From this inclusion it follows the existence of a constant $M_\varepsilon > 0$ (we can choose M_ε to be the same as the M_ε of above) such that

$$\|A_i^n\| \leqslant \varepsilon^n M_\varepsilon \quad \text{for every} \quad n \geqslant 0 \quad \text{and} \quad 1 \leqslant i \leqslant n_\varepsilon. \tag{4}$$

We obtain from (3) and (4)

$$\|(T_i - A_i)^{[n]}\| \leqslant \sum_{k=0}^{n} \binom{n}{k} \|T_i^k\| \cdot \|A_i^{n-k}\| \leqslant M_\varepsilon^2 \sum_{k=0}^{n} \binom{n}{k} \varepsilon^k \varepsilon^{n-k} = M_\varepsilon^2 (2\varepsilon)^n. \tag{5}$$

Let $\mathscr{Y} = \mathscr{Y}_1 \oplus \cdots \oplus \mathscr{Y}_{n_\varepsilon}$. The linear mapping $y_1 \oplus \cdots \oplus y_{n_\varepsilon} \to \sum_{i=1}^{n_\varepsilon} y_i$ from $\mathscr{Y}$ to $\mathscr{X}$ being continuous and surjective, it follows from the theorem of closed graph (Ref. 47, Theorem 2.12.1) that there exists a constant $M \geqslant 0$ such that for every $x \in \mathscr{X}$ there is a $y_1 \oplus \cdots \oplus y_{n_\varepsilon} \in \mathscr{Y}$ with $x = \sum_{i=1}^{n_\varepsilon} y_i$ and

$$\sum_{i=1}^{n_\varepsilon} \|y_i\| \leqslant M \|x\|. \tag{6}$$

From (3), (4), (5), and (6) it follows, for every $x \in \mathscr{X}$,

$$\begin{aligned}\|(T - A)^{[n]} x\| &\leqslant \sum_{i=1}^{n_\varepsilon} \|(T - A)^{[n]} y_i\| = \sum_{i=1}^{n_\varepsilon} \|(T_i - A_i)^{[n]} y_i\| \\ &\leqslant \sum_{i=1}^{n_\varepsilon} \|(T_i - A_i)^{[n]}\| \cdot \|y_i\| \leqslant M_\varepsilon^2 (2\varepsilon)^n \sum_{i=1}^{n_\varepsilon} \|y_i\| \\ &\leqslant M M_\varepsilon^2 (2\varepsilon)^n \|x\|,\end{aligned}$$

whence

$$\|(T - A)^{[n]}\| \leqslant M M_\varepsilon^2 (2\varepsilon)^n,$$

therefore
$$\overline{\lim_{n\to\infty}} \|(T - A)^{[n]}\|^{1/n} \leqslant 2\varepsilon \lim_{n\to\infty} (MM_\varepsilon^2)^{1/n} = 2\varepsilon .$$

ε being arbitrary, we have $\lim_{n\to\infty} \|(T - A)^{[n]}\|^{1/n} = 0$. Analogously one can show that $\lim_{n\to\infty} \|(A - T)^{[n]}\|^{1/n} = 0$, so that $A \overset{a}{\sim} T$.

From this and Theorem 2.1 it follows that A is decomposable, and that

$$\mathscr{X}_A(F) = \mathscr{X}_T(F) \quad \text{for every closed set} \quad F \subset C.$$

3. The Commutator of Two Decomposable Operators

Let $\mathscr{X}$, $\mathscr{Y}$ be two Banach spaces. For $S \in \mathbf{B}(\mathscr{X})$ and $T \in \mathbf{B}(\mathscr{Y})$ we define

$$L(T), R(S), C(T, S): \quad \mathbf{B}(\mathscr{X}, \mathscr{Y}) \to \mathbf{B}(\mathscr{X}, \mathscr{Y})$$

by

$$L(T)\,A = TA,$$

$$R(S)\,A = AS,$$

and

$$C(T, S)A = TA - AS,$$

respectively [where $A \in \mathbf{B}(\mathscr{X}, \mathscr{Y})$], i.e.

$$C(T, S) = L(T) - R(S).$$

The linear operators $L(T)$, $R(S)$, hence also $C(T, S)$, are bounded since:

$$\|L(T)\,A\| = \|TA\| \leqslant \|T\| \cdot \|A\|,$$

$$\|R(S)\,A\| = \|AS\| \leqslant \|S\| \cdot \|A\|.$$

3.1. *Remark.* $L(T)\,R(S) = R(S)\,L(T)$ for all $S \in \mathbf{B}(\mathscr{X})$ and $T \in \mathbf{B}(\mathscr{Y})$. Indeed, for every $A \in \mathbf{B}(\mathscr{X}, \mathscr{Y})$ we have

$$L(T)\,R(S)\,(A) = L(T)\,(AS) = T(AS) = (TA)\,S = R(S)\,(TA)$$
$$= R(S)\,L(T)\,(A).$$

For every $n \geqslant 1$ we put

$$C^n(T, S)\,(A) = [L(T) - R(S)]^n\,(A) = \sum_{k=0}^{n} (-1)^k \binom{n}{k} L(T)^{n-k}\,R(S)^k\,(A)$$
$$= \sum_{k=0}^{n} (-1)^k \binom{n}{k} T^{n-k}\,AS^k.$$

3.2. *Remark.* $C^{n+1}(T,S)(A) = TC^n(T,S)(A) - C^n(T,S)(A)S$. Indeed

$$\begin{aligned} C^{n+1}(T,S)(A) &= C(T,S)[C^n(T,S)(A)] \\ &= [L(T) - R(S)][C^n(T,S)(A)] \\ &= L(T)[C^n(T,S)(A)] - R(S)[C^n(T,S)(A)] \\ &= TC^n(T,S)(A) - C^n(T,S)(A)S. \end{aligned}$$

$\mathbf{B}(\mathscr{X}, \mathscr{Y})$ may be considered as a left $\mathbf{B}(\mathscr{Y})$-module and as a right $\mathbf{B}(\mathscr{X})$-module, i.e. as a $(\mathbf{B}(\mathscr{X}), \mathbf{B}(\mathscr{Y}))$-bimodule.

3.3. THEOREM. *Let $S \in \mathbf{B}(\mathscr{X})$, $T \in \mathbf{B}(\mathscr{Y})$ be two decomposable operators, and let $A \in \mathbf{B}(\mathscr{X}, \mathscr{Y})$. Then the following two assertions are equivalent:*

(i) *$A\mathscr{X}_S(F) \subset \mathscr{X}_T(F)$ for every closed set $F \subset C$.*
(ii) $\lim_{n\to\infty} \|C^n(T,S)(A)\|^{1/n} = 0$.

Proof.
(i) $\Rightarrow$ (ii). For any $\varepsilon > 0$ let $\{G_i\}_{1 \leqslant i \leqslant n_\varepsilon}$ be an open covering of $\sigma(S)$ with $d(G_i) < \varepsilon$ [where $d(G_i)$ denotes the diameter of G_i]. The operator S being decomposable, there exists a system $\{\mathscr{X}_i\}_{1 \leqslant i \leqslant n_\varepsilon}$ of spectral maximal spaces of S such that

$$\sigma(S|\mathscr{X}_i) \subset G_i, \quad (1 \leqslant i \leqslant n_\varepsilon)$$

and

$$\mathscr{X} = \sum_{i=1}^{n_\varepsilon} \mathscr{X}_i.$$

Take

$$\sigma_i = \sigma(S|\mathscr{X}_i)$$

and

$$\mathscr{Y}_i = \mathscr{Y}_T(\sigma_i).$$

By Theorem 1.5 we have

$$\mathscr{X}_i = \mathscr{X}_S(\sigma_i).$$

For $\lambda_i \in G_i$ we put

$$S_i = (S - \lambda_i I)|\mathscr{X}_i \quad \text{and} \quad T_i = (T - \lambda_i I)|\mathscr{Y}_i;$$

obviously $S_i \in \mathbf{B}(\mathscr{X}_i)$ and $T_i \in \mathbf{B}(\mathscr{Y}_i)$.

Applying the "mapping spectral theorem" we obtain:

$$\sigma(S_i) = \{\lambda - \lambda_i | \lambda \in \sigma_i\} \subset \{\lambda - \lambda_i | \lambda \in G_i\} \subset \{\lambda \,|\, |\lambda| \leqslant \varepsilon\},$$

whence

$$\lim_{n\to\infty} \|S_i^n\|^{1/n} = \sup_{\lambda \in \sigma_i} |\lambda| \leqslant \varepsilon, \quad (1 \leqslant i \leqslant n_\varepsilon).$$

From this inequality it follows the existence of a constant $M'_\varepsilon > 0$ such that

$$\|S_i^n\| \leqslant \varepsilon^n M'_\varepsilon \quad \text{for every} \quad n \geqslant 0 \quad \text{and} \quad 1 \leqslant i \leqslant n_\varepsilon. \tag{1}$$

Since

$$\sigma(T_i) = \sigma(T|\mathscr{Y}_i) = \sigma(T|\mathscr{Y}_T(\sigma_i)) \subset \sigma_i \subset G_i,$$

in the same way as above there follows the existence of another constant $M''_\varepsilon > 0$ such that

$$\|T_i^n\| \leqslant \varepsilon^n M''_\varepsilon \quad \text{for every} \quad n \geqslant 0 \quad \text{and} \quad 1 \leqslant i \leqslant n_\varepsilon. \tag{2}$$

Using the same argument as in Theorem 2.6 we obtain a constant $M \geqslant 0$ such that for every $x \in \mathscr{X}$ there exists an $x_1 \oplus \cdots \oplus x_{n_\varepsilon} \in \mathscr{X}_1 \oplus \cdots \oplus \mathscr{X}_{n_\varepsilon}$ with $x = \sum_{i=1}^{n_\varepsilon} x_i$ and

$$\sum_{i=1}^{n_\varepsilon} \|x_i\| \leqslant M\|x\|. \tag{3}$$

We remark that

$$C^n(T, S)(A)\, x_i = C^n(T_i, S_i)(A)\, x_i \quad \text{for every} \quad 1 \leqslant i \leqslant n_\varepsilon. \tag{4}$$

From the relations (1)–(4) it follows

$$\begin{aligned}
\|C^n(T, S)(A)\, x\| &= \left\|\sum_{i=1}^{n_\varepsilon} C^n(T, S)(A)\, x_i\right\| = \left\|\sum_{i=1}^{n} C^n(T_i, S_i)(A)\, x_i\right\| \\
&= \left\|\sum_{i=1}^{n_\varepsilon} \sum_{k=0}^{n} (-1)^k \binom{n}{k} T_i^{n-k} A S_i^k x_i\right\| \\
&\leqslant \sum_{i=1}^{n_\varepsilon} \sum_{k=0}^{n} \binom{n}{k} \|T_i^{n-k}\| \cdot \|A\| \cdot \|S_i^k\| \cdot \|x_i\| \\
&\leqslant M'_\varepsilon M''_\varepsilon \|A\| \sum_{i=1}^{n_\varepsilon} \left(\sum_{k=0}^{n} \binom{n}{k} \varepsilon^{n-k}\varepsilon^k\right) \|x_i\| \\
&= M'_\varepsilon M''_\varepsilon \|A\| \cdot (2\varepsilon)^n \sum_{i=1}^{n_\varepsilon} \|x_i\| \leqslant M_\varepsilon (2\varepsilon)^n \|x\|
\end{aligned}$$

(where $M_\varepsilon = M'_\varepsilon M''_\varepsilon \cdot \|A\| \cdot M$), whence

$$\|C^n(T, S)(A)\| \leqslant M_\varepsilon (2\varepsilon)^n \quad \text{for all} \quad n \geqslant 1,$$

therefore

$$\overline{\lim_{n\to\infty}} \|C^n(T, S) A\|^{1/n} \leqslant 2\varepsilon.$$

$\varepsilon > 0$ being arbitrary, it follows

$$\lim_{n\to\infty} \|C^n (T, S) (A)\|^{1/n} = 0.$$

(ii) $\Rightarrow$ (i). Let $x \in \mathscr{X}_S(F)$, i.e. $\sigma_S(x) \subset F$, and let $x(\lambda)$ be the $\mathscr{X}$-valued analytic function on $\varrho_S(x)$ verifying

$$(\lambda I - S)\, x(\lambda) \equiv x. \tag{5}$$

Let $\lambda_0 \in \varrho_S(x)$ be arbitrary and $0 < r_1 < r_2$ such that $D_2 \subset \varrho_S(x)$ (where $D_i = \{\lambda \in C \,|\, |\lambda - \lambda_0| < r_i\}, i = 1, 2$). Denote by M the maximum of $\|x(\lambda)\|$ on $\{\lambda \in C \,|\, |\lambda - \lambda_0| = r_2\}$. For $\lambda \in D_1$ we then have

$$\left\|\frac{x^{(n)}(\lambda)}{n!}\right\| = \left\|\frac{1}{2\pi i}\int_{|\xi - \lambda_0| = r_2} \frac{x(\xi)\, d\xi}{(\xi - \lambda)^{n+1}}\right\| \leqslant \frac{Mr^2}{(r_2 - r_1)^{n+1}}. \tag{6}$$

Since $\lim_{n\to\infty} \|C^n (T, S) (A)\|^{1/n} = 0$ it results that for every $\varepsilon > 0$ there exists a $M_\varepsilon > 0$ such that

$$\|C^n (T, S) (A)\| < \varepsilon^n M_\varepsilon \quad \text{for every} \quad n \geqslant 0. \tag{7}$$

From (6) and (7) it follows that

$$\left\|C^n (T, S) (A) \frac{x^{(n)}(\lambda)}{n!}\right\| \leqslant \|C^n (T, S) (A)\| \cdot \left\|\frac{x^{(n)}(\lambda)}{n!}\right\|$$
$$< \frac{M_\varepsilon M_{r_2}}{r_2 - r_1}\left(\frac{\varepsilon}{r_2 - r_1}\right)^n$$

from which, by taking $\varepsilon = \frac{1}{2}(r_2 - r_1)$, we obtain

$$\left\|C^n (T, S) (A) \frac{x^{(n)}(\lambda)}{n!}\right\| < \frac{M_0}{2^n}, \quad \text{for every} \quad n \geqslant 0, \tag{8}$$

where M_0 does not depend on $\lambda \in D_1$.

This relation shows that the series

$$\sum_{n=0}^{\infty} (-1)^n C^n (T, S) (A) \frac{x^{(n)}(\lambda)}{n!}$$

[where $C^0 (T, S) (A) = A$] converges absolutely and uniformly in D_1, therefore, $D_1 \subset \varrho_S(x)$ being arbitrary [because $\lambda_0 \in \varrho_S(x)$ is arbitrary] it converges absolutely and uniformly on every compact $K \subset \varrho_S(x)$. It follows that the $\mathscr{Y}$-valued function

$$y(\lambda) = \sum_{n=0}^{\infty} (-1)^n C^n (T, S) (A) \frac{x^{(n)}(\lambda)}{n!} \tag{9}$$

is analytic on $\varrho_S(x)$. We shall show that

$$(\lambda I - T) y(\lambda) \equiv Ax \quad \text{on } \varrho_S (x). \tag{10}$$

For this, recall first the following relation:

$$(\lambda I - S) x^{(n)}(\lambda) \equiv -n x^{(n-1)}(\lambda), \quad \lambda \in \varrho_S (x). \tag{11}$$

Using the relations (9), (11), (5) as well as Remark 3.2, we obtain

$$(\lambda I - T) y(\lambda) = \sum_{n=0}^{\infty} (-1)^n (\lambda I - T) C^n (T, S) (A) \frac{x^{(n)}(\lambda)}{n!}$$

$$= \sum_{n=0}^{\infty} (-1)^n C^n (T, S) (A) \frac{\lambda x^{(n)}(\lambda)}{n!} - \sum_{n=0}^{\infty} (-1)^n T C^n (T, S) (A) \frac{x^{(n)}(\lambda)}{n!}$$

$$= \sum_{n=0}^{\infty} (-1)^n C^n (T, S) (A) \frac{\lambda x^{(n)}(\lambda)}{n!} - \sum_{n=0}^{\infty} (-1)^n C^{n+1} (T, S) (A) \frac{x^{(n)}(\lambda)}{n!}$$

$$- \sum_{n=0}^{\infty} (-1)^n C^n (T, S) (A) S \frac{x^{(n)}(\lambda)}{n!}$$

$$= \sum_{n=0}^{\infty} (-1)^n C^n (T, S) (A) (\lambda I - S) \frac{x^{(n)}(\lambda)}{n!}$$

$$- \sum_{n=0}^{\infty} (-1)^n C^{n+1} (T, S) (A) \frac{x^{(n)}(\lambda)}{n!} = A (\lambda I - S) x(\lambda)$$

$$+ \sum_{n=1}^{\infty} (-1)^n C^n (T, S) (A) (\lambda I - S) \frac{x^{(n)}(\lambda)}{n!}$$

$$- \sum_{n=0}^{\infty} (-1)^n C^{n+1} (T, S) (A) \frac{x^{(n)}(\lambda)}{n!}$$

$$= Ax + \sum_{n=1}^{\infty} (-1)^{n-1} C^n (T, S) \frac{x^{(n-1)}(\lambda)}{(n-1)!}$$

$$- \sum_{n=0}^{\infty} (-1)^n C^{n+1} (T, S) (A) \frac{x^{(n)}(\lambda)}{n!} = Ax.$$

Thus the identity (10) is verified, therefore $\varrho_S(x) \subset \varrho_T(Ax)$, i.e. $\sigma_T(Ax) \subset \sigma_S(x) \subset F$, hence $Ax \in \mathscr{Y}_T(F)$. Consequently

$$A\mathscr{X}_S(F) \subset \mathscr{Y}_T(F).$$

If $\mathscr{X} = \mathscr{Y}$ and $S = T$, we then put

$$C_T^n(A) = C^n(T, T)(A).$$

3.4. Corollary. *Let $T \in \mathbf{B}(\mathscr{X})$ be a decomposable operator and let $A \in \mathbf{B}(\mathscr{X})$. Then the following two statements are equivalent:*

(i) *$A\mathscr{X}_T(F) \subset \mathscr{X}_T(F)$, for all closed set $F \subset C$,*

(ii) $\lim_{n\to\infty} \|C_T^n(A)\|^{1/n} = 0$.

The following corollary gives a short proof of Corollary 2.2.

3.5. Corollary. *If $T, S \in \mathbf{B}(\mathscr{X})$ are two decomposable operators, then the following two statements are equivalent*

(i) *$\mathscr{X}_S(F) = \mathscr{X}_T(F)$, for all closed set $F \subset C$*

(ii) $S \overset{q}{\sim} T$.

Proof. We remark firstly that

$$C^n(T, S)(I) = (T - S)^{[n]}.$$

Taking in Theorem 3.3 $\mathscr{X} = \mathscr{Y}$ and $A = I$, we obtain that

$$\mathscr{X}_S(F) \subset \mathscr{X}_T(F) \quad \text{for all closed} \quad F \subset C$$

if and only if

$$\lim_{n\to\infty} \|(T - S)^{[n]}\|^{1/n} = 0.$$

Replacing T by S and vice-versa we obtain also

$$\mathscr{X}_T(F) \subset \mathscr{X}_S(F) \quad \text{for all closed} \quad F \subset C$$

if and only if

$$\lim_{n\to\infty} \|(S - T)^{[n]}\|^{1/n} = 0.$$

This proves the corollary.

3.6. COROLLARY. *Let $S, T \in \mathbf{B}(\mathscr{X})$ be two spectral operators in Dunford's sense. Then*

$$\|(S - T)^{[n]}\|^{1/n} \to 0 \tag{i}$$

implies also

$$\|(T - S)^{[n]}\|^{1/n} \to 0. \tag{ii}$$

Proof. By the above argument, (i) implies

$$\mathscr{X}_S(F) \subset \mathscr{X}_T(F) \tag{1}$$

for all closed set $F \subset C$. Let $\mathbf{E}_S(\sigma)$ and $\mathbf{E}_T(\sigma)$ be the spectral measures of S and T, respectively. Then (1) is equivalent to

$$\mathbf{E}_T(F)\,\mathbf{E}_S(F) = \mathbf{E}_S(F).$$

Now using the same argument as in the proof of Corollary 2.4 we can deduce

$$\mathbf{E}_T(B)\,\mathbf{E}_S(B) = \mathbf{E}_S(B)$$

for any Borel set $B \subset C$, whence

$$\mathbf{E}_T\,(C \setminus B)\,\mathbf{E}_S(B) = (I - \mathbf{E}_T(B))\,\mathbf{E}_S(B) = \mathbf{E}_S(B) - \mathbf{E}_S(B) = 0,$$

therefore (using the last relation for $C \setminus B$ instead of B)

$$\mathbf{E}_T(B) = \mathbf{E}_T(B)\,[\mathbf{E}_S\,(C \setminus B) + \mathbf{E}_S(B)] = \mathbf{E}_T(B)\,\mathbf{E}_S\,(C \setminus B) + \mathbf{E}_T(B)\,\mathbf{E}_S(B) = \mathbf{E}_S(B).$$

It follows

$$\mathscr{X}_S(F) = \mathbf{E}_S(F)\,\mathscr{X} = \mathbf{E}_T(F)\,\mathscr{X} = \mathscr{X}_T(F) \tag{2}$$

for all closed set $F \subset C$, thus by Theorem 2.2, (ii) holds.

4. Quasisimilarity of Decomposable Operators

It is well known that $T_i \in \mathbf{B}(\mathscr{X})$ $(i = 1, 2)$ are said similar if there exists $A \in \mathbf{B}\,(\mathscr{X}_1, \mathscr{X}_2)$ such that $A^{-1} \in \mathbf{B}\,(\mathscr{X}_2, \mathscr{X}_1)$ and

$$T_1 = A^{-1} T_2 A.$$

It is obvious that if T_1 or T_2 is decomposable so is the other. In the theory of operators there is still place for another weak similarity.

4.1. DEFINITION. Let $T_i \in \mathbf{B}(\mathscr{X}_i)$ $(i = 1, 2)$. T_1 is a *quasiaffine transformation* of T_2 if there exists an $A \in \mathbf{B}(\mathscr{X}_1, \mathscr{X}_2)$ such that A^{-1} exists, is densely defined, and

$$T_1 = A^{-1}T_2A.$$

If T_1 and T_2 are each a quasiaffine transformation of the other, T_1 and T_2 are said *quasisimilar*.

4.2. LEMMA. *If $T_i \in \mathbf{B}(\mathscr{X}_i)$ are decomposable and $A \in \mathbf{B}(\mathscr{X}_1, \mathscr{X}_2)$ verifies $AT_1 = T_2A$, then*

$$A\mathscr{X}_{T_1}(F) \subset \mathscr{X}_{T_2}(F),$$

for every closed set $F \subset C$.

Proof. Let $x \in \mathscr{X}_{1T}(F)$, then $\complement F \subset \varrho_T(x)$, hence there exists an analytic $\mathscr{X}_1$-valued function f defined on $\complement F$ such that

$$(\lambda I_1 - T_1) f(\lambda) \equiv x, \quad (\lambda \in \complement F).$$

Applying A we obtain

$$(\lambda I_2 - T_2)\, Af(\lambda) = A\,(\lambda I_1 - T_1) f(\lambda) \equiv Ax, \quad (\lambda \in \complement F)$$

so that (since $Af: \complement F \to \mathscr{X}$ is analytic) $\complement F \subset \varrho_{T_2}(Ax)$, i.e. $\varrho_{T_2}(Ax) \subset F$, therefore $Ax \in \mathscr{X}_{T_2}(F)$.

4.3. LEMMA. *If $T \in \mathbf{B}(\mathscr{X})$ is decomposable and F is a closed set $\subset \sigma(T)$ such that $\mathscr{X}_T(F) = \{0\}$, then F has no interior point in $\sigma(T)$.*

Proof. Suppose the contrary. Let λ_0 be a point of F such that there exists an open set G_1 of C verifying $\lambda \in G_1 \cap \sigma(T) \subset F$.

Let G_2 be an open set such that $G_1 \cup G_2 = C$ and

$$\lambda \notin \overline{G}_2. \tag{1}$$

The operator T being decomposable there are two spectral maximal spaces $\mathscr{Y}_i$ $(i = 1, 2)$ such that

$$\sigma\,(T|\mathscr{Y}_i) \subset G_i \tag{2}$$

and

$$\mathscr{X} = \mathscr{Y}_1 + \mathscr{Y}_2. \tag{3}$$

As (Corollary 1.3.3) $\sigma(T|\mathscr{Y}_1) \subset \sigma(T)$, from (2) and $\sigma(T) \cap G_1 \subset F$ it results that $\sigma(T|\mathscr{Y}_1) \subset F \cap \sigma(T)$, hence by Theorem 2.1.5 and Proposition 1.1.2 (i), we have

$$\mathscr{Y}_1 = \mathscr{X}_T(\sigma(T|\mathscr{Y}_1)) \subset \mathscr{X}_T(F \cap \sigma(T)) = \mathscr{X}_T(F) = \{0\},$$

therefore [by (2)] $\mathscr{Y}_2 = \mathscr{X}_2$, whence

$$\sigma(T) = \sigma(T|\mathscr{Y}_2) \subset G_2. \tag{4}$$

From (1) and (4) it follows that $\lambda \notin \sigma(T)$ in contradiction with the choice of λ.

4.4. THEOREM. *If $T_i \in \mathbf{B}(\mathscr{X}_i)$ $(i = 1, 2)$ are decomposable and T_1 is a quasiaffine transformation of T_2, then*

$$\sigma(T_1) = \sigma(T_2).$$

Proof. Let $\lambda_0 \in \sigma(T_1)$ such that $\lambda_0 \in \sigma(T_2)$, then [since $\sigma(T_2)$ is closed] there exists a closed disk D_0 with center in λ_0 such that

$$D_0 \cap \sigma(T_2) = \varnothing. \tag{1}$$

As [Proposition 1.1.2 (iii)] $\sigma_{T_2}(x) = \varnothing$ only if $x = 0$, and $\sigma_{T_2}(x) \subset \sigma(T_2)$ for any $x \in \mathscr{X}_2$, it follows from (1) that

$$\mathscr{X}_{T_2}(D_0) = \{0\}. \tag{2}$$

By Lemma 4.2, we have $A\mathscr{X}_{T_1}(D_0) \subset \mathscr{X}_{T_2}(D_0)$, therefore by (2),

$$\mathscr{X}_{T_1}(D_0) \subset \operatorname{Ker} A = \{0\}$$

(since A is injective), whence by Lemma 4.3

$$\sigma(T_1) \subset \complement D_0 \not\ni \lambda_0,$$

a contradiction. Consequently $\sigma(T_1) \subset \sigma(T_2)$.

If there is a $\lambda_0 \in \sigma(T_2)$ with $\lambda_0 \notin \sigma(T_1)$, then

$$d_0 = \operatorname{dist}(\lambda_0, \sigma(T_1)) = \inf_{\lambda \in \sigma(T_1)} |\lambda_0 - \lambda| > 0.$$

Put

$$F_0 = \{\lambda \in C \mid |\lambda - \lambda_0| \geqslant d_0/2\},$$

obviously $\sigma(T_1) \subset F_0$. Therefore

$$\mathscr{X}_1 = \mathscr{X}_{T_1}(\sigma(T_1)) = \mathscr{X}_{T_1}(\sigma(T_1) \cap F_0) = \mathscr{X}_{T_1}(F_0),$$

and by Lemma 4.2 $A\mathscr{X}_1 = A\mathscr{X}_{T_1}(F_0) \subset \mathscr{X}_{T_2}(F_0)$, whence $\mathscr{X}_2 = \overline{A\mathscr{X}_1} \subset \overline{\mathscr{X}_{T_2}(F_0)} = \mathscr{X}_2(F_0)$, therefore $\mathscr{X}_{T_2}(F_0) = \mathscr{X}_2$, so that

$$\sigma(T_2) = \sigma\,(T_2|\mathscr{X}_{T_2}(F)) \subset F_0 \not\ni \lambda_0 .$$

This contradiction shows that $\sigma(T_2) \subset \sigma(T_1)$.

4.5. THEOREM. *Let $T_i \in \mathbf{B}(\mathscr{X}_i)$ $(i = 1, 2, 3)$ such that T_i is a quasiaffine transformation of T_{i+1} $(i = 1, 2)$. Suppose moreover that T_1 and T_3 are decomposable. Then to every closed set $F \subset C$ there corresponds a closed linear subspace $\mathscr{X}_2(F)$ of $\mathscr{X}$, ultrainvariant to T_2, such that*

(i) *if* $F' \subset F''$, *then* $\mathscr{X}_2(F') \subset \mathscr{X}_2(F'')$;

(ii) $\mathscr{X}_2(\varnothing) = \{0\}$, $\mathscr{X}_2\,(\sigma(T_1)) = \mathscr{X}_2$;

(iii) *if* $F' \cap F'' = \varnothing$, *then* $\mathscr{X}_2(F') \cap \mathscr{X}_2(F'') = \{0\}$.

(iv) $\mathscr{X}_2(F) \neq \{0\}$ *if* $\mathscr{X}_{T_1}(F) \neq \{0\}$ *and*

$\mathscr{X}_2(F) \neq \mathscr{X}_2$ *if* $\mathscr{X}_{T_3}(F) \neq \mathscr{X}_3$.

In particular, if $\sigma(T_1)$ does not reduce to one point, T_2 possesses nontrivial ultrainvariant subspaces.

Proof. Let

$$XT_1 = T_2X \quad \text{and} \quad YT_2 = T_3Y.$$

For any closed set $F \subset C$, we put

$$\mathscr{X}_2^-(F) = \overline{X\mathscr{X}_{T_1}(F)}, \quad \mathscr{X}_2^+(F) = Y^{-1}\,(\mathscr{X}_{T_3}(F)),$$

and†

$$\mathscr{X}_2(F) = \bigvee_{\substack{A \in \mathbf{B}(\mathscr{X}_2) \\ AT_2 = T_2A}} A\mathscr{X}_2^-(F). \tag{1}$$

$\mathscr{X}_2(F)$ is ultrainvariant to T_2, since if A, B are two operators commuting with T_2 then AB also commutes with T_2.

Let now $A \in \mathbf{B}(\mathscr{X}_2)$ be an operator commuting with T_2, then

$$YAXT_1 = YAT_2X = YT_2AX = T_3YAX,$$

† If $\{\mathscr{Y}_\gamma\}_{\gamma \in \Gamma}$ is a system of subsets of a linear normed space $\mathscr{X}$, then by $\bigvee_{\gamma \in \Gamma} \mathscr{Y}_\gamma$ we mean the closed linear subspace spanned by this system, i.e. the smallest closed linear subspace containing the set $\bigcup_{\gamma \in \Gamma} \mathscr{Y}_\gamma$.

hence by Lemma 4.2

$$YAX\mathscr{X}_{T_1}(F) \subset \mathscr{X}_{T_3}(F),$$

therefore

$$AX\mathscr{X}_{T_1}(F) \subset \mathscr{X}_2^+(F),$$

whence

$$A\mathscr{X}_2^-(F) = A\overline{X\mathscr{X}_{T_1}(F)} \subset \overline{AX\mathscr{X}_{T_1}(F)} \subset \overline{\mathscr{X}_2^+(F)} = \mathscr{X}_2^+(F) \tag{2}$$

and by (1) we have

$$\mathscr{X}_2(F) \subset \mathscr{X}_2^+(F). \tag{3}$$

Taking $A = I_2$ in (2) we get $\mathscr{X}_2^-(F) \subset \mathscr{X}_2^+(F)$. Property (iv) results readily from (3) and (1); moreover (i) is evident and so is (ii). For what concerns (iii) we remark that from (3) and Proposition 1.1.2 (iii) it follows that

$$\begin{aligned}\mathscr{X}_2(F') \cap \mathscr{X}_2(F'') \subset \mathscr{X}_2^+(F') \cap \mathscr{X}_2^+(F'') &= Y^{-1}(\mathscr{X}_{T_3}(F') \cap \mathscr{X}_{T_3}(F''))\\ &= Y^{-1}(\mathscr{X}_T(F' \cap F''))\\ &= Y^{-1}(\mathscr{X}_{T_3}(\varnothing))\\ &= Y^{-1}(\{0\}) = \{0\}.\end{aligned}$$

Notes and Remarks

The concept of decomposable operator was introduced in Ref. 41. Let us remark, however, that every decomposable operator admits a duality theory of type 3 in Bishop's sense (Ref. 12, Definition 5).

We remark that Definition 1.1 is equivalent to the following.

DEFINITION 1.1′. The operator $T \in \mathbf{B}(\mathscr{X})$ is called decomposable if for every finite open covering $\{G_i\}_{1 \leqslant i \leqslant n}$ of $\sigma(T)$ there exists spectral maximal spaces $\{\mathscr{X}_i\}_{1 \leqslant i \leqslant n}$ of T such that

$$\sigma(T|\mathscr{Y}_i) \subset \overline{G}_i \quad (1 \leqslant i \leqslant n); \tag{i'}$$

$$\mathscr{X} = \sum_{i=1}^{n} \mathscr{Y}_i. \tag{ii}$$

Obviously Definition 1.1 implies Definition 1.1′. Conversely let us suppose that T is decomposable in the sense of Definition 1.1′, and let $\{G_i\}_{1 \leq i \leq n}$ be an arbitrary finite open covering of $\sigma(T)$. There exists an open covering $\{D_i\}_{1 \leq i \leq n}$ of $\sigma(T)$ such that $\overline{D}_i \subset G_i$. By hypothesis there exist spectral maximal spaces $\{\mathscr{Y}_i\}_{1 \leq i \leq n}$ of T with

$$\sigma(T|\mathscr{Y}) \subset D_i \; (\subset \overline{D}_i \subset G_i)$$

and

$$\mathscr{X} = \sum_{i=1}^{n} \mathscr{Y}_i .$$

Definition 1.1′ was used in Refs. 15, 16 and 17.

The relation $\sigma(T) = \sigma_l(T)$ has been proved by S. R. Foguel in Ref. 36 for the case of spectral operators and extended to decomposable operators [Theorem 1.4 (ii)] in Ref. 41.

The results from 2.1–2.5 were published in Ref. 19. Theorems 2.1 and 2.2 are the noncommutative correspondents of Theorems 3.1 and 3.2, respectively, from Ref. 41. Theorem 2.6 and 3.3 as well as Corollary 3.4 are new.

The notion of quasiaffine transformation is due to B. Sz.-Nagy and C. Foiaş, in Refs. 118 and 119. All results of § 4 were suggested in Ref. 119.

In this order of ideas let us make some additional remarks.

In Ref. 118 it is shown that there exists a contraction $T \in \mathbf{B}(\mathscr{H})$, where $\mathscr{H}$ is a Hilbert space, which is quasisimilar with a unitary operator and such that $\sigma(T) = \{\lambda \in C \,\big|\, |\lambda| \leq 1\}$. Theorem 4.4 shows that this T is not decomposable, hence the quasisimilarity does not conserve the class of decomposable operators. Nor does quasisimilarity conserve the spectral properties of the operators. In spite of these facts and in virtue of Theorem 4.5, quasisimilarity conserves in a certain sense the structure of the ultrainvariant subspaces of the operators.

Chapter 3

$\mathfrak{A}$-Spectral Operators

1. Admissible Algebras of Functions and $\mathfrak{A}$-spectral Functions

1.1. DEFINITION. Let Ω be a set of the complex plane. An algebra $\mathfrak{A}$ of C-valued functions defined on Ω is called *normal*, if for every open finite covering $\{G_i\}_{1 \leqslant i \leqslant n}$ of $\overline{\Omega}$ there exists functions $f_i \in \mathfrak{A}$ such that

$$f_i(\Omega) \subset [0, 1], \quad (1 \leqslant i \leqslant n); \tag{1}$$

$$\operatorname{supp}(f_i) \subset G_i, \quad (1 \leqslant i \leqslant n); \tag{2}$$

$$\sum_{i=1}^{n} f_i = 1 \quad \text{on} \quad \Omega. \tag{3}$$

Here we put for a function $f : \Omega \to C$

$$\operatorname{supp}(f) \stackrel{\text{def}}{=} \overline{\{\lambda \in \Omega \mid f(\lambda) \neq 0\}}.$$

1.2. DEFINITION. An algebra $\mathfrak{A}$ of C-valued functions defined on Ω is called *admissible* if

(i) $\lambda \in \mathfrak{A}$ and $1 \in \mathfrak{A}$ [where λ denotes the identical function $f(\lambda) \equiv \lambda$ and 1 the $f(\lambda) \equiv 1$];

(ii) $\mathfrak{A}$ is normal;

(iii) for every $f \in \mathfrak{A}$ and every $\xi \notin \operatorname{supp}(f)$, the function

$$f_\xi(\lambda) = \begin{cases} \dfrac{f(\lambda)}{\xi - \lambda} & \text{for} \quad \lambda \in \Omega \setminus \{\xi\}, \\ 0 & \text{for} \quad \lambda \in \Omega \cap \{\xi\}, \end{cases}$$

belongs to $\mathfrak{A}$.

1.3. DEFINITION. Let $\mathfrak{A}$ be an admissible algebra, and let $\mathscr{X}$ be a Banach space. A mapping $\mathbf{U} : \mathfrak{A} \to \mathbf{B}(\mathscr{X})$ is called an $\mathfrak{A}$-*spectral function* if

(i) $\mathbf{U}$ is an algebraic homomorphism, and $\mathbf{U}_1 = I$;

(ii) the $\mathbf{B}(\mathscr{X})$-valued function $\xi \to \mathbf{U}_{f_\xi}$ is analytic on $\complement \operatorname{supp}(f)$.

1.4. EXAMPLES

(1) $\Omega = C$, $\mathfrak{A} = \{f: C \to C | f$ Borel bounded function$\}$, E a spectral measure, and $\mathbf{U}_f = \int f\, dE$.

(2) $\mathscr{X} = L^p(\Omega)$ $(1 \leqslant p \leqslant \infty)$, $\mathfrak{A} = L^\infty(\Omega)$, and $\mathbf{U}_f g = fg$.

(3) Let Ω be an open set of R^n, and k a positive integer. For $1 \leqslant p \leqslant \infty$ we denote by $W_k^p(\Omega)$ the Sobolev's space, i.e. the set of complex-valued functions f defined on Ω such that f and its distributional derivates $D^\alpha f$ of order $|\alpha| \leqslant k$ belong to $L^p(\Omega)$. $W_k^p(\Omega)$ (for $1 \leqslant p < \infty$) is a Banach space with respect to the norm

$$\|f\|_k^p = \left(\sum_{|\alpha| \leq k} \int_\Omega |D^\alpha f(x)^p|\, dx \right)^{1/p}.$$

The Banach space $W_k^\infty(\Omega)$ is endowed with the norm

$$\|f\|_k^\infty = \sum_{|\alpha| \leq k} \operatorname*{vrai\,sup}_{x \in \Omega} |D^\alpha f(x)|.$$

If we take $\mathscr{X} = W_k^p(\Omega)$ $(1 \leqslant p < \infty)$, $\mathfrak{A} = W_k^\infty(\Omega)$, then $\mathbf{U}_f g = fg$ is an $\mathfrak{A}$-spectral function.

1.5. DEFINITION. The *support* of an $\mathfrak{A}$-spectral function $\mathbf{U}$ is defined as the smallest closed set $F \subset \overline{\Omega}$ such that $\mathbf{U}_f = 0$ for any $f \in \mathfrak{A}$ with $\operatorname{supp}(f) \cap F = \emptyset$. We denote by supp ($\mathbf{U}$) the support of $\mathbf{U}$.

1.6. THEOREM. *If* $\mathbf{U}$ *is an* $\mathfrak{A}$*-spectral function, then*

$$\operatorname{supp}(\mathbf{U}) = \sigma(\mathbf{U}_\lambda)$$

[we recall that λ is the function $f(\lambda) \equiv \lambda$].

Proof. Take $f \in \mathfrak{A}$ such that $\operatorname{supp}(f) \cap \sigma(\mathbf{U}_\lambda) = \emptyset$. The function $\xi \to \mathbf{U}_{f_\xi}$ is analytic on $\complement \operatorname{supp}(f)$, and we have

$$(\xi I - \mathbf{U}_\lambda)\, \mathbf{U}_{f_\xi} = \mathbf{U}_{(\xi - \lambda) f_\xi} = \mathbf{U}_f \quad \text{for} \quad \xi \notin \operatorname{supp}(f),$$

hence

$$\mathbf{U}_{f_\xi} = R(\xi, \mathbf{U}_\lambda)\, \mathbf{U}_f \quad \text{for} \quad \xi \in \varrho(\mathbf{U}_\lambda) \cap \complement \operatorname{supp}(f).$$

The function $h: C \to \mathbf{B}(\mathscr{X})$ defined by

$$h(\xi) = \begin{cases} R(\xi, \mathbf{U}_\lambda)\, \mathbf{U}_f & \text{for} \quad \xi \in \varrho(\mathbf{U}_\lambda) \\ \mathbf{U}_{f_\xi} & \text{for} \quad \xi \notin \operatorname{supp}(f) \end{cases}$$

is entire, and

$$\lim_{|\xi| \to \infty} \|h(\xi)\| = 0.$$

Thus, by Liouville's theorem $h(\xi) \equiv 0$. In particular $\mathbf{U}_{f_\xi} = 0$ on $\complement$ supp (f), hence $\mathbf{U}_f = 0$.

This shows that (see Definition 1.5)

$$\operatorname{supp}(\mathbf{U}) \subset \sigma(\mathbf{U}_\lambda).$$

Let now V be an arbitrary open neighborhood of supp (**U**), and put

$$G = V \cup \{\xi \in C |\, |\xi| > \|\mathbf{U}_\lambda\|\}.$$

If G_1 is an open set such that $\bar{G}_1 \cap \operatorname{supp}(\mathbf{U}) = \varnothing$ and $G \cup G_1 = C$, then there exist two functions $f, f_1 \in \mathfrak{A}$ such that

$$0 \leqslant f(\lambda), \quad f_1(\lambda) \leqslant 1, \quad \lambda \in \Omega;$$

$$\operatorname{supp}(f) \subset G, \quad \operatorname{supp}(f_1) \subset G_1;$$

$$f + f_1 = 1 \quad \text{on} \quad \Omega;$$

hence we have

$$\operatorname{supp}(1 - f) = \operatorname{supp}(f_1) \subset G_1,$$

therefore

$$\operatorname{supp}(1 - f) \cap \operatorname{supp}(\mathbf{U}) = \varnothing.$$

Whence

$$0 = \mathbf{U}_{1-f} = \mathbf{U}_1 - \mathbf{U}_f, \quad \text{i.e.} \quad \mathbf{U}_f = \mathbf{U}_1 = I.$$

Since supp $(f) \subset G$, by 1.2 (iii) we have $f_\xi \in \mathfrak{A}$ for any $\xi \notin G$. Therefore $\mathbf{U}_{f_\xi}$ makes sense and

$$\mathbf{U}_{f_\xi}(\xi I - \mathbf{U}_\lambda) = (\xi I - \mathbf{U}_\lambda)\, \mathbf{U}_{f_\xi} = \mathbf{U}_{(\xi-\lambda)f_\xi} = \mathbf{U}_f = I,$$

hence $\xi \in \varrho(\mathbf{U}_\lambda)$. Thus

$$\sigma(\mathbf{U}_\lambda) \subset G = V \cup \{\xi \in C |\, |\xi| > \|\mathbf{U}_\lambda\|\}.$$

V being an arbitrary open set containing supp (**U**), we get

$$\sigma(\mathbf{U}_\lambda) \subset \bigcap_{\substack{V \text{ open} \\ V \supset \operatorname{supp}(\mathbf{U})}} (V \cup \{\xi \in C |\, |\xi| > \|\mathbf{U}_\lambda\|\})$$

$$= \operatorname{supp}(\mathbf{U}) \cup \{\xi \in C |\, |\xi| > \|\mathbf{U}_\lambda\|\}.$$

But $\sigma(\mathbf{U}_\lambda) \subset \{\xi \in C \big|\, |\xi| \leqslant \|\mathbf{U}_\lambda\|\}$, therefore

$$\sigma(\mathbf{U}_\lambda) \subset \operatorname{supp}(\mathbf{U}).$$

1.7. COROLLARY. *The support of every $\mathfrak{A}$-spectral function is compact.*

1.8. *Remark.* In the proof of Theorem 1.6 we have shown that if $f \in \mathfrak{A}$ and $f = 1$ in the neighborhood of supp (U), then $\mathbf{U}_f = I$. Consequently

$$\bigvee_{f \in \mathfrak{A}_0} \mathbf{U}_f \mathscr{X} = \mathscr{X},$$

where $\mathfrak{A}_0$ is the set of all functions in $\mathfrak{A}$ with compact support.

1.9. LEMMA. *If $(\lambda_0 I - \mathbf{U}_\lambda)\, x_0 = 0$ $(x_0 \neq 0)$ and $f \in \mathfrak{A}$ is a function such that*

$$f(\lambda) = c \quad \textit{for} \quad \lambda \in G \cap \Omega,$$

where G is an open neighborhood of λ_0, then

$$\mathbf{U}_f x_0 = c x_0 .$$

Proof. We have

$$\lambda_0 \in \sigma_p(\mathbf{U}_\lambda) \subset \sigma(\mathbf{U}_\lambda) = \text{supp}\,(\mathbf{U}) \subset \Omega,$$

hence $G \cap \Omega \neq \varnothing$. Putting $g = f - c$ we can write

$$\mathbf{U}_f x_0 - c x_0 = \mathbf{U}_g x_0 = \mathbf{U}_{(\lambda - \lambda_0)\, g_{\lambda_0}} x_0 = \mathbf{U}_{g_{\lambda_0}} (\lambda_0 I - \mathbf{U}_\lambda)\, x_0 = 0,$$

hence $\mathbf{U}_f x_0 = cx.$

1.10. THEOREM. *If $\mathbf{U}$ is an $\mathfrak{A}$-spectral function, then the operator $\mathbf{U}_\lambda$ has the single-valued extension property.*

Proof. Let $f : G_f \to \mathscr{X}$ (G_f open $\subset C$) be an analytic function such that

$$(\xi I - \mathbf{U}_\lambda) f(\xi) \equiv 0.$$

Suppose now that there exists a connected component G_0 of G_f and $\xi_0 \in G_0$ such that $f(\xi_0) \neq 0$. Then $f(\xi) \neq 0$ for λ belonging in a disk $D_0 \subset G_0$ with center in ξ_0. Let now D be another disk with center in ξ_0 and such that $\bar{D} \subset D_0$.

The algebra $\mathfrak{A}$ being normal there exists a function $\varphi \in \mathfrak{A}$ such that

$$\varphi(\xi) = \begin{cases} 1 & \text{for} \quad \xi \in \Omega \cap \bar{D}, \\ 0 & \text{for} \quad \xi \in \Omega \setminus (\Omega \cap D_0). \end{cases}$$

Applying the preceding lemma we get

$$\mathbf{U}_\varphi f(\xi) = \begin{cases} f(\xi) & \text{for} \quad \xi \in G_0 \cap D, \\ 0 & \text{for} \quad \xi \in G_0 \setminus D_0, \end{cases}$$

hence, by analytic continuation, we have

$$\mathbf{U}_\varphi f(\xi) = 0 \quad \text{for} \quad \xi \in G_0.$$

So

$$f(\xi) = \mathbf{U}_\varphi f(\xi) = 0 \quad \text{for} \quad \xi \in G_0.$$

This shows that f vanishes on every connected component of G_f, hence also on G_f.

On account of this theorem we may speak of $\sigma_{\mathbf{U}_\lambda}(x)$ and $\mathscr{X}_{\mathbf{U}_\lambda}(F)$.

1.11. PROPOSITION. *If* $\mathbf{U}$ *is an* $\mathfrak{A}$*-spectral function, then*

$$\sigma_{\mathbf{U}_\lambda}(\mathbf{U}_f x) \subset \operatorname{supp}(f),$$

for any $f \in \mathfrak{A}$ *and* $x \in \mathscr{X}$.

Proof. For any $\xi \notin \operatorname{supp}(f)$ we have $f_\xi \in \mathfrak{A}$, and the $\mathscr{X}$-valued function $\xi \to \mathbf{U}_{f_\xi} x$ is analytic. Furthermore, $(\xi I - \mathbf{U}_\lambda)\, \mathbf{U}_{f_\xi} x = \mathbf{U}_f x$, therefore $\xi \in \varrho_{\mathbf{U}_\lambda}(\mathbf{U}_f x)$.

1.12. PROPOSITION. *If* $\sigma_{\mathbf{U}_\lambda}(x) \cap \operatorname{supp}(f) = \emptyset$, *then* $\mathbf{U}_f x = 0$.

Proof. Let $x(\xi)$ be the unique $\mathscr{X}$-valued analytic function defined on $\varrho_{\mathbf{U}_\lambda}(x)$ and satisfying

$$(\xi I - \mathbf{U}_\lambda)\, x(\xi) = x \quad \text{on} \quad \varrho_{\mathbf{U}_\lambda}(x).$$

Hence

$$(\xi I - \mathbf{U}_\lambda)\, \mathbf{U}_f\, x(\xi) = \mathbf{U}_f\, (\xi I - \mathbf{U}_\lambda)\, x(\xi) = \mathbf{U}_f\, x \quad \text{on} \quad \varrho_{\mathbf{U}_\lambda}(x),$$

therefore $\varrho_{\mathbf{U}_\lambda}(x) \subset \varrho_{\mathbf{U}_\lambda}(\mathbf{U}_f x)$, i.e.

$$\sigma_{\mathbf{U}_\lambda}(\mathbf{U}_f x) \subset \sigma_{\mathbf{U}_\lambda}(x).$$

But (Proposition 1.11)

$$\sigma_{\mathbf{U}_\lambda}(\mathbf{U}_f x) \subset \operatorname{supp}(f),$$

hence

$$\sigma_{\mathbf{U}_\lambda}(\mathbf{U}_f x) = \emptyset,$$

therefore by Proposition 1.1.2 (ii) we have $\mathbf{U}_f x = 0$.

1.13. Definition. Let $\mathbf{U}$ be an $\mathfrak{A}$-spectral function. For any open set $G \subset C$ we put

$$\mathscr{X}_{[\mathbf{U}]}(G) = \bigvee_{\operatorname{supp} f \subset G} \mathbf{U}_f \mathscr{X},$$

and for any closed set $F \subset C$ we denote

$$\mathscr{X}_{[\mathbf{U}]}(F) = \bigcap_{G \supset F} \mathscr{X}_{[\mathbf{U}]}(G).$$

1.14. Theorem. $\mathscr{X}_{[\mathbf{U}]}(F) = \mathscr{X}_{\mathbf{U}_\lambda}(F)$ $(= \{x \in \mathscr{X} \mid \sigma_{\mathbf{U}_\lambda}(x) \subset F\})$.

Proof. If $\sigma_{\mathbf{U}_\lambda}(x) \subset F$ and G is an open set containing F, by normality of $\mathfrak{A}$ there exists a function $f \in \mathfrak{A}$ such that

$$f(\xi) = \begin{cases} 1 & \text{for } \xi \text{ in a neighborhood of } \Omega \cap F, \\ 0 & \text{for } \xi \text{ in a neighborhood of } \Omega \setminus (G \cap \Omega). \end{cases}$$

Therefore $\operatorname{supp}(f) \subset G$, and

$$\operatorname{supp}(1 - f) \cap \sigma_{\mathbf{U}_\lambda}(x) \subset \operatorname{supp}(1 - f) \cap F = \varnothing,$$

whence (by Proposition 1.12) $\mathbf{U}_{1-f}x = 0$, so that

$$x = \mathbf{U}_f x \in \mathscr{X}_{[\mathbf{U}]}(G).$$

Since G is an arbitrary open set containing F we get

$$x \in \mathscr{X}_{[\mathbf{U}]}(F).$$

Conversely, let

$$x = \mathscr{X}_{[\mathbf{U}]}(F) \subset \mathscr{X}_{[\mathbf{U}]}(G), \tag{1}$$

where G is any open set containing F, and let G_1 be an arbitrary open set $\supset \bar{G}$. There exists a function $f_1 \in \mathfrak{A}$ such that

$$f_1(\xi) = \begin{cases} 1 & \text{for } \xi \in \bar{G} \cap \Omega, \\ 0 & \text{for } \xi \in \Omega \setminus (G_1 \cap \Omega), \end{cases}$$

hence $\operatorname{supp}(f_1) \subset \bar{G}_1$. So that for any $f \in \mathfrak{A}$ with $\operatorname{supp}(f) \subset G$, we have $f_1 f = f$, hence

$$\mathbf{U}_{f_1}\mathbf{U}_f = \mathbf{U}_f,$$

whence

$$\mathbf{U}_{f_1} | \mathscr{X}_{[\mathbf{U}]}(G) = I | \mathscr{X}_{[\mathbf{U}]}(G). \tag{2}$$

Thus, from (1), (2), and Proposition 1.12 it follows that

$$\sigma_{\mathbf{U}_\lambda}(x) = \sigma_{\mathbf{U}_\lambda}(\mathbf{U}_{f_1}x) \subset \operatorname{supp}(f_1) \subset \bar{G}_1,$$

hence

$$\sigma_{\mathbf{U}_\lambda}(x) = \bigcap_{\substack{G_1 \text{ open} \\ G_1 \supset \bar{G}}} \bar{G}_1 = \bar{G};$$

but G is an arbitrary open set $\supset F$, so that

$$\sigma_{\mathbf{U}_\lambda}(x) \subset \bigcap_{\substack{G \text{ open} \\ G \supset F}} \bar{G} = F,$$

i.e. $x \in \mathscr{X}_{\mathbf{U}_\lambda}(F)$.

1.15. COROLLARY. *If* $\mathbf{U}$ *is an* $\mathfrak{A}$*-spectral function, then for every closed set* $F \subset C$, $\mathscr{X}_{[\mathbf{U}]}(F)$ *is a spectral maximal space for* $\mathbf{U}_\lambda$.

This results from the preceding theorem and Proposition 1.3.8.

1.16. THEOREM. *If* $\mathbf{U}$ *is an* $\mathfrak{A}$*-spectral function, then the operator* $\mathbf{U}_\lambda$ *is decomposable.*

Proof. Let $\{G_i\}_{0 \leqslant i \leqslant n}$ be an open covering of $\sigma(\mathbf{U}_\lambda)$. If we put $G_0 = \varrho(\mathbf{U}_\lambda)$, then $\{G_i\}_{1 \leqslant i \leqslant n}$ is an open covering of $\bar{\Omega}$, and there are $n+1$ functions $f_i \in \mathfrak{A}$ such that

$$f_i(\Omega) \subset [0, 1], \quad (0 \leqslant i \leqslant n);$$

$$\operatorname{supp}(f_i) \subset G_i, \quad (0 \leqslant i \leqslant n);$$

$$\sum_{i=0}^{n} f_i = 1 \quad \text{on} \quad \Omega.$$

For every $x \in \mathscr{X}$, we have

$$x = \mathbf{U}_1 x = \mathbf{U}_{f_0} x + \sum_{i=1}^{n} \mathbf{U}_{f_i} x = \sum_{i=1}^{n} \mathbf{U}_{f_i} x,$$

because $\sigma_{\mathbf{U}_\lambda}(x) \cap \operatorname{supp}(f_0) \subset \sigma(\mathbf{U}_\lambda) \cap \varrho(\mathbf{U}_\lambda) = \varnothing$.

If we put $y_i = \mathbf{U}_{f_i} x$ and $\mathscr{Y}_i = \mathscr{X}_{[\mathbf{U}]}(\operatorname{supp} f_i)) = \mathscr{X}_{\mathbf{U}_\lambda}(\operatorname{supp}(f_i))$, and if we apply Proposition 1.11, we obtain

$$y_i \in \mathscr{Y}_i, \quad (1 \leqslant i \leqslant n).$$

On account of Theorem 1.14 and Proposition 1.3.8, we have

$$\begin{aligned}\sigma(\mathbf{U}_\lambda|\mathscr{Y}_i) &= \sigma\left(\mathbf{U}_\lambda|\mathscr{X}_{[\mathbf{U}]}((\text{supp}(f_i))\right)\\ &= \sigma\left(\mathbf{U}_\lambda|\mathscr{X}_{\mathbf{U}_\lambda}(\text{supp}(f_i))\right)\\ &\subset \text{supp}(f_i)\cap\sigma(\mathbf{U}_\lambda)\subset G_i.\end{aligned}$$

Thus $\mathbf{U}_\lambda$ is decomposable.

1.17. Proposition. *Let* $\mathbf{U}$ *be an* $\mathfrak{A}$*-spectral function,* F *closed* $\subset \Omega$, *and* $x \in \mathscr{X}$. *Then* $x \in \mathscr{X}_{\mathbf{U}_\lambda}(F)$ *if and only if* $\mathbf{U}_f x = 0$ *for every* $f \in \mathfrak{A}$ *with* supp $(f) \cap F = \varnothing$.

Proof. Let $x \in \mathscr{X}_{\mathbf{U}_\lambda}(F)$, i.e. $\sigma_{\mathbf{U}_\lambda}(x) \subset F$. If $f \in \mathfrak{A}$ with supp $(f) \cap F = \varnothing$, then supp $(f) \cap \sigma_{\mathbf{U}_\lambda}(x) = \varnothing$. Applying Proposition 1.12, we get $\mathbf{U}_f x = 0$.

Conversely, suppose that $\mathbf{U}_f x = 0$ for all $f \in \mathfrak{A}$ with supp $(f) \cap F = \varnothing$. Let G be an arbitrary open set containing F, and denote $G_0 = \complement F$. By normality of $\mathfrak{A}$ there are two functions $f_0, f_1 \in \mathfrak{A}$ such that

$$\text{supp}(f) \subset G, \quad \text{supp}(f_0) \subset G_0,$$

and

$$f + f_0 = 1 \quad \text{on} \quad \Omega.$$

We have supp $(f_0) \cap F = \varnothing$, hence (by hypothesis)

$$0 = \mathbf{U}_{f_0} x = \mathbf{U}_{1-f} x = x - \mathbf{U}_f x$$

i.e.

$$x = \mathbf{U}_f x.$$

From this equality, and from the inclusion supp$(f) \subset G$, we deduce

$$x \in \mathscr{X}_{[\mathbf{U}]}(G),$$

whence (G being an arbitrary open set $\supset F$) it follows

$$x \in \mathscr{X}_{[\mathbf{U}]}(F) = \mathscr{X}_{\mathbf{U}_\lambda}(F).$$

1.18. Definition. An operator $S \in \mathbf{B}(\mathscr{X})$ is called $\mathfrak{A}$-*scalar* if there exists an $\mathfrak{A}$-spectral function $\mathbf{U}$ such that $\mathbf{U}_\lambda = S$. Such an $\mathfrak{A}$-spectral function will be called an $\mathfrak{A}$-*spectral function of* S.

The properties of $\mathbf{U}_\lambda$ (here $\mathbf{U}$ is an $\mathfrak{A}$-spectral function) can be reformulated in terms of $\mathfrak{A}$-scalar operators. In the following theorem we summarize some of these properties.

1.19. THEOREM. *If $S \in \mathbf{B}(\mathscr{X})$ is an $\mathfrak{A}$-scalar operator, and* $\mathbf{U}$ *an $\mathfrak{A}$-spectral function of S, then*

(i) *S is decomposable;*

(ii) *$\mathscr{X}_S(F) = \mathscr{X}_{[\mathbf{U}]}(F)$ for any closed set $F \subset C$.*

1.20. EXAMPLE. Let us give a simple example of an $\mathfrak{A}$-scalar operator. Let $T \in \mathbf{B}(\mathscr{X})$ be an operator whose spectrum $\sigma(T)$ is totally disconnected. Let $\mathfrak{A}$ be the algebra of all Borel functions f defined on $\Omega = \{\lambda \in C \mid |\lambda| \leqslant \|T\| + 1\}$, which are analytic on an open neighborhood G_f of $\sigma(T)$. It is obvious [since $\sigma(T)$ is totally disconnected] that $\mathfrak{A}$ is admissible. For $f \in \mathfrak{A}$ put $\mathbf{U}_f = f(T)$, where $f(T)$ is defined by Dunford's formula

$$f(T) = \frac{1}{2\pi i} \int_\Gamma f(\xi)\, R(\xi, T)\, d\xi$$

[Γ being a system of curves $\subset G_f$ surrounding $\sigma(T)$]. By Dunford's calculus $f \to \mathbf{U}_f$ is a homomorphism of algebras and $\mathbf{U}_1 = I$; also $\mathbf{U}_\lambda = T$. Furthermore, if $g \in \mathfrak{A}$ and $\xi \notin \operatorname{supp}(g)$ we may find an open set $G \ni \xi$ such that $G \cap \operatorname{supp}(g) = \varnothing$ and the sets $\sigma_1 = \sigma(T) \cap G$ and $\sigma_2 = \sigma(T) \cap \complement G$ are separate [here we use again the fact that $\sigma(T)$ is totally disconnected]. Then σ_1 and σ_2 are spectral sets in Dunford's sense, and since $g_\xi(\lambda) = 0$ for $\lambda \in G$, we have by Dunford's calculus

$$g_\xi(T)\, \mathbf{E}(\sigma_1) = 0.$$

In this manner

$$g_\xi(T)\, \mathscr{X} = g_\xi(T)\, [\mathbf{E}(\sigma_1) + \mathbf{E}(\sigma_2)]\, \mathscr{X} = g_\xi(T)\, \mathbf{E}(\sigma_2)\, \mathscr{X} \subset \mathbf{E}(\sigma_2)\, \mathscr{X}.$$

As $\sigma\,(T|\mathbf{E}(\sigma_2)) \subset \sigma_2$, the operator

$$R(\xi) = R\,(\xi, T|\mathbf{E}(\sigma_2)\, \mathscr{X}) = (\xi I|\mathbf{E}(\sigma_2)\, \mathscr{X} - T|\mathbf{E}(\sigma_2)\, \mathscr{X})^{-1}$$

exists and is bounded on $\mathbf{E}(\sigma_2)\, \mathscr{X}$, for $\xi \in \complement\sigma_2$. The function $\xi \to R\,(\xi, T|\mathbf{E}\,(\sigma_2)\, \mathscr{X})$ is analytic on $\complement\sigma_2$.

We have

$$(\xi I - T)\, \mathbf{U}_{g_\xi} x = \mathbf{U}_{(\xi - \lambda) g_\xi} x = \mathbf{U}_g x, \quad (x \in \mathscr{X}).$$

But $\mathbf{U}_{g_\xi} x \in \mathbf{E}(\sigma_2) \mathscr{X}$, hence the above relation gives for $\xi \notin \operatorname{supp}(g) \cup \sigma_2$

$$\mathbf{U}_{g_\xi} x = R(\xi)\, \mathbf{U}_g x, \quad x \in U$$

i.e.

$$\mathbf{U}_{g_\xi} = R(\xi)\, \mathbf{U}_g .$$

It results that $\xi \to \mathbf{U}_{g_\xi}$ is analytic on G.

Since every operator T, such that $f(T)$ is compact for a function f analytic in a neighborhood of $\sigma(T)$, has its spectrum totally disconnected, it follows that T is an $\mathfrak{A}$-scalar operator. In particular *every compact operator is $\mathfrak{A}$-scalar!*

2. The Algebra Generated by an $\mathfrak{A}$-spectral Function

Let Ω be a closed set of the complex plane, and $C(\Omega)$ the algebra of all continuous complex valued functions defined on Ω. A subalgebra $\mathfrak{A}$ of $C(\Omega)$ is said *inverse closed* if $1/f \in \mathfrak{A}$ whenever $f \in \mathfrak{A}$ and $1/f$ exists in $C(\Omega)$.

In this paragraph we shall study some properties of $\mathfrak{A}$-spectral functions, where $\mathfrak{A}$ is an admissible inverse closed algebra of $C(\Omega)$.

For an $\mathfrak{A}$-spectral function $\mathbf{U} : \mathfrak{A} \to \mathbf{B}(\mathscr{X})$ denote by $\mathscr{A}$ the Banach algebra generated in $\mathbf{B}(\mathscr{X})$ by the set $\{\mathbf{U}_f \mid f \in \mathfrak{A}\}$, and by $\mathfrak{M}$ the space of maximal ideals of $\mathscr{A}$. By abuse of language $\mathscr{A}$ will be called *the Banach algebra generated by* $\mathbf{U}$.

2.1. THEOREM. *Let $\mathfrak{A}$ be an admissible inverse closed algebra of continuous complex valued functions defined on Ω, $\mathbf{U}$ an $\mathfrak{A}$-spectral function, and $\mathscr{A}$ the Banach algebra generated by $\mathbf{U}$. Then the space $\mathfrak{M}$ of maximal ideals of $\mathscr{A}$ can be identified with $\sigma(\mathbf{U}_\lambda)$, and by this identification the Gelfand representation $A \to A^\wedge$ has the following properties*

$$\mathbf{U}_f^\wedge = f|\sigma(\mathbf{U}_\lambda) \quad \textit{for} \quad f \in \mathfrak{A}, \tag{i}$$

$$\sigma(\mathbf{U}_f) = f(\sigma(\mathbf{U}_\lambda)) \quad \textit{for} \quad f \in \mathfrak{A}, \tag{ii}$$

where $\sigma(A)$ denotes the spectrum of A in $\mathbf{B}(\mathscr{X})$.

Proof. Let $f \in \mathfrak{A}$. Since the mapping $\xi \to \mathbf{U}_{f_\xi}$ is analytic on $\mathbf{C} \operatorname{supp}(f)$, and the Gelfand representation $A \to A^\wedge$ is a continuous homomorphism of $\mathfrak{A}$ into $C(\mathfrak{M})$, we have that $\xi \to \mathbf{U}_{f_\xi}^\wedge(M)$ is an analytic complex valued function on $\complement$ supp (f), for every $M \in \mathfrak{M}$. From

$$(\xi I - \mathbf{U}_\lambda)\,\mathbf{U}_{f_\xi} = \mathbf{U}_f$$

we deduce

$$[\xi - \mathbf{U}_\lambda\hat{}(M)]\,\mathbf{U}_{f_\xi}\hat{}(M) = \mathbf{U}_f\hat{}(M),$$

whence

$$\mathbf{U}_f\hat{}(M) = 0 \quad \text{if} \quad \mathbf{U}_\lambda\hat{}(M) = \xi \notin \operatorname{supp}(f). \tag{1}$$

Let $\xi \notin \sigma(\mathbf{U}_\lambda)$, then there are two open sets G_0 and G_1 such that $\sigma(\mathbf{U}_\lambda) \subset G_1 \subset \bar{G}_1 \subset G_0 \subset \bar{G}_0 \not\ni \xi$. By normality of $\mathfrak{A}$ there is a $\varphi \in \mathfrak{A}$ such that

$$\varphi(\lambda) = \begin{cases} 1 & \text{for} \quad \lambda \in \Omega \cap \bar{G}_1, \\ 0 & \text{for} \quad \lambda \in \Omega \setminus G_0. \end{cases}$$

In this case supp $(\varphi) \subset \bar{G}_0$, $\mathbf{U}_\varphi = I$, $\mathbf{U}_{\varphi_\xi}$ makes sense, and therefore

$$(\xi I - \mathbf{U}_\lambda)\,\mathbf{U}_{\varphi_\xi} = \mathbf{U}_{\varphi_\xi}\,(\xi I - \mathbf{U}_\lambda) = \mathbf{U}_\varphi = I,$$

whence

$$(\xi I - \mathbf{U}_\lambda)^{-1} = \mathbf{U}_{\varphi_\xi} \in \mathscr{A},$$

i.e. $\xi \notin \sigma_{\mathscr{A}}(\mathbf{U}_\lambda)$, where $\sigma_{\mathscr{A}}(\mathbf{U}_\lambda)$ denotes the spectrum of $\mathbf{U}_\lambda$ in $\mathscr{A}$. Thus we have shown that

$$\sigma_{\mathscr{A}}(\mathbf{U}_\lambda) \subset \sigma(\mathbf{U}_\lambda). \tag{2}$$

Or obviously

$$\sigma(A) \subset \sigma_{\mathscr{A}}(A), \quad \text{for every} \quad A \in \mathscr{A},$$

hence

$$\sigma_{\mathscr{A}}(\mathbf{U}_\lambda) = \sigma(\mathbf{U}_\lambda). \tag{3}$$

But by Gelfand's formula

$$\sigma_{\mathscr{A}}(A) = A\hat{}(\mathfrak{M}) \quad \text{for} \quad A \in \mathscr{A}, \tag{4}$$

so that

$$\sigma(\mathbf{U}_\lambda) = \mathbf{U}_\lambda\hat{}(\mathfrak{M}). \tag{5}$$

Let now $\lambda_0 \in \sigma(\mathbf{U}_\lambda)$, then there is a $M_0 \in \mathfrak{M}$ such that $\mathbf{U}_\lambda\hat{}\,(M_0) = \lambda_0$. Consider $f, g \in \mathfrak{A}$ such that $f = g$ on a neighborhood of λ_0, hence

$$\mathbf{U}_\lambda\hat{}(M_0) = \lambda_0 \notin \operatorname{supp}(f - g),$$

therefore by (1), $\mathbf{U}_{f-g}\hat{}(M_0) = 0$, whence

$$\mathbf{U}_f\hat{}(M_0) = \mathbf{U}_g\hat{}(M_0). \tag{6}$$

Let $\bar{D}(\lambda_0, r)$ be the closed disk of center λ_0 and radius $r > 0$ and let $\varphi_r \in \mathfrak{A}$ such that $0 \leqslant \varphi_r(\xi) \leqslant 1$ and

$$\varphi_r(\xi) = \begin{cases} 1 & \text{for} \quad \xi \in \Omega \cap \bar{D}(\lambda_0, r/2), \\ 0 & \text{for} \quad \xi \in \Omega \setminus \bar{D}(\lambda_0, r). \end{cases}$$

Then by (6)

$$\mathbf{U}_{\varphi_r}^{\wedge}(M_0) = \mathbf{U}_1^{\wedge}(M_0) = 1,$$

hence for every $f \in \mathfrak{A}$

$$\begin{aligned} \mathbf{U}_f^{\wedge}(M_0) - f(\lambda_0) &= \mathbf{U}_{f-f(\lambda_0)}^{\wedge}(M_0) = \mathbf{U}_{f-f(\lambda_0)}^{\wedge}(M_0)\, \mathbf{U}_{\varphi_r}^{\wedge}(M_0) \\ &= \mathbf{U}_{[f-f(\lambda_0)]\varphi_r}^{\wedge}(M_0) = \mathbf{U}_{g_r}^{\wedge}(M_0), \end{aligned} \tag{7}$$

where $g_r = [f - f(\lambda_0)]\, \varphi_r$.

Putting

$$\varepsilon_r = \sup_{\xi \in \bar{D}(\lambda_0, r)} |f(\xi) - f(\lambda_0)|,$$

we have $|g_r(\xi)| \leqslant \varepsilon_r$ for all $\xi \in \Omega$. Consequently $h_r = (\mu - g_r)^{-1} \in \mathfrak{A}$ for every $|\mu| > \varepsilon_r$ because $\mathfrak{A}$ is inverse closed. It results

$$\mathbf{U}_{h_r}(\mu I - \mathbf{U}_{g_r}) = (\mu I - \mathbf{U}_{g_r})\, \mathbf{U}_{h_r} = \mathbf{U}_{(\mu - g_r) h_r} = \mathbf{U}_1 = I,$$

hence $\mu \in \varrho_{\mathscr{A}}(\mathbf{U}_{g_r})$. Accordingly,

$$\sigma_{\mathscr{A}}(\mathbf{U}_{g_r}) \subset \{\xi \in C \mid |\xi| \leqslant \varepsilon_r\}$$

so that by (4), $|\mathbf{U}_{g_r}^{\wedge}(M_0)| \leqslant \varepsilon_r$. The function f being continuous, we have $\lim\limits_{r \to +0} \varepsilon_r = \lim\limits_{\lambda \to \lambda_0} |f(\lambda) - f(\lambda_0)| = 0$, hence $\lim\limits_{r \to +0} \mathbf{U}_{g_r}^{\wedge}(M_0) = 0$, therefore by (7)

$$\mathbf{U}_f^{\wedge}(M_0) = f(\lambda_0). \tag{8}$$

The mapping $\mathbf{U}_\lambda^{\wedge} : \mathfrak{M} \to \sigma(\mathbf{U}_\lambda)$ is *injective*. Indeed, for $M_1, M_2 \in \mathfrak{M}$ such that

$$\mathbf{U}_\lambda^{\wedge}(M_1) = \mathbf{U}_\lambda^{\wedge}(M_2) = \lambda_0 \in \sigma(\mathbf{U}_\lambda)$$

we have by (8)

$$\mathbf{U}_f^{\wedge}(M_1) = f(\lambda_0) = \mathbf{U}_f^{\wedge}(M_2) \quad \text{for every} \quad f \in \mathfrak{A},$$

hence

$$A^{\wedge}(M_1) = A^{\wedge}(M_2) \quad \text{for every} \quad A \in \mathfrak{A} \tag{9}$$

(since the set $\{\mathbf{U}_f | f \in \mathfrak{A}\}$ is dense in $\mathscr{A}$). Since the set of Gelfand transforms $\{A^{\wedge} | A \in \mathscr{A}\}$ separates $\mathfrak{M}$, it follows from (9) that $M_1 = M_2$.

The surjectivity of the mapping $\mathbf{U}_\lambda^{\wedge}$ results from (5).

$\mathbf{U}_\lambda^\wedge$ is bicontinuous because it is continuous and bijective. Identifying M with $\mathbf{U}_\lambda^\wedge(M)$ we can write

$$\mathfrak{M} = \sigma(\mathbf{U}_\lambda) \tag{10}$$

and by (8)

$$\mathbf{U}_f^\wedge(\xi) = f(\xi) \quad \text{for} \quad \xi \in \sigma(\mathbf{U}_\lambda),$$

that is

$$\mathbf{U}_f^\wedge = f|\sigma(\mathbf{U}_\lambda).$$

From (4), (3), and (10) we obtain

$$\sigma(\mathbf{U}_f) \subset \sigma_{\mathscr{A}}(\mathbf{U}_f) = \mathbf{U}_f^\wedge(\mathfrak{M}) = \mathbf{U}_f^\wedge(\sigma(\mathbf{U}_\lambda)) = f(\sigma(\mathbf{U}_\lambda)). \tag{11}$$

Denote

$$G = \varrho(\mathbf{U}_\lambda) \cup \complement f^{-1}(\sigma(\mathbf{U}_f)), \tag{12}$$

and let $\mathscr{Y}$ be a spectral maximal space of $\mathbf{U}_\lambda$ such that

$$\sigma(\mathbf{U}_\lambda|\mathscr{Y}) \subset G. \tag{13}$$

$\mathscr{Y}$ being a spectral maximal space of $\mathbf{U}_\lambda$ we have (by Corollary 1.3.3) $\sigma(\mathbf{U}_\lambda|\mathscr{Y}) \subset \sigma(\mathbf{U}_\lambda)$, therefore from (12) and (13) it results

$$\sigma(\mathbf{U}_\lambda|\mathscr{Y}) \subset \complement f^{-1}(\sigma(\mathbf{U}_f)),$$

hence there is an open set G_0 such that

$$\sigma(\mathbf{U}_\lambda|\mathscr{Y}) \subset G_0 \subset \overline{G}_0 \subset \complement f^{-1}(\sigma(\mathbf{U}_f)). \tag{14}$$

Applying Theorem 2.1.5 and Proposition 1.1.2 (i),

$$\mathscr{Y} = \mathscr{X}_{\mathbf{U}_\lambda}(\sigma(\mathbf{U}_\lambda|\mathscr{Y})) \subset \mathscr{X}_{\mathbf{U}_\lambda}(\overline{G}_0). \tag{15}$$

From the last inclusion of (14) it follows

$$f(\overline{G}_0) \cap \sigma(\mathbf{U}_f) = \emptyset.$$

Considering $\mathbf{V}_f = \mathbf{U}_f|\mathscr{X}_{\mathbf{U}_\lambda}(\overline{G}_0)$ we obtain another $\mathfrak{A}$-spectral function. By (11) we have

$$\sigma(\mathbf{V}_f) \subset f(\sigma(\mathbf{V}_\lambda)).$$

But

$$\sigma(\mathbf{V}_\lambda) = \sigma(\mathbf{U}_\lambda|\mathscr{X}_{\mathbf{U}_\lambda}(\overline{G}_0)) \subset \overline{G}_0,$$

hence

$$\sigma(\mathbf{V}_f) \subset f(\overline{G}_0).$$

For every $x \in \mathscr{X}_{\mathbf{U}_\lambda}(\bar{G}_0)$ we put

$$x(\xi) = \begin{cases} (\xi I - \mathbf{U}_f)^{-1} x & \text{for} \quad \xi \notin \sigma(\mathbf{U}_f), \\ (\xi I | \mathscr{X}_{\mathbf{U}_\lambda}(\bar{G}_0) - \mathbf{V}_f)^{-1} x & \text{for} \quad \xi \notin f(\bar{G}_0). \end{cases}$$

Obviously $x(\xi)$ is well defined for every $\xi \in C$. Furthermore, $\xi \to x(\xi)$ is an entire function, and $\lim_{\xi \to \infty} x(\xi) = 0$. Thus, by Liouville's theorem, $x(\xi) = 0$ hence for $\xi \notin \sigma(\mathbf{U}_f)$ we have

$$x = (\xi I - \mathbf{U}_f)\, x(\xi) = 0.$$

Consequently $\mathscr{X}_{\mathbf{U}_\lambda}(\bar{G}_0) = \{0\}$, therefore by (15), $\mathscr{Y} = \{0\}$.

Thus we have shown that for every spectral maximal space $\mathscr{Y}$ of $\mathbf{U}_\lambda$ such that $\sigma(\mathbf{U}_\lambda | \mathscr{Y}) \subset G$, we have $\mathscr{Y} = \{0\}$. Now applying Lemma 2.1.2, it results that

$$G \cap \sigma(\mathbf{U}_\lambda) = \varnothing,$$

and from the above and (12) we obtain $\sigma(\mathbf{U}_\lambda) \subset f^{-1}(\sigma(\mathbf{U}_f))$, hence

$$f(\sigma(\mathbf{U}_\lambda)) \subset \sigma(\mathbf{U}_f).$$

2.2. Lemma. *Let $\mathfrak{A}$ be an inverse closed admissible algebra of continuous functions defined on a closed set $\Omega \subset C$, $f \in \mathfrak{A}$, $\mathbf{U} : \mathfrak{A} \to \mathbf{B}(\mathscr{X})$ an $\mathfrak{A}$-spectral function, and F a closed set $\subset C$. Then for every closed linear subspace $\mathscr{Y}$ of $\mathscr{X}$ with properties*

$$\mathbf{U}_f \mathscr{Y} \subset \mathscr{Y}, \tag{a}$$

$$\sigma(\mathbf{U}_f | \mathscr{Y}) \subset F, \tag{b}$$

we have

$$\mathscr{Y} \subset \mathscr{X}_{\mathbf{U}_\lambda}(f^{-1}(F)).$$

Proof. It is known that the spectral maximal spaces of an operator T are ultrainvariant with respect to T (see Proposition 1.3.2). Therefore $\mathscr{X}_{\mathbf{U}_\lambda}(f^{-1}(F))$ is invariant to $\mathbf{U}_f$. Putting

$$\mathbf{V}_\varphi = \mathbf{U}_\varphi | \mathscr{X}_{\mathbf{U}_\lambda}(f^{-1}(F)), \quad (\varphi \in \mathfrak{A})$$

we have

$$\sigma(\mathbf{V}_\lambda) = \sigma\left(\mathbf{U}_\lambda | \mathscr{X}_{\mathbf{U}_\lambda}(f^{-1}(F))\right) \subset \sigma(\mathbf{U}_\lambda) \cap f^{-1}(F),$$

hence, by applying Theorem 2.1(ii) to $\mathbf{V}_f$ we obtain

$$\sigma(\mathbf{V}_f) = f(\sigma(\mathbf{V}_\lambda)) \subset f(\sigma(\mathbf{U}_\lambda)) \cap f(f^{-1}(F)) \subset f(\sigma(\mathbf{U}_\lambda)) \cap F \subset F. \quad (1)$$

Let now $\mathscr{Y}$ be a closed linear subspace of $\mathscr{X}$ with properties (a) and (b) and suppose there is a $y \in \mathscr{Y}$ such that $y \notin \mathscr{X}_{\mathbf{U}_\lambda}(f^{-1}(F))$, i.e. $\sigma_{\mathbf{U}_\lambda}(y) \not\subset f^{-1}(F)$, hence there is

$$\lambda_0 \in \sigma_{\mathbf{U}_\lambda}(y) \setminus f^{-1}(F).$$

The set $f^{-1}(F)$ being closed (since F is closed and f is continuous), there exists an open disk D with the center in λ_0 such that $\bar{D} \cap f^{-1}(F) = \varnothing$, hence

$$f(\bar{D}) \cap F = \varnothing. \quad (2)$$

Take $\psi \in \mathfrak{A}$ such that $\operatorname{supp}(\psi) \subset D$ and put $z = \mathbf{U}_\psi y$. Then by (b)

$$(\xi I - \mathbf{U}_f)\, \mathbf{U}_\psi(\xi I|\mathscr{Y} - \mathbf{U}_f|\mathscr{Y})^{-1}\, y = z,$$

for all $\xi \notin F$, whence for ξ large enough (for instance $|\xi| > \|\mathbf{U}_\psi\|$) it follows

$$\mathbf{U}_\psi(\xi I|\mathscr{Y} - \mathbf{U}_f|\mathscr{Y})^{-1} y = (\xi I - \mathbf{U}_f)^{-1} z.$$

By Proposition 1.12, we have

$$\sigma_{\mathbf{U}_\lambda}(z) = \sigma_{\mathbf{U}_\lambda}(\mathbf{U}_\psi y) \subset \operatorname{supp}(\psi) \subset D \subset \bar{D}, \quad (3)$$

hence $z \in \mathscr{X}_{\mathbf{U}_\lambda}(\bar{D})$.

On account of Theorem 2.1 (ii) and (3) we have

$$\sigma_{\mathbf{U}_\lambda}(z) \subset \sigma_{\mathbf{U}_\lambda|\mathscr{X}_{\mathbf{U}_\lambda}(\bar{D})}(z) \subset \sigma(\mathbf{U}_\lambda|\mathscr{X}_{\mathbf{U}_\lambda}(\bar{D})) = f(\sigma(\mathbf{U}_\lambda|\mathscr{X}_{\mathbf{U}_\lambda}(\bar{D}))) \subset f(\bar{D}),$$

therefore

$$[\xi I|\mathscr{X}_{\mathbf{U}_\lambda}(\bar{D}) - U_f|\mathscr{X}_{\mathbf{U}_\lambda}(\bar{D})]^{-1}\, z$$

makes sense for all $\xi \notin f(\bar{D})$. Hence on account of (2), if we put

$$z(\xi) = \begin{cases} \mathbf{U}_\psi(\xi I|\mathscr{Y} - \mathbf{U}_f|\mathscr{Y})^{-1}\, z, & \text{for } \xi \notin F, \\ [\xi I|\mathscr{X}_{\mathbf{U}_\lambda}(\bar{D}) - \mathbf{U}_f|\mathscr{X}_{\mathbf{U}_\lambda}(\bar{D})]^{-1}\, z, & \text{for } \xi \notin f(\bar{D}) \end{cases}$$

we get an analytic function $\xi \to z(\xi)$ on the whole complex plane, which verifies $\lim_{\xi \to \infty} z(\xi) = 0$. By Liouville's theorem $z(\xi) \equiv 0$, hence for $\xi \notin f(\bar{D})$

$$z = [\xi I|\mathscr{X}_{\mathbf{U}_\lambda}(\bar{D}) - U_f|\mathscr{X}_{\mathbf{U}_\lambda}(\bar{D})]^{-1}\, z(\xi) = 0.$$

Thus we have shown that $\mathbf{U}_\psi y = 0$ for every $\psi \in \mathfrak{A}$ with supp $(\psi) \subset D$, i.e. with supp $(\psi) \cap \complement D = \emptyset$. Applying Proposition 1.17 it follows that $y \in \mathscr{X}_{\mathbf{U}_\lambda}(\complement D)$, i.e.

$$\sigma_{\mathbf{U}_\lambda}(y) \cap D = \emptyset .$$

This is not possible because D is a disk with the center in $\lambda_0 \in \sigma_{\mathbf{U}_\lambda}(y)$. In this manner $\sigma_{\mathbf{U}_\lambda}(y) \subset f^{-1}(F)$, i.e. $y \in \mathscr{X}_{\mathbf{U}_\lambda}(f^{-1}(F))$. Consequently

$$\mathscr{Y} \subset \mathscr{X}_{\mathbf{U}_\lambda}(f^{-1}(F)).$$

2.3. Corollary. *In the hypothesis and with the notations of the preceding lemma, $\mathscr{X}_{\mathbf{U}_\lambda}(f^{-1}(F))$ is a spectral maximal space of $\mathbf{U}_f$.*

Proof. Let $\mathscr{Z}$ be a closed linear subspace of $\mathscr{X}$ such that $\mathbf{U}_f\mathscr{Z} \subset \mathscr{Z}$ and

$$\sigma(\mathbf{U}_f|\mathscr{Z}) \subset \sigma\big(\mathbf{U}_f|\mathscr{X}_{\mathbf{U}_\lambda}(f^{-1}(F))\big).$$

But we have seen [relation 2.2(1)] that

$$\sigma\big(\mathbf{U}_f|\mathscr{X}_{\mathbf{U}_\lambda}(f^{-1}(F))\big) = \sigma(\mathbf{V}_f) \subset F,$$

hence

$$\sigma(\mathbf{U}_f|\mathscr{Z}) \subset F.$$

Applying the preceding lemma for $\mathscr{Y} = \mathscr{Z}$, we get

$$\mathscr{Z} \subset \mathscr{X}_{\mathbf{U}_\lambda}(f^{-1}(F))).$$

2.4. Theorem. *Let $\mathfrak{A}$, f, $\mathbf{U}$ and F as in the Lemma 2.2. Then*

(i) *$\mathbf{U}_f$ is decomposable*

and

(ii) $\mathscr{X}_{\mathbf{U}_f}(F) = \mathscr{X}_{\mathbf{U}_\lambda}(f^{-1}(F))$.

Proof. Let $\{G_i\}_{1\leqslant i\leqslant n}$ be an open covering of $\sigma(\mathbf{U}_f) = f(\sigma(\mathbf{U}_\lambda))$. Putting $H_i = f^{-1}(G_i)$ $(1 \leqslant i \leqslant n)$ we get an open covering of $\sigma(\mathbf{U}_\lambda)$, hence by the decomposability of $\mathbf{U}_\lambda$ there are n spectral maximal spaces $\mathscr{Y}_i$ of $\mathbf{U}_\lambda$ such that

$$\sigma(\mathbf{U}_\lambda|\mathscr{Y}_i) \subset H_i$$

and

$$\mathscr{X} = \sum_{i=1}^{n} \mathscr{Y}_i . \tag{1}$$

Putting $F_i = \sigma(\mathbf{U}_\lambda|\mathscr{Y}_i)$, we have

$$\mathscr{Y}_i = \mathscr{X}_{\mathbf{U}_\lambda}(F_i) \subset \mathscr{X}_{\mathbf{U}_\lambda}\left(f^{-1}(f(F_i))\right). \tag{2}$$

By the preceding corollary $\mathscr{X}_{\mathbf{U}_\lambda}\left(f^{-1}(f(F_i))\right)$ are spectral maximal spaces of $\mathbf{U}_f$. From (1) and (2), we get

$$\mathscr{X} = \sum_{i=1}^{n} \mathscr{X}_{\mathbf{U}_\lambda}\left(f^{-1}(f(F_i))\right).$$

On the other hand by Theorem 2.1 (ii)

$$\begin{aligned}\sigma\left(\mathbf{U}_f|\mathscr{X}_{\mathbf{U}_\lambda}\left(f^{-1}(f(F_i))\right)\right) &= f\left(\sigma\left(\mathbf{U}_\lambda|\mathscr{X}_{\mathbf{U}_\lambda}\left(f^{-1}(f(F))\right)\right)\right)\\ &\subset f\left(f^{-1}(f(F_i))\right) \subset f\left(f^{-1}(G_i)\right) \subset G_i\end{aligned}$$

so that $\mathbf{U}_f$ is decomposable.

$\mathscr{X}_{\mathbf{U}_\lambda}(f^{-1}(F))$ being a spectral maximal space of the decomposable operator $\mathbf{U}_f$ we have

$$\mathscr{X}_{\mathbf{U}_\lambda}(f^{-1}(F)) = \mathscr{X}_{\mathbf{U}_f}\left(\sigma\left(\mathbf{U}_f|\mathscr{X}_{\mathbf{U}_\lambda}(f^{-1}(F))\right)\right) \subset \mathscr{X}_{\mathbf{U}_f}(F).$$

But

$$\sigma\left(\mathbf{U}_f|\mathscr{X}_{\mathbf{U}_f}(F)\right) \subset F,$$

therefore by Lemma 2.3, we have

$$\mathscr{X}_{\mathbf{U}_f}(F) \subset \mathscr{X}_{\mathbf{U}_f}\left(f^{-1}(F)\right).$$

2.5. Corollary. *Let $\mathfrak{A}$ be an admissible inverse closed algebra of continuous functions defined on a closed set $\Omega \subset C$. If $\mathbf{U}$ and $\mathbf{V}$ are two $\mathfrak{A}$-spectral functions such that $\mathbf{U}_\lambda = \mathbf{V}_\lambda$, then*

$$\mathbf{U}_f \overset{q}{\sim} \mathbf{V}_f, \quad \textit{for every} \quad f \in \mathfrak{A}.$$

Proof. On account of the preceding theorem we have

$$\mathscr{X}_{\mathbf{U}_f}(F) = \mathscr{X}_{\mathbf{U}_\lambda}(f^{-1}(F)) = \mathscr{X}_{\mathbf{V}_\lambda}(f^{-1}(F)) = \mathscr{X}_{\mathbf{V}_\lambda}(F),$$

whence, by Theorem 2.2.2, it follows

$$\mathbf{U}_f \overset{q}{\sim} \mathbf{V}_f \quad \text{for every} \quad f \in \mathfrak{A}.$$

Summing up, we have

2.6. THEOREM. *Let* $\mathfrak{A}$ *be as in the above. If* $\mathbf{U}$ *and* $\mathbf{V}$ *are two* $\mathfrak{A}$*-spectral functions of the same* $\mathfrak{A}$*-scalar operator* S, *then*

$$\mathbf{U}_f \overset{q}{\sim} \mathbf{V}_f \quad \textit{for every} \quad f \in \mathfrak{A}.$$

3. $\mathfrak{A}$-decomposable and $\mathfrak{A}$-spectral Operators. Elementary Properties

3.1. THEOREM. *For an operator* $T \in \mathbf{B}(\mathscr{X})$ *the following two assertions are equivalent:*

(I) *There exists an* $\mathfrak{A}$*-spectral function* $\mathbf{U}$ *such that* T *is quasinilpotent equivalent to* $\mathbf{U}_\lambda$ *(see Definition* 1.2.1*).*

(II) *There exists an* $\mathfrak{A}$*-spectral function* $\mathbf{U}$ *such that for any closed set* $F \subset C$, *we have*

(a) $T\mathscr{X}_{\mathbf{U}_\lambda}(F) \subset \mathscr{X}_{\mathbf{U}_\lambda}(F)$,

and

(b) $\sigma\,(T|\mathscr{X}_{\mathbf{U}_\lambda}(F)) \subset F$.

Proof

(I) $\Rightarrow$ (II). Since $\mathbf{U}_\lambda$ is decomposable (Theorem 1.16) and $T \overset{q}{\sim} \mathbf{U}_\lambda$, it follows by Theorem 2.2.1 that T is decomposable, and

$$\mathscr{X}_T(F) = \mathscr{X}_{\mathbf{U}_\lambda}(F), \tag{1}$$

for any closed set $F \subset C$. But $\mathscr{X}_T(F)$ is invariant to T, and

$$\sigma\,(T|\mathscr{X}_T(F)) \subset F,$$

so that [by (1)] we get

$$T\mathscr{X}_{\mathbf{U}_\lambda}(F) \subset \mathscr{X}_{\mathbf{U}_\lambda}(F)$$

and

$$\sigma\,(T|\mathscr{X}_{\mathbf{U}_\lambda}(F)) \subset F.$$

(II) $\Rightarrow$ (I). Assuming (II) fulfilled, we deduce from Theorem 2.2.6 that T is decomposable, and that the equality (1) holds for any closed set $F \subset C$. Applying 2.2.2, we get $T \overset{q}{\sim} \mathbf{U}_\lambda$.

3.2. DEFINITION. An operator $T \in \mathbf{B}(\mathscr{X})$ is called $\mathfrak{A}$-*decomposable* if it verifies one of the equivalent assertions of Theorem 3.1. An $\mathfrak{A}$-spectral function verifying the assertions of Theorem 3.1 will be called an $\mathfrak{A}$-*spectral function of* T.

3.3. *Remark. If* $T \in \mathbf{B}(\mathscr{X})$ is $\mathfrak{A}$-decomposable and $\mathbf{U}$ is one of its $\mathfrak{A}$-spectral functions, then

(i) T is decomposable;

(ii) $\mathscr{X}_T(F) = \mathscr{X}_{\mathbf{U}_\lambda}(F)$, for every closed set $F \subset C$;

(iii) if $\mathbf{V}$ is another $\mathfrak{A}$-spectral function of T, then $\mathbf{U}_\lambda \overset{q}{\sim} \mathbf{V}_\lambda$;

(iv) if in addition $\mathfrak{A}$ is an inverse closed algebra of continuous functions defined on a closed set of C, and if $\mathbf{V}$ is another $\mathfrak{A}$-spectral function of T, then

$$\mathbf{U}_f \overset{q}{\sim} \mathbf{V}_f \quad \text{for every} \quad f \in \mathfrak{A}.$$

Indeed, in proving Theorem 3.1 we have seen that assertions (i) and (ii) hold. The third assertion follows from Definition 3.2 and from the transitivity of the relation $A \overset{q}{\sim} B$.

To prove (iv) we remark that by (iii) and by Theorem 2.2.1, we have

$$\mathscr{X}_{\mathbf{U}_\lambda}(F) = \mathscr{X}_{\mathbf{V}_\lambda}(F) \quad \text{for every closed} \quad F \subset C,$$

whence by Theorem 2.4, we get

$$\mathscr{X}_{\mathbf{U}_f}(F) = \mathscr{X}_{\mathbf{U}_\lambda}(f^{-1}(F)) = \mathscr{X}_{\mathbf{V}_\lambda}(f^{-1}(F)) = \mathscr{X}_{\mathbf{V}_f}(F),$$

for every $f \in \mathfrak{A}$. Applying now Theorem 2.2.2, we obtain

$$\mathbf{U}_f \overset{q}{\sim} \mathbf{V}_f.$$

3.4. THEOREM. *Let T be a bounded linear operator on a Banach space $\mathscr{X}$. The following four assertions are equivalent*

(I) *T is $\mathfrak{A}$-decomposable and commutes with one of its $\mathfrak{A}$-spectral functions.*

(II)
- (II_1) *T is decomposable;*
- (II_2) *there is an $\mathfrak{A}$-spectral function* $\mathbf{U}$ *commuting with T*, i.e. $T\mathbf{U}_f = \mathbf{U}_f T$, *for any $f \in \mathfrak{A}$;*
- (II_3) *$\mathscr{X}_T(F) = \mathscr{X}_{\mathbf{U}_\lambda}(F)$, for any closed set $F \subset \Omega$.*

(III)
- (III_1) *there is an $\mathfrak{A}$-spectral function* $\mathbf{U}$ *commuting with T;*
- (III_2) *$\sigma(T|\mathscr{X}_{\mathbf{U}_\lambda}(F)) \subset F$, for any closed set $F \subset \Omega$.*

(IV) *$T = S + Q$, where S is an $\mathfrak{A}$-scalar operator and Q is a quasinilpotent operator commuting with an $\mathfrak{A}$-spectral function of S.*

Proof

(II) $\Rightarrow$ (III). T being decomposable, we have

$$\sigma\,(T|\mathscr{X}_T(F)) \subset F \cap \sigma(T),$$

hence [by (II_3)]

$$\sigma\,(T|\mathscr{X}_{\mathbf{U}_\lambda}(F)) = \sigma\,(T|\mathscr{X}_T(F)) \subset F.$$

(I) $\Longleftrightarrow$ (III). Evident.

(III) $\Rightarrow$ (II). We remark that if $\mathbf{U}$ is an $\mathfrak{A}$-spectral function, then $\mathbf{U}_\lambda$ is an $\mathfrak{A}$-scalar operator.

In the hypothesis (III_1) $\mathbf{U}_\lambda$ is an $\mathfrak{A}$-scalar operator, hence (by Theorem 1.19) decomposable, therefore (by Proposition 1.3.2)

$$T\mathscr{X}_{\mathbf{U}_\lambda}(F) \subset \mathscr{X}_{\mathbf{U}_\lambda}(F),$$

for any closed set $F \subset \Omega$, thus (III_2) makes sense.

On account of Theorem 2.2.6 it results that T is decomposable and

$$\mathscr{X}_T(F) = \mathscr{X}_{\mathbf{U}_\lambda}(F).$$

(II) $\Rightarrow$ (IV). In the hypothesis (II) $\mathbf{U}_\lambda$ is an $\mathfrak{A}$-scalar operator. From (II_3) and Theorem 2.2.2 it results that T and $\mathbf{U}_\lambda$ are quasinilpotent equivalent, but T commutes with $\mathbf{U}_\lambda$, hence $T - \mathbf{U}_\lambda$ is a quasinilpotent operator commuting with $\mathbf{U}$. Putting $S = \mathbf{U}_\lambda$ and $Q = T - \mathbf{U}_\lambda$, we have

$$T = S + Q.$$

(IV) $\Rightarrow$ (II). The operator S, being $\mathfrak{A}$-scalar, is decomposable. Applying Theorem 2.2.1 to T and S, we get that T is decomposable and

$$\mathscr{X}_T(F) = \mathscr{X}_S(F),$$

for any closed set $F \subset \Omega$.

Let $\mathbf{U}$ be an $\mathfrak{A}$-spectral function of S commuting with Q. Then $S + Q$ commutes with $\mathbf{U}$.

3.5. Definition. An operator $T \in \mathbf{B}(\mathscr{X})$ is called $\mathfrak{A}$-*spectral* if it verifies one of the equivalent assertions of Theorem 2.4. The writing of an $\mathfrak{A}$-spectral operator in the form $T = S + Q$ is called *canonical decomposition of* T.

S is called the *scalar part* of T and Q the *radical part* of T.

An $\mathfrak{A}$-spectral function $\mathbf{U}$ verifying the conditions of Theorem 3.1 is called an $\mathfrak{A}$-*spectral function attached to* T (or $\mathfrak{A}$-spectral function of T).†

† If T is $\mathfrak{A}$-spectral, then $\mathbf{U}$ must be as in Th. 3.4.

3.6. LEMMA. *Let* $A_i, B_i \in \mathbf{B}(\mathscr{X}_i)$ *such that* $A_i \overset{a}{\sim} B_i$ $(i = 1, 2)$. *Then* $A_1 \oplus A_2 \overset{a}{\sim} B_1 \oplus B_2$.

Proof. This results from the equality

$$(A_1 \oplus A_2 - B_1 \oplus B_2)^{[n]} = (A_1 - B_1)^{[n]} \oplus (A_2 - B_2)^{[n]}$$

and the definition of norm in $\mathscr{X}_1 \oplus \mathscr{X}_2$.

3.7. LEMMA. *Let* $A, B \in \mathbf{B}(\mathscr{X})$ *such that* $A \overset{a}{\sim} B$, *and let* $\mathscr{Y}$ *be a closed linear subspace of* $\mathscr{X}$ *invariant to* A *and to* B. *Then* $A|\mathscr{Y} \overset{a}{\sim} B|\mathscr{Y}$.

Proof. This results from the equality

$$(A|\mathscr{Y} - B|\mathscr{Y})^{[n]} = (A - B)^{[n]}|\mathscr{Y},$$

and from the inequality $\|T|\mathscr{Y}\| \leqslant \|T\|$, which holds for every operator $T \in \mathbf{B}(\mathscr{X})$.

3.8. LEMMA. *Let* $A, B \in \mathbf{B}(\mathscr{X})$ *such that* $A \overset{a}{\sim} B$, *and let* $h : \mathbf{B}(\mathscr{X}) \to \mathbf{B}(\mathscr{Y})$ *be a continuous homomorphism or an antihomomorphism.*† *Then* $h(A) \overset{a}{\sim} h(B)$.

Proof. If h is a homomorphism (respectively an antihomomorphism) then

$$h\left((A - B)^{[n]}\right) = (h(A) - h(B))^{[n]}$$

$$\{\text{respectively } h\left((A - B)^{[n]}\right) = (-1)^n \left[(h(B) - h(A))^{[n]}\right]\}.$$

h being continuous, we have

$$\|(h(A) - h(B))^{[n]}\| \leqslant \|h\| \cdot \|(A - B)^{[n]}\|$$

or

$$\|(h(A) - h(B))^{[n]}\| \leqslant \|h\| \cdot |(B - A)^{[n]}\|.$$

Thus in both cases $h(A) \overset{a}{\sim} h(B)$.

With the help of these lemmas we can prove some elementary properties of 𝔄-decomposable or 𝔄-spectral operators.

---

† By an antihomomorphism we mean a mapping h verifying

$$h(\alpha A + \beta B) = \alpha h(A) + \beta h(B)$$

and

$$h(AB) = h(B)\, h(A).$$

3.9. PROPOSITION. *Let $\mathfrak{A}$ be an admissible algebra, and let $\mathscr{X}_1$ and $\mathscr{X}_2$ be two Banach spaces. If $T_i \in \mathbf{B}(\mathscr{X}_i)$ $(i = 1, 2)$ is $\mathfrak{A}$-decomposable (respectively $\mathfrak{A}$-spectral or $\mathfrak{A}$-scalar), then so is also $T_1 \oplus T_2 \in \mathbf{B}(\mathscr{X}_1 \oplus \mathscr{X}_2)$.*

Proof. If T_1 and T_2 are $\mathfrak{A}$-decomposable operators, then there are two $\mathfrak{A}$-spectral functions $\mathbf{U}^1$ and $\mathbf{U}^2$ such that

$$\mathbf{U}^1_\lambda \overset{q}{\sim} T_1 \quad \text{and} \quad \mathbf{U}^2_\lambda \overset{q}{\sim} T_2 .$$

The mapping $f \to \mathbf{U}^1_f \oplus \mathbf{U}^2_f$ is evidently an $\mathfrak{A}$-spectral function. Furthermore, by Lemma 3.6, we have

$$\mathbf{U}^1_\lambda \oplus \mathbf{U}^2_\lambda \overset{q}{\sim} T_1 \oplus T_2 ,$$

that is $T_1 \oplus T_2$ is $\mathfrak{A}$-decomposable.

It is clear that if $\mathbf{U}^i$ commutes with T_i $(i = 1, 2)$, then $\mathbf{U}^1 \oplus \mathbf{U}^2$ commutes with $T_1 \oplus T_2$. Thus if T_1 and T_2 are $\mathfrak{A}$-spectral operators, then $T_1 \oplus T_2$ is also an $\mathfrak{A}$-spectral operator. If $\mathbf{U}^i_\lambda = T_i$ $(i = 1, 2)$, then $\mathbf{U}^1_\lambda \oplus \mathbf{U}^2_\lambda = T_1 \oplus T_2$. That is, if T_1 and T_2 are $\mathfrak{A}$-scalar operators, then $T_1 \oplus T_2$ is also an $\mathfrak{A}$-scalar operator.

3.10. PROPOSITION. *Let $T \in \mathbf{B}(\mathscr{X})$ be an $\mathfrak{A}$-decomposable (respectively, $\mathfrak{A}$-spectral or $\mathfrak{A}$-scalar) operator, and let $\mathscr{Y}$ be a closed linear subspace of $\mathscr{X}$ which is invariant to T and to one of its $\mathfrak{A}$-spectral functions. Then so is also $T|\mathscr{Y}$.*

Proof. Let us suppose that T is $\mathfrak{A}$-decomposable and let $\mathbf{U}$ be an $\mathfrak{A}$-spectral function of T such that

$$\mathbf{U}_f \mathscr{Y} \subset \mathscr{Y} \quad \text{for any} \quad f \in \mathfrak{A}.$$

Putting $\mathbf{V}_f = \mathbf{U}_f|\mathscr{Y}$ we obtain a $\mathbf{B}(\mathscr{Y})$-valued $\mathfrak{A}$-spectral function. Thus, by Lemma 3.7, $T|\mathscr{Y}$ is $\mathfrak{A}$-decomposable and $\mathbf{V}$ is one of its $\mathfrak{A}$-spectral functions.

If in addition $\mathbf{U}$ commutes with T, then $\mathbf{V}$ commutes with $T|\mathscr{Y}$. That is, if T is $\mathfrak{A}$-spectral, so is also $T|\mathscr{Y}$.

If $\mathbf{U}_\lambda = T$, then $\mathbf{V}_\lambda = T|\mathscr{Y}$.

3.11. PROPOSITION. *Let $\mathscr{X}$ and $\mathscr{Y}$ be two Banach spaces, $T \in \mathbf{B}(\mathscr{X})$ an $\mathfrak{A}$-decomposable ($\mathfrak{A}$-spectral or $\mathfrak{A}$-scalar) operator, and $h : \mathbf{B}(\mathscr{X}) \to \mathbf{B}(\mathscr{Y})$ a continuous homomorphism or antihomomorphism. Then so is also $h(T)$.*

Proof. Let $\mathbf{U}$ be a $\mathbf{B}(\mathscr{X})$-valued $\mathfrak{A}$-spectral function. The mapping $h(\mathbf{U})$: $\mathfrak{A} \to B(\mathscr{Y})$ defined by $h(\mathbf{U})_f = h(\mathbf{U}_f)$ is an $\mathfrak{A}$-spectral function.

If $\mathbf{U}_\lambda \overset{a}{\sim} T$, then (by Lemma 3.8) $h(\mathbf{U}_\lambda) \overset{a}{\sim} h(T)$, i.e. $h(T)$ is $\mathfrak{A}$-decomposable.

If in addition $\mathbf{U}$ commutes with T, then obviously $h(\mathbf{U})$ commutes with $h(T)$, that is T is $\mathfrak{A}$-spectral.

If $\mathbf{U}_\lambda = T$, then $h(\mathbf{U})_\lambda = h(\mathbf{U}_\lambda) = h(T)$.

3.12. Corollary. *If $T \in \mathbf{B}(\mathscr{X})$ is an $\mathfrak{A}$-decomposable (respectively $\mathfrak{A}$-spectral or $\mathfrak{A}$-scalar) operator,* $\mathbf{U}$ *one of its $\mathfrak{A}$-spectral functions, and $\mathscr{Y}$ a closed linear subspace of $\mathscr{X}$ which is invariant to T and to* $\mathbf{U}$, *then*

$$\dot{T} \in B(\dot{\mathscr{X}}) \quad \left(\dot{\mathscr{X}} = \mathscr{X}/\mathscr{Y}, \quad \dot{T}x = \widehat{\dot{T}\mathbf{x}}\right)$$

is also $\mathfrak{A}$-decomposable (respectively $\mathfrak{A}$-spectral or $\mathfrak{A}$-scalar).

This is an immediate consequence of the preceding proposition.

3.13. Corollary. *If $T \in \mathbf{B}(\mathscr{X})$ is an $\mathfrak{A}$-decomposable (respectively $\mathfrak{A}$-spectral or $\mathfrak{A}$-scalar) operator, then so is also $T^* \in \mathbf{B}(\mathscr{X}^*)$. Conversely, if T^* is $\mathfrak{A}$-decomposable (etc. ...) and $\mathscr{X}$ is reflexive, then so is also T.*

Proof. The mapping $A \to A^*$ $(:\mathbf{B}(\mathscr{X}) \to \mathbf{B}(\mathscr{X}^*))$ being a continuous anti-homomorphism, the corollary results from Proposition 3.11.

4. Nests of Ultrainvariant Spaces of $\mathfrak{A}$-decomposable Operators

In this paragraph the term *subspace* will be used to describe a closed linear manifold.

4.1. Definition. Let $\mathscr{X}$ be a Banach space and $\mathscr{N} = \{\mathscr{X}_\alpha\}_{\alpha \in A}$ a family of subspaces of $\mathscr{X}$. $\mathscr{N}$ is called a *nest*, if it is totally ordered by inclusion, that is

(i) A is totally ordered;

and

(ii) $\mathscr{H}_\alpha \subsetneqq \mathscr{H}_\beta$ for $\alpha < \beta$.

Consider an operator $T \in \mathbf{B}(\mathscr{X})$ and the system $\mathfrak{N}$ of all the nests $\mathscr{N} = \{\mathscr{X}_\alpha\}_{\alpha \in A}$ of ultrainvariant subspaces of T (i.e. the $\mathscr{X}_\alpha$ are ultrainvariant subspaces of T). $\mathscr{N}$ is nonvoid since $\{\{0\}, \mathscr{X}\} \in \mathfrak{N}$. Ordering $\mathfrak{N}$ by inclusion of the nests and "zornifying" (i.e. applying Zorn's lemma) one obtains a maximal nest of ultrainvariant subspaces of T. Thus for every $T \in \mathbf{B}(\mathscr{X})$ there exists at least one maximal nest of ultrainvariant subspaces of T.

4.2. PROPOSITION. *Let* $T \in \mathbf{B}(\mathscr{X})$ *and let* $\mathscr{N} = \{\mathscr{X}_\alpha\}_{\alpha \in A}$ *be a maximal nest of ultrainvariant subspaces of* T. *Then for every* $\alpha \in A$ *there exists an element* $\beta \in A$ *such that*

$$\beta \leqslant \alpha; \tag{a}$$

$$\text{if } \beta \leqslant \gamma \leqslant \alpha \quad \text{then} \quad \gamma = \beta \quad \text{or} \quad \gamma = \alpha. \tag{b}$$

Proof. Take

$$\mathscr{Y} = \bigvee_{\gamma < \alpha} \mathscr{X}_\gamma.$$

Then $\mathscr{Y}$ is an ultrainvariant subspace of T and

$$\mathscr{X}_\gamma \subset \mathscr{Y} \subset \mathscr{X}_\alpha \quad \text{for} \quad \gamma < \alpha.$$

If $\mathscr{X}_\gamma \neq \mathscr{Y} \neq \mathscr{X}_\alpha$ for $\gamma < \alpha$, then the family

$$\{\mathscr{X}_\gamma\}_{\gamma < \alpha} \cup \{\mathscr{Y}\} \cup \{\mathscr{X}_\gamma\}_{\gamma \geq \alpha}$$

is a nest of ultrainvariant subspaces which majorizes $\mathscr{N} = \{\mathscr{X}_\alpha\}_{\alpha \in A}$ in $\mathfrak{N}$ This would contradict the maximality of $\mathscr{N}$. Thus

$$\mathscr{Y} = \mathscr{X}_\beta \quad \text{for some} \quad \beta < \alpha,$$

or

$$\mathscr{Y} = \mathscr{X}_\alpha.$$

In the second case put $\beta = \alpha$. In the first case $\beta < \alpha$ verifies (b).

4.3. DEFINITION. The element β constructed in the preceding proposition will be denoted by $\alpha - 0$.

α is called a *point of continuity* of the nest $\mathscr{N}$ if $\alpha - 0 = \alpha$, or a *point of discontinuity* if $\alpha - 0 < \alpha$.

4.4. PROPOSITION. *Let* $T \in \mathbf{B}(\mathscr{X})$ *be* $\mathfrak{A}$*-spectral and* $\mathscr{N} = \{\mathscr{X}_\alpha\}_{\alpha \in A}$ *a maximal nest of ultrainvariant subspaces of* T. *Let* α *be a point of discon-*

tinuity of $\mathcal{N}$, $\dot{\mathcal{X}}_\alpha = \mathcal{X}_\alpha/\mathcal{X}_{\alpha-0}$ *and* $\dot{T}_\alpha$ *the operator induced in* $\dot{\mathcal{X}}_\alpha$ *by* T. *Then* $\sigma(\dot{T}_\alpha)$ *reduces to a point* ξ_0 *which belongs to* $\sigma(T)$.

Proof. By Proposition 2.10, $T|\mathcal{X}_\alpha$ is $\mathfrak{A}$-spectral, and by Proposition 2.12, $\dot{T}_\alpha = \widehat{T|\mathcal{X}_\alpha}$ is also $\mathfrak{A}$-spectral. The Lemma 2.1.2 shows that if the spectrum of $\dot{T}_\alpha$ does not reduce to a single point there exists a nontrivial spectral maximal space $\dot{\mathcal{Y}} \subset \dot{\mathcal{X}}_\alpha$, i.e.

$$\{\dot{0}\} \neq \dot{\mathcal{Y}} \neq \dot{\mathcal{X}}_\alpha. \tag{1}$$

Since $\dot{\mathcal{Y}}$ is a spectral maximal space of $\dot{T}_\alpha$, it is ultrainvariant to $\dot{T}_\alpha$. Put

$$\mathcal{Y} = \{x \in \mathcal{X}_\alpha | \dot{x} \in \dot{\mathcal{Y}}\}.$$

Then $\mathcal{Y}$ is a subspace of $\mathcal{X}_\alpha$ containing $\mathcal{X}_{\alpha-0}$, which in virtue of (1) verifies

$$\mathcal{X}_{\alpha-0} \subsetneqq \mathcal{Y} \subsetneqq \mathcal{X}_\alpha. \tag{2}$$

On the other hand, if $X \in \mathbf{B}(\mathcal{X})$ and $XT = TX$, then

$$X\mathcal{X}_\alpha \subset \mathcal{X}_\alpha \quad \text{and} \quad X\mathcal{X}_{\alpha-0} \subset \mathcal{X}_{\alpha-0},$$

since the spaces $\mathcal{X}_\alpha$, $\mathcal{X}_{\alpha-0}$ are ultrainvariant to T. Thus $\dot{X}\dot{\mathcal{Y}} \subset \dot{\mathcal{Y}}$ and consequently

$$X\mathcal{Y} \subset \mathcal{Y}.$$

In this manner $\mathcal{Y}$ is also an ultrainvariant space of T. This conclusion, together with (2) and the maximality of $\mathcal{N}$, yields a contradiction. Hence $\sigma(\dot{T}_\alpha)$ reduces to a single point ξ_α.

It remains to prove that $\xi_\alpha \in \sigma(T)$. Suppose the contrary, that is $\xi_\alpha \notin \sigma(T)$. Then $\xi_\alpha \notin \sigma(T|\mathcal{X}_\alpha)$ since $\sigma(T|\mathcal{Y}) \subset \sigma(T)$ for every ultrainvariant space $\mathcal{Y}$ of T. Therefore there is an open set G such that $\xi_\alpha \in G$ and

$$G \cap \sigma(T|\mathcal{X}_\alpha) = \varnothing. \tag{3}$$

If $G \cap \Omega = \varnothing$, then $\{f \in \mathfrak{A} | \operatorname{supp}(f) \subset G\} = \{0\}$, hence

$$\mathcal{X}_{[\dot{U}_\alpha]}(G) = \{0\},$$

where $\dot{U}_\alpha$ is an $\mathfrak{A}$-spectral function of $\dot{T}_\alpha$. Therefore

$$\dot{\mathcal{X}}_\alpha = \mathcal{X}_{\dot{T}_\alpha}(\{\xi_\alpha\}) \subset \mathcal{X}_{[\dot{U}_\alpha]}(G) = \{0\},$$

whence $\mathscr{X}_\alpha = \mathscr{X}_{\alpha-0}$, i.e. α is a point of continuity. Contradiction! Consequently $G \cap \Omega \neq \emptyset$. In this case there exists $0 \neq f_0 \in \mathfrak{A}$ such that $\operatorname{supp}(f_0) \subset G$. T being $\mathfrak{A}$-decomposable means that there exists an $\mathfrak{A}$-spectral function $\mathbf{U}$ such that $T \overset{q}{\sim} \mathbf{U}_\lambda$, hence by Lemma 3.7, $T|\mathscr{X}_\alpha \overset{q}{\sim} \mathbf{U}_\lambda|\mathscr{X}_\alpha$, therefore by Theorem 1.2.2

$$\sigma(T|\mathscr{X}_\alpha) = \sigma(\mathbf{U}_\lambda|\mathscr{X}_\alpha). \tag{4}$$

But by Theorem 1.6

$$\operatorname{supp}(\mathbf{U}|\mathscr{X}_\alpha) = \sigma(\mathbf{U}_\lambda|\mathscr{X}_\alpha). \tag{5}$$

From (3), (4), (5) and $\operatorname{supp}(f_0) \subset G$ it results

$$(\mathbf{U}|\mathscr{X}_\alpha)_{f_0} = \mathbf{U}_{f_0}|\mathscr{X}_\alpha = 0,$$

hence

$$\dot{\mathbf{U}}_{f_0}\dot{x} = \dot{\widehat{\mathbf{U}_f x}} = \dot{0} \quad \text{for every} \quad x \in \mathscr{X}_\alpha,$$

thus $\dot{\mathbf{U}}_{f_0} = 0$. Consequently

$$\operatorname{supp}(\dot{\mathbf{U}}) \cap G = \emptyset.$$

But

$$\operatorname{supp}(\dot{\mathbf{U}}) = \sigma\left(\dot{\widehat{\mathbf{U}_\lambda|\mathscr{X}_\alpha}}\right) = \sigma(\dot{T}_\alpha) = \{\xi_\alpha\} \subset G,$$

so that we have obtained again a contradiction. This shows that $\xi_\alpha \in \sigma(T)$.

4.5. PROPOSITION. *Let $T \in \mathbf{B}(\mathscr{X})$ be $\mathfrak{A}$-spectral and $\mathscr{N} = \{\mathscr{X}_\alpha\}_{\alpha \in A}$ a maximal nest of ultrainvariant subspaces of T. Then*

$$\sigma(T|\mathscr{X}_\alpha) \subset \sigma(T|\mathscr{X}_{\beta-0}) \quad \textit{for} \quad \alpha < \beta, \tag{a}$$

$$\sigma(T|\mathscr{X}_{\alpha-0}) = \overline{\bigcup_{\gamma<\alpha} \sigma(T|\mathscr{X}_\gamma)}, \tag{b}$$

and

$$\sigma(T|\mathscr{X}_{\alpha-0}) \subset \sigma(T|\mathscr{X}_\alpha), \tag{c}$$

where the inequality occurs if and only if $\xi_\alpha \notin \sigma(T|\mathscr{X}_{\alpha-0})$ and $\mathscr{X}_T(\{\xi_\alpha\}) \cap \mathscr{X}_\alpha \neq \{0\}$.

Proof:

(a) Let $\mathbf{U}$ be an $\mathfrak{A}$-spectral function of T. Then $\mathbf{U}^{(\alpha)}: \mathfrak{A} \to \mathbf{B}(\mathscr{X}_\alpha)$ defined by

$$\mathbf{U}_f^{(\alpha)} = \mathbf{U}_f|\mathscr{X}_\alpha, \quad (f \in \mathfrak{A})$$

is an $\mathfrak{A}$-spectral function of $T_\alpha = T|\mathscr{X}_\alpha$. Hence for $\alpha < \beta$ we have

$$\sigma(T_\alpha) = \text{supp}\,(\mathbf{U}^{(\alpha)}) \subset \text{supp}\,(\mathbf{U}^{(\beta-0)}) = \sigma(T_{\beta-0}),$$

where we use the fact that $\mathbf{U}_f^{(\alpha)} = \mathbf{U}_f|\mathscr{X}_\alpha = (\mathbf{U}_f|\mathscr{X}_{\beta-0})|\mathscr{X}_\alpha$, since $\mathscr{X}_\alpha \subset \mathscr{X}_{\beta-0}$, and that the support of an $\mathfrak{A}$-spectral function obviously decreases by taking the restriction to an invariant subspace (for all operators $\mathbf{U}_f$, $f \in \mathfrak{A}$).

(b) Let now $f_0 \in \mathfrak{A}$ such that

$$\text{supp}\,(f_0) \cap \overline{\bigcup_{\gamma<\alpha} \sigma(T_\gamma)} = \emptyset. \tag{1}$$

Then, in particular,

$$\text{supp}\,(f_0) \cap \text{supp}\,(\mathbf{U}^{(\gamma)}) = \text{supp}\,(f_0) \cap \sigma(T_\gamma) = \emptyset$$

for all $\gamma < \alpha$, hence

$$\mathbf{U}_{f_0}|\mathscr{X}_\gamma = \mathbf{U}_{f_0}^{(\gamma)} = 0 \quad \text{for all} \quad \gamma < \alpha.$$

As $\mathscr{X}_{\alpha-0}$ is spanned by $\mathscr{X}_\gamma$, $\gamma < \alpha$, it results

$$\mathbf{U}_{f_0}^{(\alpha-0)} = \mathbf{U}_{f_0}|\mathscr{X}_{\alpha-0} = 0 \tag{2}$$

for every $f_0 \in \mathfrak{A}$ satisfying (1), hence (by Definition 1.5)

$$\text{supp}\,(\mathbf{U}^{(\alpha-0)}) \subset \overline{\bigcup_{\gamma<\alpha} \sigma(T_\gamma)}.$$

But $\text{supp}\,(\mathbf{U}^{(\alpha-0)}) = \sigma(T_{\alpha-0})$, so that

$$\sigma(T_{\alpha-0}) \subset \overline{\bigcup_{\gamma<\alpha} \sigma(T_\gamma)}.$$

The converse inclusion results directly from (a).

(c) The inclusion follows easily by the same argument as that used in proving (a).

The sufficiency of the conditions stated in order to have

$$\sigma(T_{\alpha-0}) = \sigma\,(T|\mathscr{X}_{\alpha-0}) \neq \sigma\,(T|\mathscr{X}_\alpha) = \sigma(T_\alpha)$$

is evident since then

$$\mathscr{X}_{T_\alpha}(\{\xi_\alpha\}) = \mathscr{X}_T(\{\xi_\alpha\}) \cap \mathscr{X}_\alpha \neq \{0\},$$

hence $\xi_\alpha \in \sigma(T_\alpha)$.

Conversely, suppose now that $\sigma(T_{\alpha-0}) \neq \sigma(T_\alpha)$, and that $\xi_\alpha \in \sigma(T_{\alpha-0}) = \sigma_{\alpha-0}$. Take an arbitrary $f \in \mathfrak{A}$ with $\text{supp}(f) \cap \sigma_{\alpha-0} = \varnothing$. Choose another $g \in \mathfrak{A}$ such that

$$\text{supp}(g) \cap \sigma_{\alpha-0} = \varnothing \quad \text{and} \quad gf = f.$$

Then

$$\mathbf{U}_f | \mathscr{X}_{\alpha-0} = \mathscr{X}_f^{(\alpha-0)} = 0$$

since $\text{supp}(\mathbf{U}^{(\alpha-0)}) = \sigma(T_{\alpha-0}) = \sigma_{\alpha-0}$. Moreover, using the notations of Proposition 4.4, we have $\dot{\mathbf{U}}_g = 0$, because $\dot{\mathbf{U}}$ is an $\mathfrak{A}$-spectral function of $\dot{T}_\alpha$ and $\sigma(\dot{T}_\alpha) = \{\xi_\alpha\} \subset \sigma_{\alpha-0}$.

Consequently

$$\mathbf{U}_g \mathscr{X}_\alpha \subset \mathscr{X}_{\alpha-0},$$

therefore

$$\mathbf{U}_f x = \mathbf{U}_{fg} x = \mathbf{U}_f \mathbf{U}_g x = 0 \quad \text{for all} \quad x \in \mathscr{X}_\alpha.$$

As a result

$$\text{supp}(\mathbf{U}^{(\alpha)}) \subset \sigma_{\alpha-0},$$

thus $\sigma(T_\alpha) \subset \sigma_{\alpha-0}$, a contradiction.

In this manner we have $\xi_\alpha \notin \sigma_{\alpha-0} = \sigma(T_{\alpha-0})$. A simple inspection of the above argument shows that we have

$$\sigma(T_\alpha) \subset \sigma(T_{\alpha-0}) \cup \{\xi_\alpha\}, \tag{3}$$

because $\mathbf{U}_f x = 0$ for all $x \in \mathscr{X}_\alpha$ and $f \in \mathfrak{A}$ such that

$$\text{supp}(f) \cap (\sigma(T_{\alpha-0}) \cup \{\xi_\alpha\}) = \varnothing.$$

Now $\sigma(T_{\alpha-0}) \subset \sigma(T_\alpha)$ (because $\alpha - 0 \leqslant \alpha$), so that if $\xi_\alpha \notin \sigma(T_\alpha)$ we should have $\sigma(T_{\alpha-0}) = \sigma(T_\alpha)$ in contradiction with the hypothesis. Concluding, we have instead of (3) the more precise relation

$$\sigma(T_\alpha) = \sigma(T_{\alpha-0}) \cup \{\xi_\alpha\}. \tag{3'}$$

Now, since $\{\xi_\alpha\}$ is open in $\sigma(T_\alpha)$, by Lemma 2.4.3 it results that [T_α being decomposable by Remark 3.3 (i)] $\mathscr{X}_{\alpha T_\alpha}(\{\xi_\alpha\}) \neq \{0\}$, hence there exists $0 \neq x \in \mathscr{X}_\alpha$ such that $\sigma_{T_\alpha}(x) \subset \{\xi_\alpha\}$. Now it is obvious that $\sigma_T(x) \subset \sigma_{T_\alpha}(x)$, thus $\sigma_T(x) \subset \{\xi_\alpha\}$; we have obtained

$$0 \neq x \in \mathscr{X}_T(\{\xi_\alpha\}) \cap \mathscr{X}_\alpha,$$

and this concludes the proof.

The preceding proposition has the following corollary:

4.6. THEOREM. *Let* $T \in \mathbf{B}(\mathscr{X})$ *be such that* T^n *is compact for an integer* $n > 0$, *and let* $\mathscr{N} = \{\mathscr{X}_\alpha\}_{\alpha \in A}$ *be a maximal nest of ultrainvariant subspaces of* T. *Then*

(a) *If* α *is a point of discontinuity of* $\mathscr{N}$, $\dot{\mathscr{X}}_\alpha = \mathscr{X}_\alpha / \mathscr{X}_{\alpha-0}$ *is either finite dimensional and* $\dot{T}_\alpha$ *is a multiple of the identity in* $\dot{\mathscr{X}}_\alpha$, *or* $\dot{\mathscr{X}}_\alpha$ *is infinite dimensional and* $\dot{T}_\alpha$ *is quasinilpotent.*

(b) *If* $\dot{T}_\alpha$ *is quasinilpotent for all points of discontinuity* α *of* $\mathscr{N}$, *then* T *is also quasinilpotent.*

Proof. Since $(\sigma(T))^n = \sigma(T^n)$ (by the Mapping Spectral Theorem), it follows that $\sigma(T)$ is totally disconnected, hence by Example 1.19 there exists an admissible algebra $\mathfrak{A}$ such that T is an $\mathfrak{A}$-scalar operator. Therefore we may apply to T and $\mathscr{N}$ Propositions 4.4 and 4.5. It results that if α is a point of discontinuity of $\mathscr{N}$, then $\sigma(\dot{T}_\alpha) = \{\xi_\alpha\}$. We have only to investigate the case $\xi_\alpha \neq 0$.

Since T^n is compact and the canonical mapping $k_\alpha : \mathscr{X} \to \dot{\mathscr{X}}_\alpha$ $[k_\alpha(x) = \dot{x} = x + \mathscr{X}_{\alpha-0}]$ is bounded linear, it results (Ref. 30, VI, § 5, Theorem 4) that $\dot{T}_\alpha^n = k_\alpha \circ T^n$ is compact. We have $\sigma(\dot{T}_\alpha^n) = \{\xi_\alpha^n\} \neq \{0\}$, hence $0 \in \varrho(\dot{T}_\alpha^n)$, therefore $(\dot{T}_\alpha^n)^{-1}$ exists. Thus the identity operator of $\dot{\mathscr{X}}_\alpha$,

$$\dot{I}_\alpha = (\dot{T}_\alpha^n)^{-1}\, \dot{T}_\alpha^n,$$

is compact, so that by the classical theorem of F. Riesz (Ref. 30, IV, § 3, Theorem 5) $\dot{\mathscr{X}}_\alpha$ is finite dimensional.

By the Mapping Spectral Theorem and by $\sigma(\dot{T}_\alpha) = \{\xi_\alpha\}$, we have

$$\sigma\,(\dot{T}_\alpha - \xi_\alpha \dot{I}_\alpha) = \{\lambda - \xi_\alpha |\, \lambda \in \sigma(\dot{T}_\alpha)\} = \{0\},$$

hence $\dot{T}_\alpha - \xi_\alpha \dot{I}_\alpha$ is a quasinilpotent operator on the finite dimensional space $\dot{\mathscr{X}}_\alpha$, therefore it is nilpotent; so there exists an integer $m > 0$ such that

$$(\dot{T}_\alpha - \xi_\alpha \dot{I}_\alpha)^m = 0. \tag{1}$$

Let m_α be the least integer $m > 0$ verifying (1). If $m_\alpha > 1$, then

$$\mathscr{Z}_\alpha = (\dot{T}_\alpha - \xi_\alpha \dot{I}_\alpha)^{m_\alpha - 1} \dot{\mathscr{X}}_\alpha \tag{2}$$

is ultrainvariant to $\dot{T}_\alpha$, and by the definition of m_α, $\mathscr{Z}_\alpha \neq \{0\}$. If $\mathscr{Z}_\alpha = \dot{\mathscr{X}}_\alpha$, then by (2) and (1)

$$(\dot{I}_\alpha - \xi_\alpha \dot{I}_\alpha)\, \dot{\mathscr{X}}_\alpha = (\dot{T}_\alpha - \xi_\alpha \dot{I}_\alpha)^{m_\alpha}\, \dot{\mathscr{X}}_\alpha = \{0\},$$

therefore $m_\alpha = 1$, contradicting $m_\alpha > 1$.

Consequently

$$\{0\} \neq \mathscr{Z}_\alpha \neq \dot{\mathscr{X}}_\alpha.$$

Putting

$$\mathscr{Y}_\alpha = k_\alpha^{-1}(\mathscr{Z}_\alpha) = \{x \in \mathscr{X}_\alpha | \dot{x} \in \mathscr{Z}_\alpha\},$$

the nest

$$\{\mathscr{X}_\gamma\}_{\gamma < \alpha} \cup \{\mathscr{Y}_\alpha\} \cup \{\mathscr{X}_\gamma\}_{\gamma \geq \alpha}$$

majorizes $\mathscr{N}$; contradiction. Thus $m_\alpha = 1$, i.e. $\dot{T}_\alpha = \xi_\alpha \dot{I}_\alpha$.

Concerning (b), let us suppose the contrary, that $\sigma(\dot{T}_\alpha) = \{\xi_\alpha\} = \{0\}$ for all points of discontinuity α of $\mathscr{N}$ and although $\sigma(T) \neq \{0\}$. Let $0 \neq \xi \in \sigma(T)$ be fixed. Since $\{0\}, \mathscr{X} \in \mathscr{N}$ and $\sigma(T|\{0\}) = \emptyset, \sigma(T|\mathscr{X}) = \sigma(T)$, it follows that

$$A^+ = \{\gamma \in A | \sigma(T|\mathscr{X}_\gamma) \ni \xi\},$$

$$A^- = \{\gamma \in A | \sigma(T|\mathscr{X}_\gamma) \not\ni \xi\},$$

are nonvoid subsets of A; obviously $A = A^- \cup A^+$, and $A^- \cap A^+ = \emptyset$.

Define

$$\mathscr{X}^- = \overline{\bigcup_{\gamma \in A^-} \mathscr{X}_\gamma}, \quad \mathscr{X}^+ = \bigcap_{\gamma \in A^+} \mathscr{X}_\gamma.$$

These spaces $\mathscr{X}^-$ and $\mathscr{X}^+$ are ultrainvariant to T and verify

$$\mathscr{X}_{\gamma^-} \subset \mathscr{X}^- \subset \mathscr{X}^+ \subset \mathscr{X}_{\gamma^+} \quad \text{for all} \quad \gamma^\pm \in A^\pm.$$

Using the maximality property of $\mathscr{N}$ we deduce that there exists an $\alpha \in A$ such that

$$\mathscr{X}^- = \mathscr{X}_{\alpha - 0}, \quad \mathscr{X}^+ = \mathscr{X}_\alpha.$$

Since ξ is isolated in $\sigma(T)$ [because ξ^n is isolated in $\sigma(T^n)$] and $\sigma(T|\mathscr{X}_\gamma) \subset \sigma(T)$, for all $\gamma \in A$, it follows

$$\xi \notin \overline{\bigcup_{\lambda \in A^-} \sigma(T|\mathscr{X}_\gamma)}.$$

By Proposition 4.5(b), we have

$$\xi \notin \sigma(T|\mathscr{X}_{\alpha-0}). \tag{3}$$

Since $\sigma(T) \supset \sigma(T|\mathscr{X}_\gamma) \ni \xi$, for all $\gamma \in A^+$, we have

$$\mathscr{X}_T(\{\xi\}) \cap \mathscr{X}_\gamma \neq \{0\} \quad \text{for all} \quad \gamma \in A^+. \tag{4}$$

Indeed, ξ is isolated in $\sigma(T|\mathscr{X}_\gamma)$, thus $\{\xi\}$ is open in $\sigma(T|\mathscr{X}_\gamma)$, hence (by Lemma 2.4.3)

$$\mathscr{X}_{T|\mathscr{X}_\gamma}(\{\xi\}) \neq \{0\};$$

or

$$\mathscr{X}_{T|\mathscr{X}_\gamma}(\{\xi\}) = \mathscr{X}_T(\{\xi\}) \cap \mathscr{X}_\gamma,$$

so that (4) holds. As T^n is compact, hence decomposable, it results that $T^n|\mathscr{X}_{T^n}(\{\xi^n\})$ has a bounded inverse S, thus

$$T^nS = I|\mathscr{X}_{T^n}(\{\xi^n\})$$

is compact. By the theorem of F. Riesz (Ref. 30, IV, § 3, Theorem 5) $\mathscr{X}_{T^n}(\{\xi^n\})$ is finite dimensional. On the other hand

$$\mathscr{X}_{T|\mathscr{X}_\gamma}(\{\xi\}) \subset \mathscr{X}_{T^n|\mathscr{X}_\gamma}(\{\xi^n\}) \tag{6}$$

[by the relation (1) from the proof of Theorem 2.1.10]. $\mathscr{X}_\gamma$ being invariant to T, we have $\sigma_{T^n|\mathscr{X}_\gamma}(x) = \sigma_{T^n}(x)$ for all $x \in \mathscr{X}_{T^n|\mathscr{X}_\gamma}(\{\xi^n\})$, therefore

$$\mathscr{X}_{T^n|\mathscr{X}_\gamma}(\{\xi^n\}) \subset \mathscr{X}_{T^n}(\{\xi^n\}). \tag{7}$$

Since $\mathscr{X}_{T^n}(\{\xi^m\})$ is finite dimensional, it follows from (6) that $\mathscr{X}_{T|\mathscr{X}_\gamma}(\{\xi\})$ is also finite dimensional.

$\mathscr{N}$ being totally ordered, it results that

$$\{\mathscr{X}_T(\{\xi\}) \cap \mathscr{X}_\gamma\}_{\gamma \in A^+}$$

is a totally ordered system of subspaces $\neq \{0\}$ [by (4)] of the finite-dimensional space $\mathscr{X}_{T|\mathscr{X}_\gamma}(\{\xi\})$, therefore there must exist a $\gamma_0 \in A^+$ such that

$$\mathscr{X}_T(\{\xi\}) \cap \mathscr{X}_\gamma = \mathscr{X}_T(\{\xi\}) \cap \mathscr{X}_{\gamma_0} \quad \text{for all} \quad \gamma \leqslant \gamma_0, \gamma \in A^+.$$

It follows

$$\mathscr{X}_T(\{\xi\}) \cap \mathscr{X}_\alpha = \mathscr{X}_T(\{\xi\}) \cap \mathscr{X}^+ = \mathscr{X}_T(\{\xi\}) \cap \mathscr{X}_{\gamma_0} \neq \{0\},$$

hence there is a $0 \neq x \in \mathscr{X}_\alpha$ such that

$$\sigma_{T|\mathscr{X}_\alpha}(x) = \sigma_T(x) \subset \{\xi\}. \tag{8}$$

As $x \neq 0$, it results from Proposition 1.1.2 (iii) that $\sigma_{T|\mathscr{X}_\gamma}(x) \neq \emptyset$, hence by (7)

$$\sigma_{T|\mathscr{X}_\alpha}(x) = \{\xi\};$$

but $\sigma_{T|\mathscr{X}_\gamma}(x) \subset \sigma(T|\mathscr{X}_\gamma)$, so $\xi \in \sigma(T|\mathscr{X}_\alpha)$.

In this manner $\sigma(T|\mathscr{X}_{\alpha-0}) \neq \sigma(T|\mathscr{X}_\alpha)$, hence $\mathscr{X}_{\alpha-0} \neq \mathscr{X}_\alpha$, i.e. α is a point of discontinuity of $\mathscr{N}$.

We shall show that this point of discontinuity contradicts the hypothesis, i.e. we shall prove that $\sigma(\dot{T}_\alpha) \neq \{0\}$. Indeed, suppose that $\{\xi_\alpha\} = \sigma(\dot{T}_\alpha) = \{0\}$, then $\xi_\alpha \neq \xi$. Let $0 \neq x \in \mathscr{X}$ verify (8), and let $x(\lambda)$ be the $\mathscr{X}_\alpha$-valued analytic function satisfying

$$(\lambda I - T)\, x(\lambda) \equiv x \quad \text{for} \quad \lambda \neq \xi,$$

whence

$$(\lambda \dot{I} - \dot{T}_\alpha)\, \dot{\widehat{x(\lambda)}} \equiv \dot{x} \quad \text{for} \quad \lambda \neq \xi,$$

therefore $\sigma_{\dot{T}_\alpha}(\dot{x}) \subset \{\xi\}$. But $\sigma_{\dot{T}_\alpha}(\dot{x}) \subset \sigma(\dot{T}_\alpha) = \{\xi_\alpha\}$, so that $\sigma_{\dot{T}_\alpha}(x) \subset \{\xi\} \cap \{\xi_\alpha\} = \emptyset$, therefore by Proposition 1.1.2 (iii), $\dot{x} = 0$, i.e. $x \in \mathscr{X}_{\alpha-0}$. In this case

$$\sigma_{T|\mathscr{X}_\alpha}(x) \subset \sigma_{T|\mathscr{X}_{\alpha-0}}(x) \subset \sigma(T|\mathscr{X}_{\alpha-0}). \tag{9}$$

From (8), (9), and (3) we get

$$\sigma_{T|\mathscr{X}_\alpha}(x) \subset \{\xi\} \cap \sigma(T|\mathscr{X}_{\alpha-0}) = \emptyset,$$

whence $x = 0$, in contradiction with the choice of x. This implies that $\sigma(\dot{T}_\alpha) \neq \{0\}$: Contradiction! Consequently T is quasinilpotent.

5. Continuous $\mathfrak{A}$-spectral Functions

5.1. Definition. Let $\mathfrak{A}$ be an algebra of complex valued functions defined on the closed set $\Omega \subset C$. $\mathfrak{A}$ will be called *topologically admissible* if

(i) $\lambda \in \mathfrak{A}$ and $1 \in \mathfrak{A}$ (see Definition 1.2);

(ii) $\mathfrak{A}$ is normal;

(iii) $\mathfrak{A}$ is endowed with a locally convex topology $\mathcal{T}$ such that if $\{f_n\}_{n\in N} \subset \mathfrak{A}$ is a Cauchy sequence in $\mathcal{T}$ and $f_n(\lambda) \to 0$ for every $\lambda \in \Omega$, then $f_n \to 0$ in $\mathcal{T}$.

(iv) for every $f \in \mathfrak{A}$ and every $\xi \notin \operatorname{supp}(f)$ the function

$$f_\xi(\lambda) = \begin{cases} \dfrac{f(\lambda)}{\xi - \lambda} & \text{for } \lambda \in \Omega \setminus \{\xi\}, \\ 0 & \text{for } \lambda \in \Omega \cap \{\xi\}, \end{cases}$$

belongs to $\mathfrak{A}$, and the mapping $\xi \to f_\xi$ of $\complement\operatorname{supp}(f)$ into $\mathfrak{A}$ is continuous.

5.2. *Remarks*

(1) Evidently every topological admissible algebra is admissible in the sense of Definition 1.2.

(2) If $\mathfrak{A}$ is sequentially complete and $\mathcal{T}$ is stronger than the pointwise convergence topology on Ω, then (iii) is evidently verified.

5.3. DEFINITION. Let $\mathfrak{A}$ be a topologically admissible algebra, and let $\mathcal{X}$ be a Banach space. A mapping $\mathbf{U}$: $\mathfrak{A} \to \mathbf{B}(\mathcal{X})$ is called a *continuous $\mathfrak{A}$-spectral function* if

(i) $\mathbf{U}$ is an algebraic homomorphism and $\mathbf{U}_1 = I$;

(ii) $\mathbf{U}$ is continuous.

5.4. THEOREM. *Every continuous $\mathfrak{A}$-spectral function U is an $\mathfrak{A}$-spectral function in the sense of Definition 1.3.*

Proof. Let Γ be a simple closed rectifiable curve included together with its "interior" in $G = \complement \operatorname{supp}(f)$ and let $\xi_k \in \Gamma$ $(0 \leqslant k \leqslant n+1;\ n \in N)$. Putting

$$g_n = \sum_{k=0}^{n} f_{\xi_k}(\xi_{k+1} - \xi_k),$$

we obtain a Cauchy sequence (in $\mathcal{T}$) of $\mathfrak{A}$. We have

$$\lim_{n\to\infty} g_n(\lambda) = \begin{cases} f(\lambda) \displaystyle\int_\Gamma \frac{d\xi}{\xi - \lambda} = 0 & \text{for } \lambda \in \operatorname{supp}(f), \\ 0 & \text{for } \lambda \in \Omega \setminus \operatorname{supp}(f). \end{cases}$$

Therefore by condition (iii) of Definition 5.1, it results that

$$\lim_{n\to\infty} (\mathscr{T})\, g_n = 0,$$

where lim ($\mathscr{T}$) means the limit in the topology $\mathscr{T}$ of $\mathfrak{A}$.

The $\mathbf{B}(\mathscr{X})$-valued function $\xi \to \mathbf{U}_{f_\xi}$ is continuous on G, hence integrable (in the usual Cauchy sense) on Γ, and

$$\int_\Gamma \mathbf{U}_{f_\xi}\, d\xi = \lim_{n\to\infty} \sum_{k=0}^{n} \mathbf{U}_{f_{\xi_k}} (\xi_{k+1} - \xi_k)$$

$$= \lim_{n\to\infty} \mathbf{U}_{g_n} = \mathbf{U}_{\lim\limits_{n\to\infty} (\mathscr{T}) g_n} = \mathbf{U}_0 = 0.$$

Since Γ is chosen arbitrarily in G with the above properties, it results (Refs. 30, 47) that $\xi \to \mathbf{U}_{f_\xi}$ is analytic on G.

Notes and Remarks

The notion of spectral distribution was introduced in Ref. 39. F.Y.Maeda in Ref. 81 replaces the algebra $C^\infty(C)$ with a topological algebra Φ of complex-valued Borel locally bounded functions defined on C; this algebra is subjected to the following conditions:

(i) Φ is normal.

(ii) Φ has a topology $\mathscr{T}$ which is stronger than the topology of uniform convergence on compact parts of C; the set Φ_0 of all functions in Φ with compact support is dense in Φ.

(iii) If $f \in \Phi$ and $g \in H(\operatorname{supp}(f))$ [= the set of the locally holomorphic functions in a neighborhood of supp(f)], then $fg \in \Phi$ and $g \to fg$ is continuous.

Maeda calls such algebra, *basic algebra*. A continuous homomorphism $\mathbf{U}: \Phi \to L(\mathscr{X})$ (= the space of the linear continuous transformations of a locally convex quasi-complete space $\mathscr{X}$) is called by Maeda a *Φ-spectral representation*. Obviously if $\mathscr{X}$ is a Banach space the notion of a continuous $\mathfrak{A}$-spectral function where $\mathfrak{A}$ is a topologically admissible algebra is larger than the former one due to Maeda.

Theorem 1.6 was proved for spectral distributions in Ref. 39, for Φ-spectral representations by F.Y.Maeda (Ref. 81, Proposition 1.4) and S.Kantorovitz (Ref. 55, Lemma 2.2). Seemingly, Theorem 1.10 appears explicitly in the article by Dunford,[27] who proves it for the case of spectral operators. For spectral distributions, Theorem 1.10 is proved in Ref. 39 and for a Φ-spectral representation it is proved in the above-mentioned paper[81] of Maeda. The same can be said of all the results contained in the sequel to paragraph 1.

Theorem 2.1 was proved by F. Vasilescu[126] for the case of spectral distributions. Our proof for the general case was suggested by his proof. Theorem 2.4 (ii) belongs to Maeda,[83] for the case of $\mathfrak{A} = C_c^m(R^2)$ [= the space of functions $f \in C^m(R^2)$ with compact support].

The notion of $\mathfrak{A}$-decomposable operator is new. That of generalized spectral operator (see also Definition 4.1.2) was introduced independently by Maeda[81] and the first of the authors.[15] This notion is contained in that of $\mathfrak{A}$-spectral operator.

The elementary properties proved in Secs. 3.9–3.13 are extensions to the case of $\mathfrak{A}$-spectral operators and $\mathfrak{A}$-decomposable operators of some results established in Ref. 17 for generalized spectral operators.

All results in Sec. 4 were suggested by the paper[98] of Ringrose.

Chapter 4

Generalized Scalar and Spectral Operators

1. The Uniqueness of the Spectral Distributions of the Generalized Scalar Operators

1.1. DEFINITION. If in Definition 3.5.3 we take $\Omega = R^2 (= C)$ and $\mathfrak{A} = C^\infty =$ the algebra of all infinitely differentiable functions on R^2 (with the topology of uniform convergence of functions and of all their derivates), then a continuous C^∞-spectral function is in fact an operator-valued distribution in the L. Schwartz's sense.[113] Such a continuous C^∞-spectral function will be called a *spectral distribution.*

1.2. DEFINITION. A C^∞-scalar (spectral) operator which has a spectral distribution (as a C^∞-spectral function) will be called a *generalized scalar (spectral) operator.*

The following examples show that the spectral distribution of a generalized scalar operator may not be unique.

1.3. EXAMPLES.

(a) Let $\mathscr{X}$ be a Banach space, $A \in \mathbf{B}(\mathscr{X})$ such that $A^2 = 0$, and let δ_1 be the Dirac's distribution $f \to f(1)$ $(f \in C^\infty)$. Then, putting $D = \partial/\partial \operatorname{Re} \lambda + i\partial/\partial \operatorname{Im} \lambda$ $(\lambda \in C)$,

$$\mathbf{U}_A = I \otimes \delta_1 + \tfrac{1}{2}A \otimes D\delta_1$$

is a spectral distribution of the identity operator. Consequently, a generalized scalar operator S (for instance $S = I$) may have different spectral distributions, which do not commute with all operators commuting with S.

(b) Let S be a generalized scalar operator, and let $\mathbf{U}$ be one of its spectral distributions. If Q is a nilpotent operator (say $Q^{m+1} = 0$) commuting with all $\mathbf{U}_f$ ($f \in C^\infty$) then

$$\mathbf{V}_f = \sum_{k=0}^{m} \frac{Q^k}{k!} \mathbf{U}_{D^k f}$$

is a spectral distribution of S. Indeed, the function $\lambda \to \lambda$ being analytic, we have $D^k \lambda = 0$ for all $k \geqslant 1$, hence $\mathbf{V}_\lambda = \mathbf{U}_\lambda = S$.

Let $\mathscr{X}$ and $\mathscr{Y}$ be two Banach spaces, and let $\mathbf{B}(\mathscr{X}, \mathscr{Y})$ be the Banach space of linear bounded operators of $\mathscr{X}$ into $\mathscr{Y}$. For $U \in \mathbf{B}(\mathscr{X})$ and $V \in \mathbf{B}(\mathscr{Y})$ fixed, let $C(V, U) : \mathbf{B}(\mathscr{X}, \mathscr{Y}) \to \mathbf{B}(\mathscr{X}, \mathscr{Y})$ defined by

$$C(V, U) A = VA - AU \quad \text{for} \quad A \in B(\mathscr{X}, \mathscr{Y}).$$

By induction we put

$$C^{n+1}(V, U) A = C(V, U)(C^n(V, U) A).$$

We remark that if $\mathscr{X} = \mathscr{Y}$ and $A = I$, then

$$C^n(V, U) I = (V - U)^{[n]}.$$

1.4. Lemma. *Let* $\mathbf{U}$ *(respectively* $\mathbf{V}$*) be a* $\mathbf{B}(\mathscr{X})$ *[respectively* $\mathbf{B}(\mathscr{Y})$*] valued spectral distribution of order* m *(respectively* n*). If* $A \in \mathbf{B}(\mathscr{X}, \mathscr{Y})$ *verifies*

$$C(\mathbf{V}_\lambda, \mathbf{U}_\lambda) A = 0 = C(\mathbf{V}_{\bar\lambda}, \mathbf{U}_{\bar\lambda}) A,$$

i.e.

$$\mathbf{V}_\lambda A = A\mathbf{U}_\lambda \quad \textit{and} \quad \mathbf{V}_{\bar\lambda} A = A\mathbf{U}_{\bar\lambda}, \tag{1}$$

then

$$C(\mathbf{V}_f, \mathbf{U}_f) A = 0 \quad \textit{for all} \quad f \in C^\infty.$$

Proof. For any polynomial $p(\lambda, \mu) = \sum_{k,l} a_{kl} \lambda^k \mu^l$ in two variables, we have

$$\begin{aligned} C(\mathbf{V}_{p(\lambda,\bar\lambda)}, \mathbf{U}_{p(\lambda,\bar\lambda)}) A &= C(p(V_\lambda, V_{\bar\lambda}), p(\mathbf{U}_\lambda, \mathbf{U}_{\bar\lambda})) A \\ &= \sum_{k,l} a_{kl} (\mathbf{V}_\lambda^k \mathbf{V}_{\bar\lambda}^l A - A\mathbf{U}_\lambda^k \mathbf{U}_{\bar\lambda}^l) = 0, \end{aligned}$$

since by (1)

$$\begin{aligned} \mathbf{V}_\lambda^k \mathbf{V}_{\bar\lambda}^l A - A\mathbf{U}_\lambda^k \mathbf{U}_{\bar\lambda}^l &= \mathbf{V}_\lambda^k \mathbf{V}_{\bar\lambda}^{l-1} A\mathbf{U}_{\bar\lambda} - A\mathbf{U}_\lambda^k \mathbf{U}_{\bar\lambda}^l \\ &= (\mathbf{V}_\lambda^k \mathbf{V}_{\bar\lambda}^{l-1} A - A\mathbf{U}_\lambda^k \mathbf{U}_{\bar\lambda}^{l-1}) \mathbf{U}_{\bar\lambda} \\ &\cdots\cdots\cdots\cdots\cdots\cdots \\ &= (\mathbf{V}_\lambda^k A - A\mathbf{U}_\lambda^k) \mathbf{U}_{\bar\lambda}^l \\ &\cdots\cdots\cdots\cdots\cdots\cdots \\ &= (A - A) \mathbf{U}_\lambda^k \mathbf{U}_{\bar\lambda}^l = 0. \end{aligned}$$

Since **U**, **V** and the multiplication in $\mathbf{B}(\mathscr{X})$ are continuous, and the polynomials $p(\lambda, \bar{\lambda})$ are dense in C^∞, we have $C(\mathbf{U}_f, \mathbf{U}_f) A = 0$ for all $f \in C^\infty$.

1.5. Theorem: *Let* **U** *and* **V** *be two spectral distributions as in the preceding lemma. Then there exists an integer* p $(0 \leqslant p \leqslant m + n)$ *such that for every* $A \in \mathbf{B}(\mathscr{X}, \mathscr{Y})$ *verifying*

$$C(\mathbf{V}_\lambda, \mathbf{U}_\lambda) A \equiv 0, \tag{1}$$

we have

$$C(\mathbf{V}_{f_1}, \mathbf{U}_{f_1}) C(\mathbf{V}_{f_2}, \mathbf{U}_{f_2}) \cdots C(\mathbf{V}_{f_{p+1}}, \mathbf{U}_{f_{p+1}}) A = 0, \tag{2}$$

for every system $f_1, \ldots, f_{p+1} \in C^\infty$.

Proof. For every $\xi \in C$ we have

$$C\left(\exp\left(\bar{\xi}\mathbf{V}_\lambda\right), \exp\left(\bar{\xi}\mathbf{U}_\lambda\right)\right) A = \sum_{n=1}^{\infty} \frac{\bar{\xi}^n}{n!} (\mathbf{V}_\lambda^n A - A\mathbf{U}_\lambda^n) = 0,$$

whence

$$\exp\left(-\bar{\xi}\mathbf{V}_\lambda\right) A \exp\left(\bar{\xi}\mathbf{U}_\lambda\right) = A. \tag{3}$$

Multiplying (1) by $\exp(\xi \mathbf{V}_{\bar{\lambda}})$ to the left and by $\exp(-\xi \mathbf{U}_{\bar{\lambda}})$ to the right, we obtain

$$\exp(\mathbf{V}_{-\bar{\xi}\lambda + \xi\bar{\lambda}}) A \exp(\mathbf{U}_{\bar{\xi}\lambda - \xi\bar{\lambda}}) = \exp(\xi \mathbf{V}_{\bar{\lambda}}) A \exp(-\xi \mathbf{U}_{\bar{\lambda}}),$$

hence by the C^∞-functional calculus and since $\bar{\xi}\lambda - \xi\bar{\lambda} = 2i \operatorname{Im}(\bar{\xi}\lambda)$

$$\mathbf{V}_{\exp[-2i \operatorname{Im}(\bar{\xi}\lambda)]} A \, \mathbf{U}_{\exp[2i \operatorname{Im}(\bar{\xi}\lambda)]} = \exp(\xi \mathbf{V}_{\bar{\lambda}}) A \exp(-\xi \mathbf{U}_{\bar{\lambda}}). \tag{4}$$

We have

$$\|\mathbf{U}_f\| \leqslant M \cdot \sup_{\substack{|\xi| \leqslant \|\mathbf{U}_\lambda\| + 1 \\ 0 \leqslant k + l \leqslant m}} \left| \frac{\partial^{k+l} f(\xi)}{\partial s^k \partial t^l} \right|,$$

$$\|\mathbf{V}_f\| \leqslant M' \cdot \sup_{\substack{|\xi| \leqslant \|\mathbf{V}_\lambda\| + 1 \\ 0 \leqslant k + l \leqslant m}} \left| \frac{\partial^{k+l} f(\xi)}{\partial s^k \partial t^l} \right|,$$

(where $\xi = s + it$) for every $f \in C^\infty$, whence

$$\begin{aligned} \|\mathbf{U}_{\exp[2i \operatorname{Im}(\bar{\xi}\lambda)]}\| &\leqslant M 2^m |\xi|^m, \\ \|\mathbf{V}_{\exp[-2i \operatorname{Im}(\bar{\xi}\lambda)]}\| &\leqslant M' 2^n |\xi|^n, \end{aligned} \tag{5}$$

for $\xi \in C$, $|\xi| \geqslant 1$.

From (4) and (5) we obtain

$$\|\exp(\xi \mathbf{V}_{\bar\lambda}) A \exp(-\xi \mathbf{U}_{\bar\lambda})\| \leqslant MM' 2^{m+n} |\xi|^{m+n}$$

for $\xi \in C$, $|\xi| \geqslant 1$. Therefore, by the generalized Liouville's theorem (Ref. 47, Theorem 3.13.2) the $\mathbf{B}(\mathscr{X}, \mathscr{Y})$-valued entire function

$$\xi \to \exp(\xi \mathbf{V}_{\bar\lambda}) A \exp(-\xi \mathbf{U}_{\bar\lambda})$$

is a polynomial of degree $p \leqslant m + n$, that is

$$\exp(\xi \mathbf{V}_{\bar\lambda}) A \exp(-\xi \mathbf{U}_{\bar\lambda}) = P(\xi) = \sum_{k=0}^{p} \xi^k X_k, \tag{6}$$

where $X_k \in B(\mathscr{X}, \mathscr{Y})$, $0 \leqslant k \leqslant m + n$. Then

$$P(\xi) \exp(\xi \mathbf{U}_{\bar\lambda}) = \exp(\xi \mathbf{V}_{\bar\lambda}) A. \tag{7}$$

We shall prove the theorem by induction on p. Let $p = 0$, then from (6) it results (taking $\xi = 0$) $X_0 = A$. Taking the derivative of (7) in the point $\xi = 0$, we obtain $A\mathbf{U}_\lambda = \mathbf{V}_{\bar\lambda} A$, i.e.

$$C(\mathbf{V}_{\bar\lambda}, \mathbf{U}_{\bar\lambda}) A = 0. \tag{8}$$

From (1) and (8) it follows (by Lemma 1.4) the relation (2).

Suppose now that the relations (1) and (7) imply (2) for every $p \leqslant q - 1$ and that the degree of $P(\xi)$ in (6) is q. Taking the derivative of (7) and using (6) we get

$$\begin{aligned} P'(\xi) \exp(\xi \mathbf{U}_{\bar\lambda}) &= \mathbf{V}_{\bar\lambda} \exp(\xi \mathbf{V}_{\bar\lambda}) A - P(\xi) \mathbf{U}_{\bar\lambda} \exp(\xi \mathbf{U}_{\bar\lambda}) \\ &= \exp(\xi \mathbf{V}_{\bar\lambda}) \mathbf{V}_{\bar\lambda} A - \exp(\xi \mathbf{V}_{\bar\lambda}) A \exp(-\xi \mathbf{U}_{\bar\lambda}) \mathbf{U}_{\bar\lambda} \exp(\xi \mathbf{U}_{\bar\lambda}) \\ &= \exp(\xi \mathbf{V}_{\bar\lambda}) C(\mathbf{V}_{\bar\lambda}, \mathbf{U}_{\bar\lambda}) A. \end{aligned} \tag{9}$$

We remark that

$$C(\mathbf{V}_f, \mathbf{U}_f) C(\mathbf{V}_g, \mathbf{U}_g) = C(\mathbf{V}_g, \mathbf{U}_g) C(\mathbf{V}_f, \mathbf{U}_f) \quad \text{for all} \quad f, g \in C^\infty, \tag{10}$$

hence

$$C(\mathbf{V}_\lambda, \mathbf{U}_\lambda) C(\mathbf{V}_{\bar\lambda}, \mathbf{U}_{\bar\lambda}) A = C(\mathbf{V}_{\bar\lambda}, \mathbf{U}_{\bar\lambda}) C(\mathbf{V}_\lambda, \mathbf{U}_\lambda) A = 0. \tag{11}$$

Since the degree of $P'(\xi)$ is $\leqslant q - 1$, the relations (9) and (11) show that (1) and (7) are satisfied with $C(\mathbf{V}_{\bar\lambda}, \mathbf{U}_{\bar\lambda}) A$ instead of A, and $P'(\xi)$ instead of $P(\xi)$. Therefore on account of the hypothesis, we have

$$C(\mathbf{V}_{f_2}, \mathbf{U}_{f_2}) \cdots C(\mathbf{V}_{f_{q+1}}, \mathbf{U}_{f_{q+1}})\, C(\mathbf{V}_{\bar{\lambda}}, \mathbf{U}_{\bar{\lambda}})\, A = 0,$$

whence by (10)

$$C(\mathbf{V}_{\bar{\lambda}}, \mathbf{U}_{\bar{\lambda}})\, C(\mathbf{V}_{f_2}, \mathbf{U}_{f_2}) \cdots C(\mathbf{V}_{f_{q+1}}, \mathbf{U}_{f_{q+1}})\, A = 0. \tag{12}$$

On the other hand by (1) and (10) we have

$$\begin{aligned} &C(\mathbf{V}_{\lambda}, \mathbf{U}_{\lambda})\, C(\mathbf{V}_{f_2}, \mathbf{U}_{f_2}) \cdots C(\mathbf{V}_{f_{q+1}}, \mathbf{U}_{f_{q+1}}) \\ &= C(\mathbf{V}_{f_2}, \mathbf{U}_{f_2}) \cdots C(\mathbf{V}_{f_{q+1}}, \mathbf{U}_{f_{q+1}})\, C(\mathbf{V}_{\lambda}, \mathbf{U}_{\lambda})\, A = 0. \end{aligned} \tag{13}$$

From (12), (13), and Lemma 1.4 it results that

$$C(\mathbf{V}_{f_1}, \mathbf{U}_{f_1})\, C(\mathbf{V}_{f_2}, \mathbf{U}_{f_2}) \cdots C(\mathbf{V}_{f_{q+1}}, \mathbf{U}_{f_{q+1}})\, A = 0.$$

This completes the proof.

1.6. COROLLARY. *If* $\mathbf{U}$, $\mathbf{V}$ *are two spectral distributions of order* m, n *respectively of the same generalized scalar operator, then there exists an integer* p $(0 \leqslant p \leqslant m + n)$ *such that*

$$(\mathbf{U}_f - \mathbf{V}_f)^{[p+1]} = 0 \quad \textit{for all} \quad f \in C^{\infty}.$$

Indeed, we have evidently

$$(\mathbf{U}_f - \mathbf{V}_f)^{[p+1]} = C^{p+1}(\mathbf{U}_f, \mathbf{V}_f)\, I = 0.$$

1.7. DEFINITION. A spectral distribution U is called *regular* if

$$C(\mathbf{U}_{\lambda}, \mathbf{U}_{\lambda})\, A = 0 \;[A \in \mathbf{B}(\mathscr{X})] \;\text{ implies }\; C(\mathbf{U}_f, \mathbf{U}_f)\, A = 0$$

for all $f \in C^{\infty}$. A generalized scalar (or spectral) *operator* is called *regular* if it has a regular spectral distribution.

1.8. COROLLARY. *The spectral distributions of a regular generalized scalar operator are uniquely determined except for additive nilpotent operators.*

Proof. Let $\mathbf{U}$ be a regular spectral distribution and $\mathbf{V}$ an arbitrary spectral distribution of the regular generalized scalar operator S. Then $\mathbf{U}_{\lambda}$

$= S = \mathbf{V}_\lambda$, hence $\mathbf{V}_g\mathbf{U}_\lambda = \mathbf{U}_\lambda\mathbf{V}_g$ for all $g \in C^\infty$, therefore by the regularity of $\mathbf{U}$ we have

$$\mathbf{V}_g\mathbf{U}_f = \mathbf{U}_f\mathbf{V}_g \quad \text{for all} \quad f, g \in C^\infty.$$

In particular, $\mathbf{V}_f$ commutes with $\mathbf{U}_f$, so that by Corollary 1.6, we have

$$(\mathbf{U}_f - \mathbf{V}_f)^{p+1} = (\mathbf{U}_f - \mathbf{V}_f)^{[p+1]} = 0 \quad \text{for all} \quad f \in C^\infty.$$

Example 1.3(a) shows that there exist spectral distributions which are not regular. We shall give a sufficient condition for a spectral distribution $\mathbf{U}$ to be regular. For this purpose we denote by $\mathscr{L}$ the set of all $T \in \mathbf{B}(\mathscr{X})$ such that $T = \lim_{n\to\infty} \sum_{i=1}^{n} \lambda_i E_i$, where $\lambda_i \in C$, $E_i^2 = E_i \in \mathbf{B}(\mathscr{X})$, and E_i commute with all operators commuting with T.

1.9. Proposition. *If there exists an analytic function h in a neighborhood of* supp $(\mathbf{U}) = \sigma(\mathbf{U}_\lambda)$ *such that $\mathbf{U}_g \in \mathscr{L}$ (where g is an infinitely differentiable extension of the function $\lambda \to \bar{\lambda} - h(\lambda)$ to the whole complex plane) then $\mathbf{U}$ is regular.*

Proof. Let $A \in \mathbf{B}(\mathscr{X})$ be such that

$$C(\mathbf{U}_\lambda, \mathbf{U}_\lambda) A = 0, \tag{1}$$

then by Theorem 1.5 there exists a p ($0 \leqslant p \leqslant 2 \times$ the order of $\mathbf{U}$) such that $C^{p+1}(\mathbf{U}_g, \mathbf{U}_g) A = 0$.

Let $E^2 = E \in \mathbf{B}(\mathscr{X})$ be such that

$$C(\mathbf{U}_g, \mathbf{U}_g) B = 0 \quad \text{implies} \quad C(E, E) B = 0. \tag{2}$$

Then

$$C(\mathbf{U}_g, \mathbf{U}_g)\, C(E, E)\, C^{p-1}(\mathbf{U}_g, \mathbf{U}_g) A = C(E, E)\, C^p(\mathbf{U}_g, \mathbf{U}_g) A = 0,$$

whence by (2)

$$C^2(E, E)\, C^{p-1}(\mathbf{U}_g, \mathbf{U}_g) A = 0. \tag{3}$$

Using $E^2 = E$ it is easy to obtain from (3) that

$$C(E,E)\, C^{p-1}(\mathbf{U}_g,\mathbf{U}_g) A = 0,$$

therefore using the fact that $\mathbf{U}_g \in \mathscr{L}$ we can deduce that

$$C^p(\mathbf{U}_g,\mathbf{U}_g) A = 0.$$

In this manner step by step we get

$$C(\mathbf{U}_g, \mathbf{U}_g)\, A = 0. \tag{4}$$

If $\tilde{h}$ is an infinitely differentiable extension of h to the whole complex plane, then by Dunford's functional calculus $\mathbf{U}_{\tilde{h}} = h(\mathbf{U}_\lambda)$ [here we use the equality supp $(\mathbf{U}) = \sigma(\mathbf{U}_\lambda)$], hence by (1)

$$C(\mathbf{U}_{\tilde{h}}, \mathbf{U}_{\tilde{h}})\, A = 0. \tag{5}$$

Since in a neighborhood of supp $(\mathbf{U})$, $\bar{\lambda} = g(\lambda) + \tilde{h}(\lambda)$, we have $\mathbf{U}_{\bar{\lambda}} = \mathbf{U}_g + \mathbf{U}_{\tilde{h}}$, from (4) and (5) it results

$$C(\mathbf{U}_{\bar{\lambda}}, \mathbf{U}_{\bar{\lambda}})\, A = 0.$$

Applying Lemma 1.4, we obtain

$$C(\mathbf{U}_f, \mathbf{U}_f)\, A = 0 \quad \text{for every} \quad f \in C^\infty.$$

1.10. DEFINITION. A closed subset F of the complex plane is called *thin* if the function $\lambda \to \bar{\lambda}$ on F is the restriction of the analytic function h in a neighborhood of F.

Evidently, segments of a line or of a circle are thin sets.

1.11. THEOREM. *If S is a generalized scalar operator whose spectrum $\sigma(S)$ is thin, then S is regular.*

Proof. Let $\mathbf{V}$ be a spectral distribution of S, and let n be the order of $\mathbf{V}$. Since $\sigma(S)$ is thin there exists an analytic function h in a neighbourhood of $\sigma(S)$ such that $\bar{\lambda} = h(\lambda)$. The numerical distribution $f \to \langle \mathbf{V}_f x, x^* \rangle$ has the order $\leqslant n$ for all $x \in \mathscr{X}$, $x^* \in \mathscr{X}^*$. Let $\tilde{h}$ be an infinitely differentiable extension of h to the whole complex plane, and let $\varphi(\lambda) = [\bar{\lambda} - \tilde{h}(\lambda)]^{n+1}$. Since g and all its derivates of order $\leqslant n$ vanish on $\sigma(S) = $ supp $(\mathbf{V})$, by a well-known result from the theory of distributions (Ref. 49, Theorem 1.5.4) we have

$$\langle \mathbf{V}_\varphi x, x^* \rangle = 0 \quad \text{for all} \quad x \in \mathscr{X}, x^* \in \mathscr{X}^*,$$

whence $\mathbf{V}_\varphi = 0$. But $\mathbf{V}$ is a spectral distribution, so that

$$[\mathbf{V}_{\bar{\lambda}} - h(S)]^{n+1} = (\mathbf{V}_{\bar{\lambda}} - \mathbf{V}_{\tilde{h}})^{n+1} = \mathbf{V}_{(\bar{\lambda} - \tilde{h})^{n+1}} = 0,$$

where $h(S)$ is given by Dunford's functional calculus. Putting

$$Q = \mathbf{V}_{\bar{\lambda}} - h(S)$$

we see that Q commutes with $V_{\bar{\lambda}}$ and $S = V_\lambda$, consequently with V_f for all $f \in C^\infty$. Putting

$$\mathbf{U}_f = \sum_{k=0}^{n} \frac{Q^k}{k!} \mathbf{V}_{D^k f}, \quad (f \in C^\infty) \tag{1}$$

we obtain a $\mathbf{B}(\mathscr{X})$-valued distribution (of order $\leqslant 2n$). Moreover, since $D\lambda = 0$, we have $\mathbf{U}_\lambda = \mathbf{V}_\lambda = S$ and for all $f, g \in C^\infty$ we have

$$\begin{aligned}
\mathbf{U}_{fg} &= \sum_{k=0}^{n} \frac{Q^k}{k!} \mathbf{V}_{D^k(fg)} = \sum_{k=0}^{n} \frac{Q^k}{k!} \mathbf{V}_{\sum_{j=0}^{k} \binom{k}{j} D^j f D^{k-j} g} \\
&= \sum_{k=0}^{n} \frac{Q^k}{k!} \sum_{j=0}^{k} \binom{k}{j} \mathbf{V}_{D^j f} \mathbf{V}_{D^{k-j} g} \\
&= \sum_{k=0}^{n} \sum_{j=0}^{k} \frac{Q^j}{j!} \mathbf{V}_{D^j f} \frac{Q^{k-j}}{(k-j)!} \mathbf{V}_{D^{k-j} g} \\
&= \sum_{j=0}^{n} \frac{Q^j}{j!} \mathbf{V}_{D^j f} \sum_{l=0}^{n} \frac{Q^l}{l!} \mathbf{V}_{D^l f} = \mathbf{U}_f \mathbf{U}_g,
\end{aligned}$$

where we used the fact that

$$Q^j Q^l = Q^{n+p} = 0 \quad \text{for} \quad j + l = n + p \geqslant n + 1.$$

Accordingly $\mathbf{U}$ is a spectral distribution. If $A \in \mathbf{B}(\mathscr{X})$ commutes with S, then A commutes with $\mathbf{U}_\lambda = S$ and with $\mathbf{U}_{\bar{\lambda}} = \mathbf{V}_{\bar{\lambda}} - Q = h(S)$; consequently A commutes with $\mathbf{U}_f$ for all $f \in C^\infty$. So $\mathbf{U}$ is a regular spectral distribution.

2. A Theorem of Uniqueness of the Spectral Distribution of a Generalized Scalar Operator

First we shall give some facts concerning derivation in Banach algebras. With the help of these results we shall prove a theorem of real unicity of the spectral distribution of operators so called of spectral multiplicity 1.

2.1. Definition. Let $\mathscr{A}$ be an algebra over a ring $\mathscr{R}$. A *derivation* in $\mathscr{A}$ is a $\mathscr{R}$-linear mapping $D\colon \mathscr{A} \to \mathscr{A}$ such that

$$D(xy) = D(x)\, y + xD(y) \quad \text{for all} \quad x, y \in \mathscr{A}.$$

Using the relation $\binom{n}{k} = \binom{n-1}{k} + \binom{n-1}{k-1}$ it is easy to prove by induction the *Leibniz formula*

$$D^n(xy) = \sum_{k=0}^{n} \binom{n}{k} D^k(x)\, D^{n-k}(y).$$

2.2. Lemma. *Let D be a derivation in an algebra $\mathscr{A}$. If $D^2(x) = 0$ then*

$$D^n(x^n) = n!\,(Dx)^n \quad \textit{for all} \quad n \geqslant 1,$$

Proof. The lemma is obvious for $n = 1$. Assume that

$$D^{n-1}(x^{n-1}) = (n-1)!\,(Dx)^{n-1}.$$

Then, differentiating, $D^n(x^{n-1}) = 0$. From this, using the Leibniz's formula

$$D^n(x^n) = D^n(x \cdot x^{n-1}) = \sum_{u}^{k=0} \binom{k}{n} D^k(x)\, D^{n-k}(x^{n-1})$$

$$= xD^n(x^{n-1}) + nD(x)\, D^{n-1}(x^{n-1})$$

$$= nD(x)(n-1)!\,(Dx)^{n-1} = n!\,(Dx)^n.$$

2.3. Proposition. *If D is a bounded derivation in a Banach algebra $\mathscr{A}$ and x is an element of $\mathscr{A}$ with $D^2(x) = 0$, then $D(x)$ is quasinilpotent.*

Proof. By Lemma 2.2

$$(Dx)^n = (1/n!)\, D^n(x^n),$$

whence, using the fact that D is a bounded linear mapping, we obtain

$$\|(Dx)^n\| = \left\|\frac{D^n(x^n)}{n!}\right\| \leqslant \frac{\|D^n\| \cdot \|x^n\|}{n!} \leqslant \frac{(\|D\| \cdot \|x\|)^n}{n!},$$

therefore

$$\lim_{n\to\infty} \|(Dx)^n\|^{1/n} = 0.$$

2.4. Corollary. *Let a, b be two elements of a Banach algebra $\mathscr{A}$, and put $q = ab - ba$. If q commutes with a, then q is quasinilpotent.*

Proof. Let $D: \mathscr{A} \to \mathscr{A}$ be defined by

$$D(x) = ax - xa.$$

It is easy to prove that D is a derivation and that

$$D^2(b) = D(ab - ba) = D(q) = aq - qa = 0.$$

Further, since

$$\|D(x)\| = \|ax - xa\| \leqslant 2\|a\| \cdot \|x\|,$$

D is a bounded operator, and

$$\|D\| \leqslant 2\|a\|.$$

Now the corollary follows from Proposition 2.3.

2.5. Definition. Let $\mathscr{X}$ be a Banach space and $T \in \mathbf{B}(\mathscr{X})$. We say that T *is of spectral multiplicity* 1 if every quasinilpotent operator $Q \in \mathbf{B}(\mathscr{X})$ commuting with T is 0.

2.6. Theorem. *If* $S \in \mathbf{B}(\mathscr{X})$ *is a generalized scalar operator of spectral multiplicity* 1, *then*

(i) *S is regular*

(ii) *S has only one spectral distribution.*

Proof. Let $\mathbf{U}$ be a spectral distribution of S, and take $A \in \mathbf{B}(\mathscr{X})$ commuting with S.

(i) Taking in Theorem 1.5, $S = T$, $\mathbf{U} = \mathbf{V}$ and the functions f_i equal to $\bar{\lambda}$, we deduce that there exists an integer $n \geqslant 1$ such that $C^n_{U_{\bar{\lambda}}}(A) = 0$, i.e.

$$\mathbf{U}_{\bar{\lambda}} C^{n-1}_{\mathbf{U}_{\bar{\lambda}}}(A) = C^{n-1}_{\mathbf{U}_{\bar{\lambda}}}(A)\, \mathbf{U}_{\bar{\lambda}}.$$

Applying Corollary 2.4 [for $a = \mathbf{U}_{\bar{\lambda}}$, $b = C^{n-2}_{\mathbf{U}_{\bar{\lambda}}}(A)$, hence $q = C^{n-1}_{\mathbf{U}_{\bar{\lambda}}}(A)$], we have

$$\sigma\left(C^{n-1}_{\mathbf{U}_{\bar{\lambda}}}(A)\right) = \{0\}. \tag{1}$$

The operator $S = \mathbf{U}_\lambda$ commutes with $\mathbf{U}_{\bar{\lambda}}$ and with A, hence with $C^k_{U_{\bar{\lambda}}}(A)$, for all $k \in N$, so that

$$S C^{n-1}_{\mathbf{U}_{\bar{\lambda}}}(A) = C^{n-1}_{\mathbf{U}_{\bar{\lambda}}}(A)\, S. \tag{2}$$

Since S is of spectral multiplicity 1, it results from (1) and (2) that

$$C_{\mathbf{U}\bar{\lambda}}^{n-1}(A) = 0.$$

Applying n times this procedure we will obtain

$$C(\mathbf{U}_{\bar{\lambda}}, \mathbf{U}_{\bar{\lambda}})\, A = C_{\mathbf{U}\bar{\lambda}}(A) = 0.$$

But we have also

$$C(\mathbf{U}_{\lambda}, \mathbf{U}_{\lambda})\, A = C_{\mathbf{U}_{\lambda}}(A) = 0.$$

Therefore, by Lemma 1.4, we get

$$C(\mathbf{U}_{f}, \mathbf{U}_{f})\, A = 0 \quad \text{for all} \quad f \in C^{\infty}.$$

Consequently S is regular. Moreover, $\mathbf{U}$ being arbitrarily chosen we can say that all spectral distributions of S are regular.

(ii) Let $\mathbf{U}$, $\mathbf{V}$ be two spectral distributions of S, then, since S is regular there exists a $n \geqslant 1$ such that

$$(\mathbf{U}_{f} - \mathbf{U}_{f})^{n} = 0 \quad \text{for all} \quad f \in C^{\infty},$$

hence

$$\sigma(\mathbf{U}_{f} - \mathbf{V}_{f}) = \{0\}. \tag{3}$$

But we have also

$$S(\mathbf{U}_{f} - \mathbf{V}_{f}) = (\mathbf{U}_{f} - \mathbf{V}_{f})\, S. \tag{4}$$

Since S is of spectral multiplicity 1, from (3) and (4) it follows that

$$\mathbf{U}_{f} = \mathbf{V}_{f} \quad \text{for all} \quad f \in C^{\infty}.$$

3. Sums and Products of Generalized Scalar and Spectral Operators

For E, F locally convex spaces A. Grothendieck (Ref. 45, Chap. I, p. 30 and p. 74) denotes by $E \mathbin{\widehat{\otimes}} F$ (respectively $E \mathbin{\overline{\otimes}} F$) the complete projective (respectively inductive) tensor of E and F. If one of the spaces E, F is nuclear, then

$$E \mathbin{\widehat{\otimes}} F = E \mathbin{\overline{\otimes}} F.$$

The space $C^{\infty}(R^{n})$ being nuclear (Ref. 45, II, § 2, No. 3 Theorem 10) we have

$$C^{\infty}(R^{n}) \mathbin{\widehat{\otimes}} C^{\infty}(R^{m}) = C^{\infty}(R^{n}) \mathbin{\overline{\otimes}} C^{\infty}(R^{m}),$$

therefore by the Ref. 113, Proposition 28

$$C^\infty(R^n) \mathbin{\widehat{\otimes}} C^\infty(R^m) = C^\infty(R^n) \mathbin{\overline{\otimes}} C^\infty(R^m) = C^\infty(R^{n+m}).$$

3.1. PROPOSITION. *The tensor product of two commuting* $\mathbf{B}(\mathscr{X})$*-valued spectral distributions is again a spectral distribution* (on $C^2 = R^4$).

Proof. Let $\mathbf{U}, \mathbf{V}$: $C^\infty(R^2) \to \mathbf{B}(\mathscr{X})$ be two spectral distributions such that

$$\mathbf{U}_f \mathbf{V}_g = \mathbf{V}_g \mathbf{U}_f \quad \text{for all} \quad f, g \in C^\infty(R^2).$$

Since the bilinear mapping $(f, g) \to \mathbf{U}_f \mathbf{V}_g$ of $C^\infty(R^2) \times C^\infty(R^2)$ into $\mathbf{B}(\mathscr{X})$ is continuous, there exists a unique linear continuous mapping

$$\mathbf{W}: C^\infty(R^2) \otimes C^\infty(R^2) \to \mathbf{B}(\mathscr{X})$$

such that

$$\mathbf{W}_{f \otimes g} = \mathbf{U}_f \mathbf{V}_g.$$

But $C^\infty(R^2)$ is an algebra, so that $f \otimes g = f(\lambda) g(\mu) =$ usual product. Using the theorem of kernels, we have a linear continuous mapping $\mathbf{W}$ of $C^\infty(R^4)$ into $\mathbf{B}(\mathscr{X})$ such that

$$\mathbf{W}_{fg} = \mathbf{U}_f \mathbf{V}_g.$$

Evidently $\mathbf{W}_1 = \mathbf{U}_1 \mathbf{U}_1 = I$. Take $\varphi_i = (f_i, g_i) \in C^\infty(R^2) \times C^\infty(R^2) (i = 1, 2)$ then $\varphi_1 \varphi_2 = (f_1 f_2, g_1 g_2)$ and, using the commutativity of U and V, we have

$$\mathbf{W}_{\varphi_1 \varphi_2} = \mathbf{U}_{f_1 f_2} \mathbf{V}_{g_1} \mathbf{V}_{g_2} = \mathbf{U}_{f_1} \mathbf{U}_{f_2} \mathbf{V}_{g_1} \mathbf{V}_{g_2} = (\mathbf{U}_{f_1} \mathbf{V}_{g_1})(\mathbf{U}_{f_2} \mathbf{V}_{g_2}) = \mathbf{W}_{\varphi_1} \mathbf{W}_{\varphi_2}.$$

Thus $\mathbf{W}$ is a multiplication on the linear subspace $C^\infty(R^2) \times C^\infty(R^2)$ hence also in $C^\infty(R^2) \mathbin{\widehat{\otimes}} C^\infty(R^2) = C^\infty(R^4)$. Consequently $\mathbf{W}$ is multiplicative on $C^\infty(R^2)$. So $\mathbf{W}$ is a spectral distribution.

Often the mapping $\mathbf{W}$ will be denoted by $\mathbf{U} \otimes \mathbf{V}$ and is called the *tensor product* of the spectral distributions $\mathbf{U}$ and $\mathbf{V}$.

3.2. LEMMA. *If* $\mathbf{U}$ *is a spectral distribution on* R^n, *then* $\mathbf{U}_f$ *is a generalized scalar operator for every* $f \in C^\infty(R^n)$.

Proof. The mapping $g \to \mathbf{U}_{g \circ f}$ is a spectral distribution of $\mathbf{U}_f$.

3.3. THEOREM. *If S and T are two generalized scalar operators having two commuting spectral distributions, then $S + T$ and ST are again generalized scalar operators.*

Proof. Let $\mathbf{U}$ and $\mathbf{V}$ be two commuting spectral distributions of S and T, respectively, and let $\mathbf{U} \otimes \mathbf{V}$ be its tensor product. Then

$$S + T = \mathbf{U}_\lambda + \mathbf{V}_\mu = \mathbf{U}_\lambda \mathbf{V}_1 + \mathbf{U}_1 \mathbf{V}_\mu = (\mathbf{U} \otimes \mathbf{V})_{\lambda \otimes 1} + (\mathbf{U} \otimes \mathbf{V})_{1 \otimes \mu}$$

$$= (\mathbf{U} \otimes \mathbf{V})_{\lambda \otimes 1 + 1 \otimes \mu} = (\mathbf{U} \otimes \mathbf{V})_{\lambda + \mu} \tag{1}$$

and

$$ST = \mathbf{U}_\lambda \mathbf{V}_\mu = (\mathbf{U}_\lambda \mathbf{V}_1)(\mathbf{U}_1 \mathbf{V}_\mu) = (\mathbf{U} \otimes \mathbf{V})_{\lambda \otimes 1} \cdot (\mathbf{U} \otimes \mathbf{V})_{1 \otimes \mu}$$

$$= (\mathbf{U} \otimes \mathbf{V})_{(\lambda \otimes 1)(1 \otimes \mu)} = (\mathbf{U} \otimes \mathbf{V})_{\lambda \mu}, \tag{2}$$

where λ and μ denote the identic mappings in the variables λ and μ respectively.

Since $\mathbf{W}_\varphi$ is (by Lemma 3.2) a generalized scalar operator for all $\varphi \in C^\infty(R^n)$, from (1) and (2) it results that $S + T$ and ST are generalized scalar operators.

3.4. COROLLARY. *The sum and the product of two commuting regular generalized scalar operators are generalized scalar operators.*

3.5. LEMMA. *If Q is a quasinilpotent operator which is also generalized scalar, then Q is nilpotent.*

Proof. Let $\mathbf{U}$ be a spectral distribution of Q, then by Theorem 3.1.6

$$\operatorname{supp}(\mathbf{U}) = \sigma(Q) = \{0\},$$

hence putting for $x \in \mathscr{X}$ and $x^* \in \mathscr{X}^*$

$$\mathbf{A}_{x,x^*}(f) = \langle \mathbf{U}_f x, x^* \rangle,$$

we obtain a numerical distribution $\mathbf{A}_{x,x^*}$ such that

$$\operatorname{supp}(\mathbf{A}_{x,x^*}) \subset \{0\},$$

therefore (see for instance Ref. 49, Theorem 1.5.3) of the form

$$\mathbf{A}_{x,x^*} = \sum_{|p| \leqslant n} a_p \delta^{(p)},$$

where δ is the Dirac distribution, and n is the order of $\mathbf{U}$. Consequently

$$|\langle \mathbf{U}_g x, x^* \rangle| = |\mathbf{A}_{x,x^*}(f)| \leqslant M_{x,x^*} \sup_{|p| \leqslant n} |f^{(p)}(0)|.$$

Let

$$C_1^\infty = \{f \in C^\infty | \sup_{|p| \leqslant n} |f^{(p)}(0)| \leqslant 1\}.$$

By Steinhaus-Banach's theorem there exists a constant $0 \leqslant M < \infty$ such that

$$\|\mathbf{U}_f\| \leqslant M \quad \text{for all} \quad f \in C_1^\infty,$$

hence

$$\|\mathbf{U}_f\| \leqslant M \sup_{|p| \leqslant n} |f^{(p)}(0)| \quad \text{for all} \quad f \in C^\infty.$$

In particular for $f_0(\lambda) = \lambda^m$ with $m > n$, we have

$$\|Q^m\| = \|\mathbf{U}_{f_0}\| \leqslant M \sup_{|p| \leqslant n} |(\lambda^m)^{(p)}_{\lambda=0}|,$$

consequently Q is nilpotent.

3.6. THEOREM. *A spectral operator is a generalized scalar operator if and only if it is of finite type.*

Proof. Let $T = S + Q$ be a spectral operator where $S = \int_{\sigma(T)} \lambda \, d\mathbf{E}_\lambda$ is its scalar part and Q is its radical part; we have $QS = SQ$.

Assume that Q is nilpotent and let n be the least positive integer such that $Q^{n+1} = 0$. Then the mapping $\mathbf{U} : C^\infty \to \mathbf{B}(\mathscr{X})$ defined by

$$\mathbf{U}_f = \sum_{k=0}^{n} \frac{Q^k}{k!} \int_{\sigma(T)} D^k f(\lambda) \, d\mathbf{E}_\lambda$$

[where $D = \frac{1}{2}(\partial/\partial s + i \, \partial/\partial t), \lambda = s + it$) is a regular spectral distribution such that

$$\mathbf{U}_\lambda = \int_{\sigma(T)} \lambda \, d\mathbf{E}_\lambda + Q,$$

hence T is a regular generalized scalar operator.

Suppose now conversely that T is a generalized scalar operator, and let $\mathbf{U}$ be one of its spectral distributions. Then for every $f \in C^\infty$, $\mathbf{U}_f$ commutes with T, hence also with $\mathbf{E}(\sigma)$ for all Borelian sets $\sigma \subset C$ (Ref. 27, Theorem 5), therefore $\mathbf{U}_f$ commutes with all

$$\mathbf{V}_g = \int_{\sigma(T)} g(\lambda)\, d\mathbf{E}_\lambda, \quad (g \in C^\infty).$$

But $\mathbf{V}$ so defined is a spectral distribution of S, so that we have two generalized scalar operators, R and S, such that their spectral distributions $\mathbf{U}$ and $\mathbf{V}$, respectively, commute. Applying Theorem 3.3, it results that the quasinilpotent operator

$$T - S = Q$$

is also a generalized scalar operator, therefore by Lemma 3.5, Q is nilpotent. Consequently $T = S + Q$ is of finite type.

As an immediate consequence of Theorem 3.3 and 3.5 we obtain the following

3.7. Proposition. *The sum and product of two commuting spectral operators of finite type, are generalized scalar operators.*

3.8. Lemma. *The sum of two commuting quasinilpotent operators as well as the product of two bounded commuting operators one of which is quasinilpotent, are quasinilpotent operators.*

Proof. Denote by

$$r(T) = \sup_{\lambda \in \sigma(T)} |\lambda| = \lim_{n \to \infty} \sqrt[n]{\|T^n\|}$$

the spectral radius of the bounded linear operator T. In Ref. 133 (Chap. XI, No. 149) it is proved that

$$r(A + B) \leqslant r(A) + r(B) \quad \text{and} \quad r(AB) \leqslant r(A)\, r(B)$$

for all commuting $A, B \in \mathbf{B}(\mathscr{X})$. The lemma follows from these inequalities.

3.9. Theorem. *If T_1 and T_2 are two commuting generalized spectral operators such that they have two commuting spectral distributions $\mathbf{U}^1$ and $\mathbf{U}^2$, respectively, then $T_1 + T_2$ and T_1T_2 are generalized spectral operators.*

Proof. Let $T_i = S_i + Q_i$ $(i = 1, 2)$ be the canonical decompositions given by $\mathbf{U}^i$ (see Definition 3.3.5), then

$$T_1 + T_2 = (S_1 + S_2) + (Q_1 + Q_2) = S + Q.$$

From the fact that $\mathbf{U}^1$ commutes with $\mathbf{U}^2$, it results that S_1 commutes with S_2, hence by Theorem 3.3, $S = S_1 + S_2$ is a generalized scalar operator.

Since quasinilpotent operators Q_1 and Q_2 commute (because $T_1T_2 = T_2T_1$ and $S_1S_2 = S_2S_1$), it results by Lemma 3.8 that $Q_1 + Q_2$ is a quasinilpotent operator.

In order to prove that $S + Q$ is a generalized spectral operator it is necessary to show also that Q commutes with a spectral distribution of S. A spectral distribution of S is expressed by $\mathbf{U}^1 \otimes \mathbf{U}^2$. Using the fact that T_1 commutes with T_2, and that $\mathbf{U}^1$ commutes with $\mathbf{U}^2$, we obtain for all $f_1, f_2 \in C^\infty$

$$Q_i (\mathbf{U}^1 \otimes \mathbf{U}^2)_{f_1 \otimes f_2} = Q_i \mathbf{U}^1_{f_1} \mathbf{U}^2_{f_2} = \mathbf{U}^1_{f_1} \mathbf{U}^2_{f_2} Q_i = (\mathbf{U}^1 \otimes \mathbf{U}^2)_{f_1 \otimes f_2} Q_i,$$
$$(i = 1, 2)$$

hence

$$Q (\mathbf{U}^1 \otimes \mathbf{U}^2)_{f_1 \otimes f_2} = (\mathbf{U}^1 \otimes \mathbf{U}^2)_{f_1 \otimes f_2} Q,$$

therefore

$$Q (\mathbf{U}^1 \otimes \mathbf{U}^2)_\varphi = (\mathbf{U}^1 \otimes \mathbf{U}^2)_\varphi Q \quad \text{for every} \quad \varphi \in C^\infty(R^4).$$

Consequently $T_1 + T_2 = S + Q$ is a generalized spectral operator.

Analogously, $T_1T_2 = S + Q$, where $S = S_1S_2$ is a generalized scalar operator (by Theorem 3.3) and $Q = Q_1Q_2 + Q_1S_2 + Q_2S_1$ is a quasinilpotent operator (by Lemma 3.8) commuting with $\mathbf{U}^1 \otimes \mathbf{U}^2$. Thus T_1T_2 is a generalized spectral operator.

3.10. Corollary. *If T_1 and T_2 are two commuting spectral operators (not necessarily of finite type), then $T_1 + T_2$ and T_1T_2 are generalized spectral operators.*

Proof. If $\mathbf{E}^i$ $(i = 1, 2)$ is the spectral measure of T_i, then

$$\mathbf{U}^i_f = \int_{\sigma(T_i)} f(\lambda)\, d\mathbf{E}^i, \quad (f \in C^\infty)$$

is a spectral distribution of T_i.

From the commutativity of the spectral operators T_1 and T_2 follows (Ref. 27, Theorem 5) the commutativity of their spectral measures $\mathbf{E}^1$ and $\mathbf{E}^2$, hence the commutativity of the spectral distribution $\mathbf{U}^1$, $\mathbf{U}^2$ defined above. Now our assertion follows from Theorem 3.9.

3.11. DEFINITION. A spectral distribution $\mathbf{U}$ is called *completely regular* if from

$$A\mathscr{X}_{\mathbf{U}\lambda}(F) \subset \mathscr{X}_{\mathbf{U}\lambda}(F), \quad \text{for every closed set} \quad F \subset C,$$

with $A \in \mathbf{B}(\mathscr{X})$, follows that

$$A\mathbf{U}_f = \mathbf{U}_f A \quad \text{for every} \quad f \in C^\infty.$$

3.12. EXAMPLE. *Every spectral operator is a completely regular generalized spectral operator, i.e. has a completely regular distribution.*

Indeed, let T be a spectral operator, $\mathbf{E}$ its spectral measure, and let

$$\mathbf{U}_f = \int_{\sigma(T)} f(\lambda)\, d\mathbf{E}_\lambda$$

be the spectral distribution respect to which it is a generalized spectral operator.

Take $A \in \mathbf{B}(\mathscr{X})$ such that

$$A\mathscr{X}_{\mathbf{U}\lambda}(F) \subset \mathscr{X}_{\mathbf{U}\lambda}(F),$$

for every closed set $F \subset C$; but (Ref. 27, Theorem 4)

$$\mathscr{X}_T(F) = \mathbf{E}(F)\,\mathscr{X}$$

hence

$$A\mathbf{E}\,(F)\,\mathscr{X} \subset \mathbf{E}(F)\,\mathscr{X},$$

whence it follows that

$$A\mathbf{E}\,(F) = \mathbf{E}(F)\,A\mathbf{E}\,(F).$$

By the continuity of the measure $\mathbf{E}$, this equality may be extended firstly to the sets of type F_σ, in particular to the open sets (which in the case of the metric spaces are of type F_σ), after that to the sets of type G_δ, and finally to the Borelian sets. Consequently, for every Borelian set $\sigma \subset C$, we have

$$\mathbf{E}(\sigma)\,A = \mathbf{E}(\sigma)\,A\mathbf{E}\,(\sigma \cup \complement T) = \mathbf{E}(\sigma)\,A\mathbf{E}(\sigma) + \mathbf{E}(\sigma)\,A\mathbf{E}\,(\complement\sigma)$$

$$= A\mathbf{E}\,(\sigma) + \mathbf{E}(\sigma)\,\mathbf{E}\,(\complement\sigma)\,A\mathbf{E}\,(\sigma) = A\mathbf{E}\,(\sigma),$$

whence it results that

$$A\mathbf{U}_f = \mathbf{U}_f A \quad \text{for all} \quad f \in C^\infty.$$

3.13. LEMMA. *If T_1, T_2 are two commuting completely regular generalized spectral operators and $\mathbf{U}^1$, $\mathbf{U}^2$ are two completely regular spectral distributions of T_1, T_2 respectively, then $\mathbf{U}^1$ commutes with $\mathbf{U}^2$.*

Proof. Since $T_1T_2 = T_2T_1$ and

$$\mathscr{X}_{T_i}(F) = \mathscr{X}_{\mathbf{U}^i_\lambda}(F), \quad (F \text{ closed} \subset C;\, i = 1, 2) \tag{1}$$

it results (Proposition 1.3.2) that

$$T_2\mathscr{X}_{\mathbf{U}^1_\lambda}(F) \subset \mathscr{X}_{\mathbf{U}^1_\lambda}(F),$$

whence by the complete regularity of $\mathbf{U}^1$ we obtain

$$T_2\mathbf{U}^1_{f_1} = \mathbf{U}^1_{f_1}T_2 \quad \text{for every} \quad f_1 \in C^\infty. \tag{2}$$

Applying again Proposition 1.3.2 and using (2) and (1), we get

$$\mathbf{U}^1_{f_1}\mathscr{X}_{\mathbf{U}^2_\lambda}(F) \subset \mathscr{X}_{\mathbf{U}^2_\lambda}(F),$$

whence on the account of the complete regularity of $\mathbf{U}^2$ it follows that

$$\mathbf{U}^1_{f_1}\mathbf{U}^2_{f_2} = \mathbf{U}^2_{f_2}\mathbf{U}^1_{f_1} \quad \text{for all} \quad f_1, f_2 \in C^\infty.$$

3.14. THEOREM. *The sum and the product of two commuting completely regular generalized spectral operators are generalized spectral operators.*

Proof. This follows from Theorem 3.9 and Lemma 3.13.

4. Nilpotence Properties of the Commutators of Generalized Scalar Operators

Let $\mathscr{X}, \mathscr{Y}$, be two Banach space, $S \in \mathbf{B}(\mathscr{X})$, $T \in \mathbf{B}(\mathscr{Y})$ and let $R(S)$, $L(T)$, $C(T, S)$ be the linear bounded operators [on $\mathbf{B}(\mathscr{X}, \mathscr{Y})$] defined in chapter 2, § 3.

4.1. *Remark:* The mappings $R: S \to R(S)$ and $L: T \to L(T)$ are two bounded algebraic homomorphisms (representations) of $B(\mathscr{X})$ into

$\mathbf{B}(\mathbf{B}(\mathscr{X}, \mathscr{Y}))$ and of $\mathbf{B}(\mathscr{Y})$ into $\mathbf{B}(\mathbf{B}(\mathscr{X}, \mathscr{Y}))$, respectively, such that

$$R(I_{\mathscr{X}}) = I_{\mathbf{B}(\mathscr{X},\mathscr{Y})} = L(I_{\mathscr{Y}}).$$

4.2. PROPOSITION. *If S and T are generalized scalar operators, then $R(S)$ and $L(T)$ are also generalized scalar.*

Proof: Let $\mathbf{U}$ and $\mathbf{V}$ be spectral distributions of S and T, respectively. Then the mappings

$$R \circ \mathbf{U}, \quad L \circ \mathbf{V}: C^{\infty} \to \mathbf{B}(\mathbf{B}(\mathscr{X}, \mathscr{Y}))$$

are continuous algebraic homomorphisms (since so are R, L and $\mathbf{U}, \mathbf{V}$) and verify

$$(R \circ \mathbf{U})_1 = R(\mathbf{U}_1) = R(I_{\mathscr{X}}) = I_{\mathbf{B}(\mathscr{X},\mathscr{Y})},$$

$$(L \circ \mathbf{V})_1 = L(\mathbf{V}_1) = L(I_{\mathscr{Y}}) = I_{\mathbf{B}(\mathscr{X},\mathscr{Y})},$$

and

$$\begin{cases} (R \circ \mathbf{U})_{\lambda} = R(\mathbf{U}_{\lambda}) = R(S), \\ (L \circ \mathbf{V})_{\lambda} = L(\mathbf{V}_{\lambda}) = L(T). \end{cases}$$

Thus $R \circ \mathbf{U}$ and $L \circ \mathbf{V}$ are spectral distributions of $R(S)$ and $L(T)$, respectively. This completes the proof.

4.3. THEOREM. *If S and T are generalized scalar operators, then for every $n \geqslant 1$, $C^n(T, S)$ is also generalized scalar.*

Proof: We have seen (Remark 2.3.1) that $R(X)$ and $L(Y)$ commute for all $X \in \mathbf{B}(\mathscr{X})$ and $Y \in \mathbf{B}(\mathscr{Y})$, hence

$$R(\mathbf{U}_f)\, L(\mathbf{V}_g) = L(\mathbf{V}_g)\, R(\mathbf{U}_f) \quad \text{for all} \quad f, g \in C^{\infty}$$

(where $\mathbf{U}$ and $\mathbf{V}$ are spectral distributions of S and T, respectively), therefore by Theorem 3.3, $C(T, S) = L(T) - R(S)$ is a generalized scalar operator.

Applying Lemma 3.2, we obtain that

$$C^n(T, S) = [L(T) - R(S)]^{(n)}, \quad (n \geqslant 1)$$

is also generalized scalar.

4.4. LEMMA. *If $T \in \mathbf{B}(\mathscr{X})$ is a decomposable operator, then*

$$\mathscr{X}_T(\{0\}) = \left\{x \in \mathscr{X} \,\middle|\, \lim_{n\to\infty} \|T^n x\|^{1/n} = 0\right\}.$$

Proof: Putting

$$T_0 = T|\mathscr{X}_T(\{0\}),$$

we have

$$\sigma(T_0) = \sigma(T|\mathscr{X}_T(\{0\})) \subset \{0\},$$

hence

$$\lim_{n\to\infty} \|T_0^n\|^{1/n} = \sup_{\lambda \in \sigma(T_0)} |\lambda| = 0.$$

For every $x \in \mathscr{X}_T(\{0\})$ we have

$$\|T^n x\|^{1/n} = \|T_0^n x\|^{1/n} \leqslant \|x\|^{1/n} \cdot \|T_0^n\|^{1/n} \xrightarrow[n\to\infty]{} 0.$$

Conversely, let $x \in \mathscr{X}$ be such that

$$\lim_{n\to\infty} \|T^n x\|^{1/n} = 0.$$

Then the radius of convergence of the series

$$x(\lambda) = \sum_{n=0}^{\infty} \frac{T^n x}{\lambda^{n+1}}$$

is ∞, therefore it converges for every $\lambda \neq 0$. We remark that

$$x(\lambda) = R(\lambda, T)\, x \quad \text{for} \quad |\lambda| > \|T\|,$$

hence it verifies

$$(\lambda I - T)\, x(\lambda) = x \quad \text{for} \quad |\lambda| > \|T\|,$$

and by analytic continuation

$$(\lambda I - T)\, x(\lambda) = x \quad \text{for} \quad \lambda \neq 0.$$

Thus $C\{0\} \subset \varrho_T(x)$, i.e. $\sigma_T(x) \subset \{0\}$, that is

$$x \in \mathscr{X}_T(\{0\}).$$

4.5. THEOREM. *Let $S \in \mathbf{B}(\mathscr{X})$, $T \in \mathbf{B}(\mathscr{Y})$ be two generalized scalar operators, and let $A \in \mathbf{B}(\mathscr{X}, \mathscr{Y})$. Then the following three assertions are equivalent*

(i) *$A\mathscr{X}_S(F) \subset \mathscr{Y}_T(F)$ for every closed set $F \subset C$;*

(ii) $\lim_{n\to\infty} \|C^n(T, S)(A)\|^{1/n} = 0$;

(iii) $C^m(T, S)(A) = 0$ *for a certain* $m \geqslant 1$.

Moreover in (iii) *one can choose* m *independent of* A.

Proof. The equivalence (i) $\Longleftrightarrow$ (ii) was proved in Theorem 2.3.3. Obviously (iii) $\Rightarrow$ (ii). It remains to be proved the implication (ii) $\Rightarrow$ (iii). For this denote

$$\mathbf{B}_0 = \mathbf{B}(\mathscr{X}, \mathscr{Y})_{C(T,S)}(\{0\}).$$

By Lemma 4.4,

$$\mathbf{B}_0 = \left\{A \in \mathbf{B}(\mathscr{X}, \mathscr{Y}) \,\middle|\, \lim_{n\to\infty} \|C^n(T, S)(A)\|^{1/n} = 0\right\}.$$

We have seen (Theorem 4.3) that $C(T, S)$ is a generalized scalar operator. Since $\mathbf{B}_0$ is a spectral maximal space of $C(T, S)$, it is ultra-invariant, therefore it is invariant to every spectral distribution of $C(T, S)$. Applying now Proposition 3.3.10 it follows that $C(T, S)|\mathbf{B}_0$ is also a generalized scalar operator. But (see the proof of Lemma 4.4) $C(T, S)|\mathbf{B}_0$ is a quasinilpotent operator, therefore by Lemma 3.5 $C(T, S)|\mathbf{B}_0$ is nilpotent, that is there exists an integer $m \geqslant 1$ such that

$$C^m(T, S)(A) = 0,$$

for every $A \in \mathbf{B}_0$.

As a corollary of this theorem we have the following theorem of "uniqueness" of spectral distributions of a generalized spectral operator. (See also 1.6.)

4.6. THEOREM. *If* $\mathbf{U}$ *and* $\mathbf{V}$ *are two spectral distributions of the same generalized spectral operator, then there exists an integer* $m \geqslant 1$ *such that*

$$(\mathbf{U}_f - \mathbf{V}_f)^{[m]} = 0 = (\mathbf{V}_f - \mathbf{U}_f)^{[m]} \tag{1}$$

for all $f \in C^\infty$.

Proof. Since C^∞ is inverse closed and every generalized spectral operator is C^∞-decomposable, we may apply Remark 3.3.3 and we obtain

$$\mathbf{U}_f \overset{q}{\sim} \mathbf{V}_f \quad \text{for all} \quad f \in C^\infty.$$

By Lemma 3.2 $\mathbf{U}_f$ and $\mathbf{V}_f$ are generalized scalar operators, hence by the preceding theorem (for $\mathscr{X} = \mathscr{Y}$ and $A = I$) we deduce the validity of (1).

4.7. COROLLARY. *For every two commuting spectral distributions* $\mathbf{U}$ *and* $\mathbf{V}$ *of the same generalized spectral operator* T *there exists an integer* $m \geqslant 1$ *such that*

$$(\mathbf{U}_f - \mathbf{V}_f)^m = 0$$

for all $f \in C^\infty$.

4.8. COROLLARY. *If* T *is a completely regular generalized spectral operator, and* $\mathbf{U}$ *is one of its completely regular spectral distributions, then for every other spectral distribution* $\mathbf{V}$ *of* T, *and every* $f \in C^\infty$, $\mathbf{U}_f - \mathbf{V}_f$ *is a nilpotent operator.*

Proof. Since

$$T\mathbf{V}_g = \mathbf{V}_g T \quad \text{for every} \quad f \in C^\infty$$

and

$$\mathscr{X}_{\mathbf{U}_\lambda}(F) = \mathscr{X}_T(F) = \mathscr{X}_{\mathbf{V}_\lambda}(F),$$

for every closed set $F \subset C$, it results by Proposition 1.3.2 that

$$\mathbf{V}_g \mathscr{X}_{\mathbf{U}_\lambda}(F) \subset \mathscr{X}_{\mathbf{U}_\lambda}(F),$$

whence by the complete regularity of $\mathbf{U}$ we have

$$\mathbf{U}_f \mathbf{V}_g = \mathbf{V}_g \mathbf{U}_f \quad \text{for all} \quad f, g \in C^\infty.$$

Then our assertion follows from the preceding theorem.

5. Some Relations between a Generalized Spectral Operator and its Scalar Part

Set

$$\mathscr{A}^p = \{f \in C^p(R^2) | f^{(k)}(0) = 0, \quad 0 \leqslant k \leqslant p\},$$

$$\mathscr{B}^p = \{f \in C^p(R^2) | \operatorname{supp}(f) \not\ni 0\}.$$

5.1. LEMMA. *The set* $\mathscr{B}^p$ *is dense in* $\mathscr{A}^p$.

Proof. Let $\mathscr{B}^p$ be the closure of $\mathscr{B}^p$ in the topology of $C^p(R^n)$. We need to show that

$$\mathscr{A}^p \subset \overline{\mathscr{B}^p}.$$

Assuming that this inclusion fails, there is a function $g \in \mathscr{A}^p$ such that

$$d(g, \mathscr{B}^p) = d_0 > 0$$

(the distance between g and $\mathscr{B}^p$).

By a consequence of Hahn-Banach's theorem there is a scalar distribution $\mathbf{V}$ on $C^p(\Omega)$ such that

$$\mathbf{V}(g) = d_0; \tag{1}$$

$$\mathbf{V}(f) = 0 \quad \text{for any} \quad f \in \mathscr{B}^p. \tag{2}$$

From these two properties of the distribution $\mathbf{V}$ it results that supp $(\mathbf{V}) = \{0\}$. But by a well-known result in the theory of distribution (see Ref. 49, Theorem 1.5.3) $\mathbf{V}$ has the form

$$\mathbf{V} = \sum_{|k| \leqslant p} a_k \delta^{(k)}, \quad [k = (k_1, k_2), |k| = k_1 + k_2]$$

therefore

$$\mathbf{V}(g) = \sum_{|k| \leqslant p} a_k \delta^{(k)} g = \sum_{|k| \leqslant p} (-1)^k a_k g^{(k)}(0) = 0,$$

which is in contradiction with (1). This completes the proof.

5.2. THEOREM. *Let $\mathscr{I} \subset \mathbf{B}(\mathscr{X})$ be a uniformly closed left (right) ideal. If T is a generalized spectral operator belonging to $\mathscr{I}$, and $\mathbf{U}$ is one of its spectral distributions of order n, then*

$$\mathbf{U}_f \in \mathscr{I}$$

for every $f \in \mathscr{A}^p$ and $p \geqslant n$.

Proof. We shall first show

$$\mathbf{U}_g \in \mathscr{I} \quad \text{for any} \quad g \in \mathscr{B}^p, \quad (p \geqslant n).$$

If $g \in \mathscr{B}^p$, then there is an open neighborhood G of the origin where g vanishes, therefore

$$\text{supp}\,(g) \subset \Omega \setminus G. \tag{1}$$

$\mathbf{U}_\lambda$ being a generalized scalar operator we have

$$\sigma_{\mathbf{U}_\lambda}(\mathbf{U}_g x) \subset \text{supp}\,(g) \quad \text{for any} \quad x \in \mathscr{X},$$

hence (by Theorem 3.3.4)

$$\mathbf{U}_g x \in \mathscr{X}_{\mathbf{U}_\lambda}(\operatorname{supp}(g)) = \mathscr{X}_T(\operatorname{supp}(g))$$

for any $x \in \mathscr{X}$, whence

$$\mathbf{U}_g \mathscr{X} \subset \mathscr{X}_T(\operatorname{supp}(g)).$$

From

$$0 \notin \operatorname{supp}(g)$$

[by (1)] and

$$\sigma\left(T|\mathscr{X}_T(\operatorname{supp}(g))\right) \subset \operatorname{supp}(g)$$

it results

$$0 \notin \sigma(T|\mathscr{X}_T)(\operatorname{supp}(g)),$$

therefore $\left(T|\mathscr{X}_T(\operatorname{supp}(g))\right)^{-1}$ exists and is bounded on $\mathscr{X}_T(\operatorname{supp}(g))$. Putting

$$A_g = \left(T|\mathscr{X}_T(\operatorname{supp}(g))\right)^{-1} \mathbf{U}_g$$

we have $A_g \in \mathbf{B}(\mathscr{X})$. Therefore, from

$$A_g T = \left(T|\mathscr{X}_T(\operatorname{supp}(g))\right)^{-1} \mathbf{U}_g T = \left(T|\mathscr{X}_T(\operatorname{supp}(g))\right)^{-1} T\mathbf{U}_g = \mathbf{U}_g,$$

respectively

$$TA_g = T\left(T|\mathscr{X}_T(\operatorname{supp}(g))\right)^{-1} \mathbf{U}_g = \mathbf{U}_g,$$

we obtain $\mathbf{U}_g \in \mathscr{I}$.

$\mathbf{U}$ being continuous and $\mathscr{I}$ uniformly closed, from the preceding lemma we get

$$\mathbf{U}_f \in \mathscr{I}$$

for any $f \in \mathscr{A}^p$ and $p \geqslant n$.

5.3. Corollary. *In the hypotheses and notations of the preceding theorem, we have*

$$\mathbf{U}_\lambda^{p+1} \in \mathscr{I} \quad \textit{for any} \quad p \geqslant n. \tag{1}$$

Moreover, if $\mathscr{I}$ is a two-sided ideal, then

$$(T - \mathbf{U}_f)^{[k]}, (\mathbf{U}_f - T)^{[k]} \in \mathscr{I} \tag{2}$$

and

$$C_T^k(\mathbf{U}_f), C_{\mathbf{U}_f}^k(T) \in \mathscr{I} \tag{3}$$

for any $f \in \mathscr{A}^p$ and $k = 1, 2, \ldots$.

Proof. The function $\lambda \to \lambda^{p+1}$ belonging to $\mathscr{A}^p$, we get (by the preceding theorem)

$$\mathbf{U}_\lambda^{p+1} = \mathbf{U}_{\lambda^{p+1}} \in \mathscr{I}, \quad (p \geqslant n).$$

As $\mathscr{I}$ is a two-sided ideal, and T, $\mathbf{U}_f \in \mathscr{I}$ (for $f \in \mathscr{A}^p$) it results that

$$(T - \mathbf{U}_f)^{[k]} = \sum_{i=0}^{k} (-1)^{k-i} \binom{k}{i} T^i \mathbf{U}_f^{k-i} \in \mathscr{I},$$

and

$$C_T^k(\mathbf{U}_f) = \sum_{i=0}^{k} (-1)^{k-i} \binom{k}{i} T^i \mathbf{U}_f T^{k-i} \in \mathscr{I}.$$

Analogously

$$(\mathbf{U}_f - T)^{[k]},\ C_{\mathbf{U}_f}^k(T) \in \mathscr{I}.$$

5.4. Corollary. *If* $T \in \mathbf{B}(\mathscr{X})$ *is a* generalized spectral *(weakly) compact operator, and* $\mathbf{U}$ *is its spectral distribution of order* n, *then the following operators*

$$\mathbf{U}_f,\ (T - \mathbf{U}_f)^{[k]},\ (\mathbf{U}_f - T)^{[k]},\ C_T^k(\mathbf{U}_f),\ C_{\mathbf{U}_f}^k(T)$$

are (weakly) compact too, for any $f \in \mathscr{A}^p$ *and* $K = 1, 2, \ldots$

Proof. The set of (weakly) compact operators is a uniformly closed two-sided ideal in the Banach algebra $\mathbf{B}(\mathscr{X})$ (see Ref. 30, VI, §§ 4–5).

5.5. Corollary. *Let* $\mathscr{I} \in \mathbf{B}(\mathscr{X})$ *be a uniformly closed left (right) ideal. If* $T \in \mathscr{I}$ *is a generalized spectral operator and* $T = S + Q$ *its canonical decomposition given by a spectral distribution* $\mathbf{U}$ *of order* n, *then*

$$S^{p+1} \in \mathscr{I} \quad \text{and} \quad Q^{p+1} \in \mathscr{I}$$

for any $p \geqslant n$.

Proof. The function $\lambda \to \lambda^{p+1}$ belonging to $\mathscr{A}^p$, we get

$$S^{p+1} = (\mathbf{U}_\lambda)^{p+1} = \mathbf{U}_{\lambda^{p+1}} \in \mathscr{I}.$$

Writing S^{p+1} in the form

$$S^{p+1} = (T - Q)^{p+1} = T_1 + Q^{p+1},$$

where

$$T_1 = T^{p+1} + \sum_{k=1}^{p} (-1)^k \binom{p+1}{k} Q^k T^{p+1-k} \in \mathscr{I},$$

it results

$$Q^{p+1} = S^{p+1} - T_1 \in \mathscr{I}.$$

5.6. COROLLARY. *If $T \in \mathbf{B}(\mathscr{X})$ is a generalized spectral (weakly) compact operator, and* **U** *is a spectral distribution of order n, and if $T = S + Q$ is the canonical decomposition given by* **U**, *we have that S^{p+1} and Q^{p+1} are (weakly) compact, for any $p \geqslant n$.*

This results from the fact that the set of (weakly) compact operators is a uniformly closed 2-sided ideal in the Banach algebra $\mathbf{B}(\mathscr{X})$.

5.7. COROLLARY. *If $T \in \mathbf{B}(\mathscr{X})$ is a generalized spectral operator, and $\mathscr{X}_0$ is a closed subspace of $\mathscr{X}$ such that $T\mathscr{X} \subset \mathscr{X}_0$ then*

$$\mathbf{U}_f \mathscr{X} \subset \mathscr{X}_0, \quad (f \in \mathscr{A}^p, p \geqslant n); \tag{1}$$

$$S^{p+1}\mathscr{X} \subset \mathscr{X}_0, \quad Q^{p+1}\mathscr{X} \subset \mathscr{X}_0, \quad (p \geqslant n). \tag{2}$$

This results from the fact that the set

$$\{A \in \mathbf{B}(\mathscr{X}) | A\mathscr{X} \subset \mathscr{X}_0\}$$

is a uniformly closed right ideal.

5.8. COROLLARY. *If $T \in \mathbf{B}(\mathscr{H})$ is a generalized spectral operator, and $A_0 \in \mathbf{B}(\mathscr{H})$ verifies $A_0 T = 0$ (respectively, $TA_0 = 0$), then*

$$A_0 \mathbf{U}_f = 0 \text{ (respectively, } \mathbf{U}_f A_0 = 0) \quad \text{for every} \quad f \in \mathscr{A}^p \quad (p \geqslant n), \tag{1}$$

$$A_0 S^{p+1} = A_0 Q^{p+1} = 0 \text{ (respectively, } S^{p+1} A_0 = Q^{p+1} A_0 = 0) \quad (p \geqslant n). \tag{2}$$

This results from the fact that the set

$$\{A \in B(\mathscr{X}) | A_0 A = 0\} \text{ (respectively, } \{A \in \mathbf{B}(\mathscr{X}) | AA_0 = 0\})$$

is a uniformly closed right (respectively, left) ideal.

5.9. COROLLARY. *If T is a generalized spectral operator such that $Tx_0 = 0$, then*

$$\mathbf{U}_f x_0 = S^{p+1}x_0 = Q^{p+1}x_0 = 0, \quad (f \in \mathscr{A}^p, p \geqslant n).$$

Proof. The set

$$\{A \in \mathbf{B}(\mathscr{X}) | Bx_0 = 0\}$$

is a uniformly closed left ideal.

5.10. COROLLARY. *Let $T \in \mathbf{B}(\mathscr{X})$ be a generalized spectral operator, and let $\{x_n\} \subset \mathscr{X}$ be a bounded sequence such that $\lim_{n\to\infty} Tx_n$ exists, then the sequences*

$$\{\mathbf{U}_f x_n\}_{n\in N}, \ \{S^{p+1}x_n\}_{n\in N}, \ \{Q^{p+1}x_n\}_{n\in N}$$

have limits for any $f \in \mathscr{A}^p$ and $p \geqslant n$.

Proof. The set

$$\{A \in \mathbf{B}(\mathscr{X}) | \lim_{n\to\infty} Ax_n \text{ exists}\}$$

is a uniformly closed left ideal.

6. The Decomposition of a Generalized Spectral Operator into Real Part and Imaginary Part

6.1. LEMMA. *If S is a generalized scalar operator, then*

$$S = S_1 + iS_2,$$

where S_1 and S_2 are commuting generalized scalar operators with real spectra. S_1 will be called the real part of S, and S_2 will be called the imaginar part of S.

Proof. Let U be a spectral distribution of S, then

$$S = \mathbf{U}_\lambda = \mathbf{U}_{\mathrm{Re}\,\lambda} + i\mathbf{U}_{\mathrm{Im}\,\lambda} = S_1 + iS_2.$$

The mapping $\mathbf{U}^1 : f \to \mathbf{U}_{f \circ \mathrm{Re}\,\lambda}$ (respectively, $\mathbf{U}^2 : f \to \mathbf{U}_{f \circ \mathrm{Im}\,\lambda}$) is a spectral distribution, and

$$S_1 = \mathbf{U}^1_\lambda \text{ (respectively, } S_2 = \mathbf{U}^2_\lambda),$$

hence S_1 (respectively, S_2) is a generalized scalar operator.

By Theorem 3.2.1, we have

$$\sigma(S_1) = \sigma(U_{\mathrm{Re}\,\lambda}) \subset \mathrm{Re}\,[\mathrm{supp}\,(\mathbf{U})]$$

and

$$\sigma(S_2) = \sigma(\mathbf{U}_{\mathrm{Im}\,\lambda}) \subset \mathrm{Im}\,[\mathrm{supp}\,(\mathbf{U})].$$

The commutativity of S_1 with S_2 results from the fact that $\mathbf{U}$ is multiplicative.

6.2. THEOREM. *If T is a generalized spectral operator, then there are two operators R and I such that*

(1) *$T = R + iJ$, and $RJ = JR$;*

(2) *R and J have real spectra;*

(3) *R is a generalized scalar and J is a generalized spectral operator;*

(4) *If R_1 and J_1 satisfy conditions* (1) *and* (2), *and commute with R, then they are generalized spectral operators and there exists a quasinilpotent operator Q_1 such that*

$$R_1 = R + Q_1 \quad \textit{and} \quad J_1 = J + iQ_1.$$

Proof. Let $\mathbf{U}$ be a spectral distribution of T, and $T = S + Q$ its canonical decomposition given by $\mathbf{U}$. Then according to the preceding lemma, $S = S_1 + iS_2$.

Putting

$$R = S_1 \quad \text{and} \quad J = S_2 - iQ,$$

we have

$$T = R + iJ.$$

From the commutativity of S_1 with S_2 and of Q with $\mathbf{U}$, it results that R commutes with J.

We have

$$\sigma(R) = (S_1) \quad \text{and} \quad \sigma(J) = \sigma(S_2 - iQ) = \sigma(S_2),$$

hence R and J have real spectra.

$R = S_1$ is a generalized scalar operator, $J = S_2 + (-iQ)$ is a generalized spectral operator, since S_2 is a generalized scalar operator and Q is a quasinilpotent operator commuting with $\mathbf{U}^2$ (the spectral distribution of S_2).

Let now R_1 and J_1 be two operators with the properties (1) and (2), and commuting with R; then the operators R, J, R_1, and J_1 commute. Let $\mathscr{A}$ be the commutative Banach algebra spanned by these operators and I, and let $\mathfrak{M}$ be the space of its maximal ideals.

The operators R, J, R_1, and J_1 having real spectra, the numbers

$$R^{\wedge}(M), J^{\wedge}(M), \hat{R_1}(M), \hat{J_1}(M)$$

are real for any $M \in \mathfrak{M}$, hence

$$(R_1 - R)^{\wedge}(M), (J_1 - J)^{\wedge}(M)$$

are real too. From

$$T = R + iJ = R_1 + iJ_1$$

follows

$$0 = (R_1 - R) + i(J_1 - J),$$

hence

$$0 = (R_1 - R)^{\wedge}(M) + i(J_1 - J)^{\wedge}(M) \quad \text{for any} \quad M \in \mathfrak{M},$$

therefore

$$(R_1 - R)^{\wedge}(M) = 0 = (J_1 - J)^{\wedge}(M) \quad \text{for any} \quad M \in \mathfrak{M}.$$

This shows that $R_1 - R$ and $J_1 - J$ are quasinilpotent operators.

Putting

$$Q_1 = R_1 - R \quad \text{and} \quad Q_2 = J_1 - J,$$

it results

$$Q_2 = iQ_1,$$

therefore

$$R_1 = R + Q_1 \quad \text{and} \quad J_1 = J + iQ_1.$$

7. Roots and Logarithms of Generalized Spectral Operators

7.1. Lemma. *If $A \in \mathbf{B}(\mathscr{X})$ is an operator such that*

$$A^n = S \quad (n \geqslant 2),$$

where S is a regular generalized scalar operator whose spectrum does not separate 0 from ∞, then A is a generalized scalar operator.

Proof. The mapping $\lambda \to \sqrt[n]{\lambda}$ has n branches; let $r_1, \ldots, r_n$ be these functions. As $\sigma(T)$ does not separate 0 from ∞, it is clear that $r_k \in C^{\infty}(\Omega)$ $(1 \leqslant k \leqslant n)$, where Ω is a suitable neighborhood of $\sigma(T)$.

Putting

$$\sigma_k = r_k(\sigma(S)) \left(\subset \left\{ \lambda \in C \,\middle|\, \frac{2k\pi}{n} < \arg \lambda < \frac{2(k+1)\pi}{n} \right\} \right),$$

we have

$$\sigma(A) \subset \bigcup_{k=1}^{n} \sigma_k.$$

The sets σ_k are separated because they are closed and disjoint.

Applying to the operator A the theorem of decomposition according to the separate parts of the spectrum (Ref. 47, Theorem 5.13.1) there is a system of idempotents $\{J_k\}_{1 \leqslant k \leqslant n}$ such that

(1) $I = \sum_{k=1}^{n} J_k$, $J_k J_l = 0$ for $k \neq l$;

(2) $AJ_k = J_k A$, $(1 \leqslant k \leqslant n)$;

(3) if $XA = AX$, then $XJ_k = J_k X$, $(1 \leqslant k \leqslant n)$;

(4) denote $A_k = A|J_k\mathscr{X}$, we have

$$A = \bigoplus_{k=1}^{n} A_k \quad \text{and} \quad \sigma(A_k) = \sigma_k.$$

Let $\mathbf{U}$ be a regular distribution of S. We have

$$AS = A^{n+1} = SA,$$

i.e.

$$A\mathbf{U}_\lambda = \mathbf{U}_\lambda A$$

whence, according to the regularity of $\mathbf{U}$, it follows

$$A\mathbf{U}_f = \mathbf{U}_f A \quad \text{for any} \quad f \in C^\infty(\Omega),$$

hence [by (3)]

$$J_k\mathbf{U}_f = \mathbf{U}_f J_k \quad \text{for any} \quad f \in C(\Omega) \quad \text{and} \quad 1 \leqslant k \leqslant n.$$

If we write

$$\mathscr{X}_k = J_k\mathscr{X},$$

$$S_k = S|\mathscr{X}_k,$$

$$\mathbf{U}_f^k = \mathbf{U}_f|\mathscr{X}_k,$$

it follows $A_k, S_k, \mathbf{U}_f^k \in \mathbf{B}(\mathscr{X}_k)$.

We observe that S_k is a generalized scalar operator on $\mathscr{X}_k$ and $\mathbf{U}_f^k$ is its spectral distribution. We have

$$A_k^n = S_k,$$

whence

$$A_k = (r_k \circ \lambda^n)(A_k) = r_k(A_k^n) = r_k(S_k) = r_k(\mathbf{U}_\lambda^k) = \mathbf{U}_{r_k}^k,$$

therefore (Lemma 3.2) A_k is a generalized scalar operator.

By proposition 3.3.9

$$A = \bigoplus_{k=1}^{n} A_k$$

is a generalized scalar operator.

To extend this result to the case of generalized spectral operators we need the following result of J.T.Schwartz (Ref. 110, Corollary to Theorem 1, or Ref. 30, VII.6.12).

If Q is a quasinilpotent operator commuting with an operator S and f is an analytic function in a neighborhood of $\sigma(S)$, then

$$f(S+Q) = \sum_{p=0}^{\infty} \frac{Q^p}{p!} f^p(S)$$

and the series on the right is convergent in the uniform topology.

7.2. Theorem. *If $A \in \mathbf{B}(\mathscr{X})$ is an operator such that*

$$A^n = T, \quad (n \geqslant 2)$$

where T is a regular generalized spectral operator whose spectrum does not separate 0 from ∞, then A is a generalized spectral operator.

Proof. Let $\mathbf{U}$ be a spectral distribution of T, and let $T = S + Q$ be the canonical decomposition given by $\mathbf{U}$. Applying Schwartz's result to the operators S_k, Q_k and to the function r_k $(1 \leqslant k \leqslant n)$, we obtain

$$A_k = r(T_k) = r_k(S_k + Q_k) = \sum_{p=0}^{\infty} \frac{Q_k}{p!} r_k^{(p)}(S_k)$$

$$= r_k(\mathbf{U}_\lambda^{[k]}) + Q_k \sum_{p=1}^{\infty} \frac{Q_k^{p+1}}{p!} r_k^{(p)}(S_k) = \mathbf{U}_{r_k}^{[k]} + Q_k',$$

where

$$Q'_k = Q_k \sum_{p=1}^{\infty} \frac{Q_k^{p-1}}{p!} r_k^{(p)}(S)$$

is a quasinilpotent operator which commutes with $\mathbf{U}^k$ (because $\mathbf{U}$ commutes with Q and $r_k^{(p)}(S_k) = \mathbf{U}^k_{r_k^{(p)}}$), and $\mathbf{U}^k_{r_k}$ is a generalized scalar operator. Therefore

$$A_k = \mathbf{U}^k_{r_k} + Q'_k$$

is a generalized spectral operator. By applying Proposition 3.3.9, it follows that

$$A = \bigoplus_{k=1}^{n} A_k$$

is a generalized spectral operator.

7.3. LEMMA. *If $A \in \mathbf{B}(\mathscr{X})$ is an operator such that*

$$\exp A = S,$$

where S is a regular generalized scalar operator whose spectrum does not separate 0 from ∞, then A is a generalized scalar operator.

We remark that $\lambda \to \log \lambda$ has only a finite number of branches whose ranges intersect $\sigma(A)$; let $\{\log_k\}_{n \geqslant k \geqslant m}$ $(n, m \in Z)$ be these branches. If we put

$$\sigma_k = \log_k(\sigma(S)), \quad (n \leqslant k \leqslant m),$$

the rest of the proof is the same as for Lemma 7.1.

In the same way as for the proof of Theorem 7.2, one can show the following result.

7.4. THEOREM. *If $A \in \mathbf{B}(\mathscr{X})$ is an operator such that*

$$\exp A = S,$$

where S is a regular generalized spectral operator whose spectrum does not separate 0 from ∞, then A is a generalized scalar operator.

Notes and Remarks

The notions of spectral distribution as well as that of generalized scalar operator were introduced in Ref. 39; that of generalized spectral operator in Refs. 15 and 81. Sects. 1.4–1.11 are taken from Refs. 39 and 42.

Example 1.3(a) is due to L. Schwartz (see Ref. 39) while example 1.3(b) is a generalization, made by Maeda,[81] of the L. Schwartz example.

Proposition 2.3 is taken from Ref. 57. Corollary 2.4 was conjectured by I. Kaplanski, P. R. Halmos,[46] and C. R. Putnam.[96] For the finite-dimensional case it is a well-known theorem of N. Jacobson, while for the general case it was proved by F. V. Širokov[134] and D. C. Kleinecke.[59] Theorem 2.6 seems new.

The results of sections 3.1–3.4 have been published in Ref. 39, those of sections 3.5–3.7 in Ref. 42, and those of sections 3.9–3.14 in Ref. 15.

The results of section 4.5 are new. Their consequence, namely Theorem 4.6, constitutes an affirmative answer to Problem 2, raised in Ref. 19. Corollary 4.8 represents, in fact, a result obtained in a different way in Ref. 39.

All the results of §§ 5–6 are extensions (published in Ref. 15) to the class of generalized spectral operators of some results of S. R. Foguel concerning spectral operators.[36] The results in § 7 are partial extensions to the generalized scalar and spectral operators of the results of J. G. Stampfli[117] (for the case of roots of operators) and S. Kurepa[67] (for the case of logarithms of operators) also concerning the usual scalar and spectral operators.

Chapter 5

$\mathfrak{A}$-unitary and $\mathfrak{A}$-self-adjoint Operators

1. $\mathfrak{A}$-unitary Operators; the Case of Generalized Scalar Operators

Let $\mathscr{X}$ be a Banach space and $S \in \mathbf{B}(\mathscr{X})$.

1.1. DEFINITION. S is called an $\mathfrak{A}$-*unitary* operator if it is an $\mathfrak{A}$-scalar operator, where $\mathfrak{A}$ is an admissible of functions defined on

$$\Omega = \{\lambda \in C \,|\, |\lambda| = 1\} = C_1 .$$

In virtue of Proposition 3.1.6 it results that if S is an $\mathfrak{A}$-unitary operator then

$$\sigma(S) \subset C_1 = \{\lambda \in C \,|\, |\lambda| = 1\}.$$

1.2. PROPOSITION. *Let $S \in \mathbf{B}(\mathscr{X})$ be a generalized scalar operator [i.e. $C^\infty(R^2)$-scalar] such that $\sigma(S) \subset C_1$. Then S is an $\mathfrak{A}$-unitary operator, where $\mathfrak{A}$ is the algebra $C^\infty(C_1)$ of the functions $f: C_1 \to C$ such that the function $t \to f(e^{it})$ belongs to $C^\infty(R)$. The algebra $C^\infty(C_1)$ is endowed with the topology induced by $C^\infty(R)$, being a topologically admissible algebra.*

Proof. Let $\mathbf{V}: C^\infty(R^2) \to \mathbf{B}(\mathscr{X})$ be a spectral distribution of S, and let n be the order of $\mathbf{V}$. Take $\psi \in C^\infty(R^2)$ such that in a neighborhood $G(\not\ni 0)$ of C_1 we have $\psi(\lambda) = 1/\lambda$. Since $\lambda\psi(x) = 1$ in G and supp $(\mathbf{V}) = \sigma(S)$ $\subset C_1$, we have

$$S\mathbf{V}_\psi = \mathbf{V}_\psi S = \mathbf{V}_{\lambda\psi} = \mathbf{U}_1 = I,$$

thus $\mathbf{V}_\psi = S^{-1}$. On the other hand for

$$\varphi(\lambda) = [\bar{\lambda} - \psi(\lambda)]^{n+1}$$

all the derivates

$$\partial^{\alpha+\beta}\varphi(s+it)/\partial s^{\alpha}\,\partial t^{\beta}, \quad (0 \leqslant \alpha + \beta \leqslant n)$$

are 0 on C_1, hence also on supp $(\mathbf{V})$.

On the other hand the numerical distribution $f \to \langle \mathbf{V}_f x, x^* \rangle$ $(x \in \mathscr{X}, x^* \in \mathscr{X}^*)$ is of order $\leqslant n$ and has its support $\subset$ supp $(\mathbf{V})$. Thus, by a well-known property of the distributions (see for instance Ref. 49, Theorem 1.5.4), we have

$$\langle \mathbf{V}_{\varphi} x, x^* \rangle = 0 \quad \text{for all} \quad x \in \mathscr{X}, x^* \in \mathscr{X}^*,$$

hence

$$(\mathbf{V}_{\bar{\lambda}} - \mathbf{V}_{\psi})^n = \mathbf{V}_{(\bar{\lambda}-\psi)^n} = \mathbf{V}_{\varphi} = 0.$$

In this manner

$$N = \mathbf{V}_{\bar{\lambda}} - S^{-1}$$

is a nilpotent operator commuting with all $\mathbf{V}_f, f \in C^{\infty}(R^2)$.

Let us put

$$\mathbf{U}_f = \sum_{k=0}^{n} \frac{(-1)^k}{k!} N^k \mathbf{V}_{D^k f} \quad f \in C^{\infty}(R^2),$$

where $D = \frac{1}{2}(\partial/\partial s + i\,\partial/\partial t)$, $\lambda = s + it$. It is evident that the mapping U is a $\mathbf{B}(\mathscr{X})$-valued distribution such that $\mathbf{U}_1 = I$. Moreover, since $D\lambda = 0$, we have $\mathbf{U}_{\lambda} = S$. It remains to verify that for every $f, g \in C^{\infty}(R)$ we have $\mathbf{U}_{fg} = \mathbf{U}_f \mathbf{U}_g$. This is obtained in the following manner:

$$\mathbf{U}_{fg} = \sum_{k=0}^{n} \frac{(-1)^k}{k!} N^k \mathbf{V}_{D^k(fg)} = \sum_{k=0}^{n} \frac{(-1)^k}{k!} N^k \mathbf{V}_{\sum_{j=0}^{k} \binom{k}{j} D^j f D^{k-j} g}$$

$$= \sum_{k=0}^{n} \frac{(-1)^k}{k!} N^k \sum_{j=0}^{k} \binom{k}{j} \mathbf{V}_{D^j f} \mathbf{V}_{D^{k-j} g}$$

$$= \sum_{k=0}^{n} \sum_{j=0}^{k} \frac{(-1)^j}{j!} N^j \mathbf{V}_{D^j f} \frac{(-1)^{k-j}}{(k-j)!} N^{k-j} \mathbf{V}_{D^{k-j} g}$$

$$= \left(\sum_{j=0}^{n} \frac{(-1)^j}{j!} N^j \mathbf{V}_{D^j f} \right) \left(\sum_{l=0}^{n} (-1)^l N^l \mathbf{V}_{D^l g} \right) = \mathbf{U}_f \mathbf{U}_g,$$

where we used the fact that $N^j N^l = N^{n+p} = 0$ for $j + l = n + p \geqslant n + 1$. Thus $\mathbf{U}$ is a spectral distribution of S such that $\mathbf{U}_{\bar{\lambda}} = S^{-1}$.

Let φ and ψ be two functions of $C^\infty(R^2)$ such that

$$\varphi(\lambda) = \lambda/|\lambda| \quad \text{and} \quad \psi(\lambda) = \bar{\lambda}/|\lambda|$$

in a neighborhood $G_r = \{\lambda \in C \,|\, r \leqslant |\lambda| \leqslant 1/r\}$ $(0 < r < 1)$ of C_1. As

$$[\lambda - \varphi(\lambda)]^{2n+1} = 0 = [\bar{\lambda} - \psi(\lambda)]^{2n+1} \quad \text{on} \quad C_1,$$

we deduce

$$(S - \mathbf{U}_\varphi)^{2n+1} = 0 = (S^{-1} - \mathbf{U}_\psi)^{2n+1}. \tag{1}$$

Or, since

$$\|\mathbf{U}_f\| \leqslant M_r \sup_{\substack{\lambda \in G_r \\ \alpha+\beta \leqslant 2n}} \left| \frac{\partial^{\alpha+\beta} f(\lambda)}{\partial s^\alpha \, \partial t^\beta} \right|, \quad (\lambda = s + it),$$

we obtain

$$\begin{cases} \|\mathbf{U}_\varphi^p\| = \|\mathbf{U}_{\varphi^p}\| \leqslant p^{2n} M' \\ \|\mathbf{U}_\psi^p\| = \|\mathbf{U}_{\psi^p}\| \leqslant p^{2n} M'' \end{cases} \quad (p = 0, 1, 2, \ldots). \tag{2}$$

We can write [by (1)]

$$\begin{cases} S = \mathbf{U}_\varphi + Q_1 \\ S^{-1} = \mathbf{U}_\psi + Q_2 \end{cases} \quad (Q_1^{2n+1} = 0 = Q_2^{2n+1}). \tag{3}$$

From (2) and (3) it results

$$\|S^p\| \leqslant \sum_{k=0}^{p} \binom{p}{k} \|\mathbf{U}_\varphi^{p-k}\| \cdot \|Q_1^k\| \leqslant M_1 p^{2n},$$

$$\|S^{-p}\| \leqslant \sum_{k=0}^{p} \binom{p}{k} \|\mathbf{U}_\psi^{p-k}\| \cdot \|Q_2^k\| \leqslant M_2 p^{2n},$$

hence

$$\|S^p\| \leqslant M\,|p|^{2n} \quad \text{for any} \quad p \in Z, \tag{4}$$

where Z is the ring of integers.

If $f \in C^\infty(C_1)$, then

$$f(\lambda) = \sum_{n \in Z} a_p \lambda^p, \quad (\lambda \in C_1),$$

where

$$a_p = \frac{1}{2\pi} \int_0^{2\pi} e^{-ipt} f(e^{it})\, dt$$

tends to 0 faster than $1/|p|^{2n+2}$. Thus the series

$$\sum_{p\in Z} a_p S^p$$

converges [by (4)] in $\mathbf{B}(\mathscr{X})$. Putting by definition

$$\mathbf{U}_f = \sum_{p\in Z} a_p S^p$$

we obtain a continuous $C^\infty(C_1)$-spectral function such that $\mathbf{U}_\lambda = S$. This finishes the proof.

1.3. *Remark*. During the preceding proof we obtained the following result: *Let S be a generalized scalar operator such that $\sigma(S) \subset C_1$. Then*

$$\|S^p\| = O(|p|^\alpha), \quad (p \in Z, |p| \to \infty)$$

for a certain $\alpha \geqslant 0$. Moreover if S satisfies these inequalities, then S is a $C^\infty(C_1)$-unitary operator.

Actually this last remark may be improved.

1.4. PROPOSITION. *Let $S \in \mathbf{B}(\mathscr{X})$ verify*

$$\|S^p\| = O(|p|^\alpha), \quad (p \in Z, |p| \to \infty)$$

for an $\alpha \geqslant 0$, and let $C^m(C_1)$ denote the topologically admissible algebra of the functions $f: C_1 \to C$ such that the function $t \to f(e^{it})$ belongs to $C^m(R)$. The algebra $C^m(C_1)$ is endowed with the norm

$$\|f\| = \sup_{\substack{t\in R\\ 0\leqslant k\leqslant m}} \left|\frac{d^k f(e^{it})}{dt^k}\right|.$$

Then S is a $C^m(C_1)$-unitary operator, for every $m > \alpha + 1$ (or equivalently $m \geqslant [\alpha] + 2$).

Proof. For $f \in C^m(C_1)$ we have (by partial integrations) that

$$a_p = \frac{1}{2\pi}\int_0^{2\pi} f(e^{it})\, e^{-ipt}\, dt = \frac{1}{ip}\frac{1}{2\pi}\int_0^{2\pi} f'(e^{it})\, e^{-ipt} dt$$

$$= \frac{(-i)^m}{p^m}\frac{1}{2\pi}\int_0^{2\pi} f^{(m)}(e^{it})\, e^{-ipt}\, dt,$$

that is

$$|a_p| \leqslant \frac{1}{|p|^m} M(f^{(m)}),$$

where

$$M(f^{(m)}) = \frac{1}{2\pi} \int_0^{2\pi} |f^{(m)}(e^{it})| \, dt.$$

Taking $m > \alpha + 1$ the series $\sum_{p \in Z} a_p S^p$ converges in $\mathbf{B}(\mathscr{X})$. Denoting by $\mathbf{U}_f$ the sum of this series, we obtain an application $\mathbf{U}: C^m(C_1) \to \mathbf{B}(\mathscr{X})$. It is an easy matter to verify that actually this is a $C^k(C_1)$-function of S.

It is noteworthy to remark the following simple fact:

1.5. *Remark. If $S \in \mathbf{B}(\mathscr{X})$ is $C^\infty(C_1)$-unitary having a continuous $C^\infty(C_1)$-spectral function then S is actually a generalized scalar operator.*

Indeed if $\mathbf{U}$ is a continuous $C^\infty(C_1)$-spectral function of S, then defining $\mathbf{V}_f$ by

$$\mathbf{V}_f = \mathbf{U}_{f|C_1}$$

where $f \in C^\infty(C)$, we obtain obviously a spectral distribution such that $\mathbf{V}_\lambda = S$, hence a spectral distribution of S.

It is useful to replace the growing condition on the iteratives S^n of Proposition 1.4, by a growing condition on the resolvent of S. In this aim let us prove firstly the following.

1.6. Proposition. *Let $S \in \mathbf{B}(\mathscr{X})$ have the spectrum $\sigma(S)$ on the unit circle C_1. Then the following implications are valid*

(i) *If for an $\alpha \geqslant 0$*

$$\|S^n\| = O(|n|^\alpha), \quad (n \in Z, |n| \to \infty),$$

then

$$\|R(\lambda); S)\| = O\left(\frac{1}{||\lambda| - 1|^\beta}\right), \quad (|\lambda| \neq 1, |\lambda| \to 1) \tag{1}$$

for $\beta > [\alpha] + 1$.

(ii) *If*

$$\|R(\lambda; S)\| = O\left(\frac{1}{||\lambda| - 1|^\beta}\right), \quad (|\lambda| \neq 1, |\lambda| \to 1)$$

for a $\beta \geqslant 1$, then

$$\|S^n\| = O(|n|^\beta), \quad (n \in Z, |n| \to \infty). \tag{2}$$

Proof:
Case (i): We have for $|\lambda| > 1$:

$$\|R(\lambda; T)\| \leqslant \sum_{n=0}^{\infty} \frac{\|T^n\|}{|\lambda|^{n+1}} \leqslant \frac{M}{|\lambda|}\left(1 + \sum_{n=1}^{\infty} \frac{n^\alpha}{|\lambda|^n}\right)$$

$$\leqslant M\left(1 + \sum_{n=1}^{\infty} \frac{n^\alpha}{|\lambda|^n}\right),$$

where M is a suitable constant $\geqslant 1$. Let k be the least integer $\geqslant \alpha$ and let $\varrho = 1/|\lambda|$. Then using the fact that $\varrho < 1$, we have successively

$$\begin{aligned}\|R(\lambda; S)\| &\leqslant M(2 + 2^\alpha\varrho + 3^\alpha\varrho^2 + \cdots + n^\alpha\varrho^{n-1} + \cdots)\\ &\leqslant M(2 + 2^k\varrho + 3^k\varrho^2 + \cdots + n^k\varrho^{n-1} + \cdots)\\ &\leqslant M[2 + 2\cdot 3\cdots(k+1)\varrho + 3\cdot 4\cdots(k+2)\varrho^2\\ &\quad + \cdots + n(n+1)\cdots(k+n-1)\varrho^{n-1} + \cdots]\\ &= M\left[2 + \left(\frac{d}{d\varrho}\right)^k(\varrho^{k+1} + \varrho^{k+2} + \cdots + \varrho^{k+n-1} + \cdots)\right]\\ &= M\left[2 + \left(\frac{d}{d\varrho}\right)^k \frac{\varrho^{k+1}}{1-\varrho}\right] = M\frac{P_k(\varrho)}{(1-\varrho)^{k+1}},\end{aligned}$$

where $P_k(\varrho)$ is a certain polynomial of ϱ. For $\frac{1}{2} \leqslant \varrho < 1$, this polynomial is bounded, hence we obtain

$$\|R(\lambda; S)\| \leqslant \frac{M_1}{(1 - 1/|\lambda|)^{k+1}}, \quad \left(\frac{1}{2} < \frac{1}{|\lambda|} < 1\right),$$

from which we get (1) for $|\lambda| > 1$, $|\lambda| \to 1$. The case $|\lambda| < 1$ can be deduced in the same manner.

Case (ii): We shall consider only S^n for $n > 0$; the case $n < 0$ being analogous. We have for every $r > 1$

$$S^n = \frac{1}{2\pi i}\int_{|\lambda|=r} \lambda^n R(\lambda; S)\,d\lambda, \quad (r > 1)$$

whence for $1 < r < 2$

$$\|S^n\| \leqslant Mr^{n+1}/(r-1)^\beta, \tag{3}$$

where M is again a suitable constant. Let us take in (3), for n large enough,

$$r_n = \frac{n+1}{n+1-\beta};$$

we obtain

$$\frac{\|S^n\|}{n^\beta} \leqslant \frac{M}{n^\beta} \frac{[(n+1)/(n+1-\beta)]^{n+1}}{[\beta/(n+1-\beta)]^\beta} \to M \frac{e^\beta}{\beta^\beta} \quad \text{for} \quad n \to \infty,$$

i.e. the estimation (2) for $n \to \infty$.

As a corollary we obtain finally the following

1.7. Proposition. *Let $S \in \mathbf{B}(\mathcal{X})$ be such that $\sigma(S) \subset C_1$, and suppose that S verifies the following growing condition*

$$\|R(\lambda, S)\| = O\left(\frac{1}{|1-|\lambda||^\beta}\right), \quad (|\lambda| \neq 1; |\lambda| \to 1)$$

for a $\beta \geqslant 1$. Then S is a $C^m(C_1)$-unitary operator, for every $m > \beta + 1$.

Proof. By Proposition 1.6 (ii), S verifies the growing condition of Proposition 1.4, hence this last proposition applies to S.

Before finishing this paragraph let us give two applications involving $C^m(C_1)$-unitary operators. The first application concerns the existence of ultra-invariant subspaces for a certain class of operators while the second concerns a multiplicative spectral property of the automorphisms of a Banach algebra.

1.8. Lemma. *If A is a quasiaffinity† from a reflexive Banach space $\mathcal{X}$ in a Banach space $\mathcal{Y}$, then A^* is also a quasiaffinity of $\mathcal{Y}^*$ in $\mathcal{X}^*$.*

Proof;

(a) If $A^*y^* = 0$, then $\langle Ax, y^*\rangle = 0$ for all $x \in \mathcal{X}$. Or $\overline{A\mathcal{X}} = \mathcal{Y}$, thus $y^* \perp \mathcal{Y}$, i.e. $y^* = 0$.

(b) If $\overline{A^*\mathcal{Y}^*} \neq \mathcal{X}^*$, using the reflexivity of $\mathcal{X}$ we can choose a $x \neq 0$, $x \in \mathcal{X}$, such that $x \perp A^*\mathcal{Y}^*$, i.e. $\langle x, A^*y^*\rangle = 0$ for all $y^* \in \mathcal{Y}^*$. It results $\langle Ax, y^*\rangle = 0$ for all $y^* \in \mathcal{Y}^*$, hence $Ax = 0$, $x = 0$: contradiction. Consequently $\overline{A^*\mathcal{Y}^*} = \mathcal{X}$ and this completes the proof.

† This is if A is injective and $\overline{A\mathcal{X}} = \mathcal{Y}$.

1.9. THEOREM. *Let $\mathscr{X}$ be a reflexive Banach space and $T \in \mathbf{B}(\mathscr{X})$ be such that*

(i) $$\|T^n\| \leqslant \varrho_n, \quad n = 1, 2, \ldots,$$

where $\varrho_n \leqslant \varrho_{n+m}$ *and*

$$\limsup_{n\to\infty} \frac{\varrho_{n+m}}{\varrho_m} \leqslant Mm^\alpha, \quad (n = 0, 1 \ldots; m = 1, 2, \ldots),$$

$0 < M < \infty$ *and* $0 \leqslant \alpha < \infty$ *being constants;*

(ii) *neither* $\{T/\varrho_n\}_{n=0}$ *nor* $\{T^{*n}/\varrho_n\}_{n=0}^{\infty}$ *converge strongly to* 0.

Then T has either an ultra-invariant non trivial subspace or $T = cI$ *where* $|c| = 1$.

Proof:

(a) Let
$$\mathscr{Y} = \{x \in \mathscr{X} | \varrho_n^{-1} T^n x \to 0\}.$$

By the assumption (ii) $\mathscr{Y} \neq \mathscr{X}$. If $\mathscr{Y} \neq \{0\}$, then it constitutes obviously an ultra-invariant *nontrivial* subspace of T.

(b) Let
$$\mathscr{Z}_* = \{x^* | x^* \in \mathscr{X}^*, \varrho_n^{-1} T^{*n} x^* \to 0\}.$$

By the assumption (ii) $\mathscr{Z}_* \neq \mathscr{X}^*$. If $\mathscr{Z}_* \neq \{0\}$, then $\mathscr{Z}_*^\perp = \{x | x \in \mathscr{X}, x \perp \mathscr{Z}_*\}$ is a *nontrivial* subspace obviously ultra-invariant for T.

(c) Thus we have only to consider the case when $\mathscr{Y} = \{0\} = \mathscr{Z}_*$, that is the case when for all $x \in \mathscr{X}$, $x \neq 0$, and $x^* \in \mathscr{X}^*$, $x^* \neq 0$, we have

$$\inf_{n=1,2,\ldots} \frac{\|T^n x\|}{\varrho_n} > 0, \quad \inf_{n=1,2,\ldots} \frac{\|T^* x^*\|}{\varrho_n} > 0. \tag{1}$$

For $x \in \mathscr{X}$, put
$$\|x\|_2 = \limsup_{n\to\infty} \frac{\|T^n x\|}{\varrho_n}.$$

On account of (i) and (1) we have that $\| \ \|_2$ is a norm on $\mathscr{X}$, verifying

$$\|x\|_2 \leqslant \|x\|, \quad (x \in \mathscr{X}).$$

Denote by $\mathscr{X}_2$ the Banach space obtained completing $\mathscr{X}$ with respect to the norm $\| \ \|_2$, and by A the linear operator from $\mathscr{X}$ in $\mathscr{X}_2$ corresponding to the natural imbedding of $\mathscr{X}$ into $\mathscr{X}_2$. Obviously A is a quasi-affinity from $\mathscr{X}$ in $\mathscr{X}_2$. We have for all $x \in \mathscr{X}$ and $m \geqslant 1$:

$$\|T^m x\|_2 = \limsup_{n\to\infty} \frac{\|T^{n+m}x\|}{\varrho_n} = \limsup_{n\to\infty} \frac{\|T^{n+m}x\|}{\varrho_{n+m}} \frac{\varrho_{n+m}}{\varrho_n}$$

$$\leqslant Mm^\alpha \limsup_{n\to\infty} \frac{\|T^n x\|}{\varrho_n} = Mm^\alpha \|x\|_2.$$

Thus T can be extended by continuity to an operator T_2 of $\mathscr{X}_2$ verifying

$$\|T_2^m\| \leqslant Mm^\alpha, \quad m = 1, 2, \ldots. \tag{2}$$

Moreover we have for every $x \in \mathscr{H}$ and $m \geqslant 0$,

$$\|x\|_2 = \limsup_{n\to\infty} \frac{\|T^{n+m}x\|}{\varrho_{n+m}} = \limsup_{n\to\infty} \frac{\|T^n T^m x\|}{\varrho_n} \frac{\varrho_n}{\varrho_{n+m}}$$

$$\leqslant \limsup_{n\to\infty} \frac{\|T^n T^m x\|}{\varrho_n} = \|T^m x\|_2 = \|T_2^m x\|_2,$$

since $\varrho_n \leqslant \varrho_{n+m}$ for $m \geqslant 0$. Now $T_2\mathscr{X}_2 \supset T\mathscr{X}$ which is dense in $\mathscr{X}$ [because if not, $T^*x^* = 0$ for a $x^* \neq 0$ and consequently the second relation in (1) would not hold], hence by the continuity of the imbedding, $T_2\mathscr{X}_2$ is dense in $\mathscr{X}_2$; we deduce that T_2^{-1} exists, it belongs to $\mathbf{B}(\mathscr{X}_2)$, and it verifies

$$\|T_2^{-1}\| \leqslant 1. \tag{3}$$

Applying Proposition 1.4 we see by (2) and (3) that T_2 is $C^{[\alpha]+2}(C_1)$-unitary, hence decomposable. Moreover we have obviously

$$XT = T_2 X. \tag{4}$$

Applying the same argument to T^* instead of T, we obtain that

$$T^* = X_*^{-1} T_{*1} X_*,$$

where T_{*1} is a $C^{[\alpha]+2}(C_1)$-unitary operator and X_* a quasi-affinity of $\mathscr{X}^*$ into $\mathscr{X}_{*1}$. Put $\mathscr{X}_1 = \mathscr{X}_{*1}^*$, $X_1 = (X_*)^*$, and $T_1 = (T_{*1})^*$. Then T_1 is also $C^{[\alpha]+2}(C_1)$-unitary, hence decomposable; X_1 is, by Lemma 1.8, also a quasiaffinity from $\mathscr{X}_1$ in $\mathscr{X}$ and

$$X_1T_1 = TX_1. \tag{5}$$

Applying now the Theorem 2.4.5 we deduce that either T has an ultra-invariant nontrivial subspace or $\sigma(T_1)$ reduces to one point $\{c\}$. Since T_1 is generalized unitary, $|c| = 1$, and since moreover $T_1 - cI$ is a generalized scalar operator having the spectrum reduced to $\{0\}$ we have by Lemma 4.3.5, $(T_1 - cI)^n = 0$ for a certain $n \geqslant 1$.

Using (5) we deduce easily

$$(T - cI)^n X_1 = X_1 (T_1 - cI)^n = 0$$

and since $\overline{X_1\mathscr{X}_1} = \mathscr{X}$ we obtain

$$(T - cI)^n = 0 \tag{6}$$

when $n \geqslant 1$. If the smallest integer verifying (6) is $n \geqslant 2$ then putting

$$\mathscr{Y} = \{x|x \in \mathscr{X}, Tx = cx\}$$

we obtain an ultra-invariant subspace of T which is nontrivial. Indeed if $\mathscr{Y} = \mathscr{X}$, then in (6) we may take $n = 1$, contradicting the hypothesis $n \geqslant 2$. If $\mathscr{Y} = \{0\}$, then from (6) we deduce

$$(T - cI)(T - cI)^{n-1} = 0, \quad (T - cI)^{n-1} = 0$$

contradicting the choice of n. Thus if $n \geqslant 2$, T has an ultrainvariant nontrivial subspace. The only case which remains is that when $n = 1$, thus when $T = cI$. This completes the proof.

1.10. COROLLARY. *Let $T \in \mathbf{B}(\mathscr{X})$ be a power bounded* (i.e. $\|T^n\| \leqslant M$, $n = 1, 2, \ldots$) *operator in a reflexive Banach space $\mathscr{X}$, such that neither $\{T^n\}$ nor $\{T^{*n}\}$ converge strongly to 0. Then either T has an ultra-invariant nontrivial subspace or $T = cI$ where $|c| = 1$.*

Indeed take $\varrho_n = 1$ and apply the above theorem.

Let us pass now to the second application. From now on in the whole remainder of this paragraph, $\mathscr{B}$ will denote a Banach (not necessarily commuting) algebra with unit element e and verifying the condition

$$\|b\|^2 \leqslant K\|b^2\|, \quad (b \in \mathscr{B}) \tag{*}$$

for a certain constant K, $1 \leqslant K < \infty$.

1.11. THEOREM. *Let T be an automorphism of $\mathscr{B}$ (i.e. a linear multiplicative one-to-one mapping of $\mathscr{B}$ onto $\mathscr{B}$). Then T is a $C^2(C_1)$-unitary operator satisfying the following multiplicative spectral property:*

For every closed sets $F_1, F_2 \subset C_1$, the set

$$\mathscr{B}_T(F_1) \cdot \mathscr{B}_T(F_2) = \{b_1 b_2 | b_1 \in \mathscr{B}_T(F_1), b_2 \in \mathscr{B}_T(F_2)\}$$

is included in $\mathscr{B}_T(F_1 \cdot F_2)$, where

$$F_1 \cdot F_2 = \{\beta_1 \beta_2 | \beta_1 \in F_1, \beta_2 \in F_2\}.$$

Proof. Obviously for every $k = 0, \pm 1; \pm 2, \ldots$ the mapping T^k (where $T^0 = I$) is also an automorphism of $\mathscr{B}$. Since an automorphism of $\mathscr{B}$ conserves the spectrum of an element $b \in \mathscr{B}$ we have, for every $b \in \mathscr{B}$,

$$\lim_{n\to\infty} \|b^n\|^{1/n} = \sup \{|\lambda| \, |\lambda \in \sigma(b)\} = \sup \{|\lambda| \, |\lambda \in \sigma(T^k b)\}$$
$$= \lim_{n\to\infty} \|(T^k b)^n\|^{1/n}.$$

Or in virtue of (*) we have by an easy computation

$$\|b\| \leqslant K^{1/2+1/2^2+\cdots+1/2^n} \|b^{2^n}\|^{1/2^n},$$

whence the well-known consequence of (*):

$$\|b\| \leqslant K \lim_{n\to\infty} \|b^n\|^{1/n}. \tag{**}$$

Consequently using (**) and the first remark made in the proof, we obtain

$$\|T^k b\| \leqslant K \lim_{n\to\infty} \|(T^k b)^n\|^{1/n} = K \lim_{n\to\infty} \|b^n\|^{1/n} \leqslant K \|b\|,$$

for all $b \in \mathscr{B}$; therefore $T^k \in \mathbf{B}(\mathscr{B})$ and

$$\|T^k\| \leqslant K, \quad (k = 0, \pm 1, \pm 2, \ldots).$$

In virtue of Proposition 1.4, T is a $C^2(C_1)$-unitary operator. In particular, T is a decomposable operator having its spectrum $\sigma(T)$ included in C_1. Thus we may consider the maximal spectral spaces $\mathscr{B}_T(F)$ of T and moreover restrict ourselves only to $F \subset C_1$, so that the multiplicative spectral property which we have still to prove, concerns all maximal spectral spaces of T. Obviously it suffices to prove for all $a, b \in \mathscr{B}$, the following formula:

$$\sigma_T(a \cdot b) \subset \sigma_T(a) \cdot \sigma_T(b) = \{\alpha\beta | \alpha \in \sigma_T(a), \beta \in \sigma_T(b)\}. \tag{1}$$

To this purpose let us remark that for an $a \in \mathscr{B}$, $\sigma(a) \subset C_1$ and that if $\sigma_T(a)$ or $\sigma_T(b)$ coincide with C_1, the inclusion (1) is hence obviously verified. In the same way let us assume that $\sigma_T(a) \neq C_1$ and $\sigma_T(b) \neq C_1$. Then $a_T(\lambda)$ and $b_T(\lambda)$ are the analytical extensions of the functions defined by the power series

$$f(\lambda) = -\sum_{n=0}^{\infty} \lambda^n T^{-n-1} a, \quad g(\lambda) = -\sum_{n=0}^{\infty} \lambda^n T^{-n-1} b$$

for $|\lambda| < 1$. Obviously $\sigma_T(a) \cdot \sigma_T(b) \subset C_1$. If the two sets coincide, then (1) is obviously valid, so that we may suppose that $C_1 \neq \sigma_T(a) \cdot \sigma_T(b)$. Let $\xi \in C_1 \setminus \sigma_T(a) \cdot \sigma_T(b)$, and let ω be an arc of C_1 centered in ξ and disjoint of $\sigma_T(a) \cdot \sigma_T(b)$. We have to show that $\xi \notin \sigma_T(ab)$. To this end, let $h(\lambda)$ be defined by

$$h(\lambda) = -\sum_{n=0}^{\infty} \lambda^n T^{-n-1} (a \cdot b) = -\sum_{n=0}^{\infty} \lambda^n T^{-n-1} a \cdot T^{-n-1} b$$

for $|\lambda| < 1$; for these values of λ we have $h(\lambda) = (ab)_T(\lambda)$. In this way it suffices to prove that $h(\lambda)$ can be analytically extended through ω, since this implies $\omega \subset \varrho_T(ab)$.

We shall need in this last part of the proof the following formula:

$$h(\lambda) = -\frac{1}{2\pi} \int_\Gamma f\left(\frac{1}{\mu}\right) g(\mu\lambda) \frac{d\mu}{\mu}, \tag{2}$$

where $|\lambda| < 1$ and Γ is a simple closed curve surrounding the origin and contained in the ring

$$\left\{\mu \middle| 1 < |\mu| < \frac{1}{|\lambda|}\right\}.$$

The proof of (2) is simple. Indeed, since the series defining $f(1/\mu)$ and $g(\mu\lambda)$ converge uniformly for $\mu \in \Gamma$ (λ and Γ being fixed) we have

$$\frac{1}{2\pi i} \int_\Gamma \left(\sum_{m=0}^{\infty} \frac{T^{-m-1}a}{\mu^m}\right)\left(\sum_{n=0}^{\infty} T^{-n-1} b \mu^n \lambda^n\right) \frac{d\mu}{\mu}$$

$$= \sum_{m=0}^{\infty} \sum_{n=0}^{\infty} \left(\frac{1}{2\pi i} \int_\Gamma \mu^{n-m-1} d\mu\right) \lambda^n T^{-m-1} a \cdot T^{-n-1} b$$

$$= \sum_{m=n=0}^{\infty} \lambda^n T^{-n-1} a \cdot T^{-n-1} b = -h(\lambda).$$

The formula (2) can be also written in the form

$$h(\lambda) = -\frac{1}{2\pi i} \int_{\Gamma} a_T \left(\frac{1}{\mu}\right) b_T(\mu\lambda) \frac{d\mu}{\mu}. \tag{3}$$

Since $b_T(\mu\lambda)$ is as function of μ analytic for $|\mu| < 1/|\lambda|$ we may replace Γ by a system of curves surrounding the origin and $\sigma_T(a)^* = \{\eta = 1/\xi | \xi \in \sigma_T(a)\}$. Let us denote this system by Γ_ε pointing out that

$$\Gamma_\varepsilon \subset \{\lambda | \operatorname{dist}(\lambda, \{0\} \cup \sigma_T(a)^*) \leqslant \varepsilon\}.$$

Denote also by $\omega_{2\varepsilon}$ the set of points λ such that dist $(\lambda, \omega) \leqslant 2\varepsilon$, for $\varepsilon > 0$. We may choose ε so small that $b_T(\mu\lambda)$ be analytic as function of λ and μ for all μ in a neighborhood of Γ_ε and $\lambda \in \omega_{2\varepsilon}$. Indeed in the opposite case we have two sequences of points $\lambda_n \in \omega_{2\varepsilon_n}$ and μ_n such that μ_n is at a distance smaller than ε_n from Γ_{ε_n}, $\lambda_n\mu_n \in \sigma_T(b)$ and $\varepsilon_n \to 0$. We may assume that $\lambda_n \to \lambda_0$, $\mu_n \to \mu_0$. Obviously $\lambda_0\mu_0 \in \sigma_T(b)$, $\mu_0 \in \sigma_T(a)^*$ or $\mu_0 = 0$ and, finally, $\lambda_0 \in \omega$. The case $\mu_0 = 0$ is impossible, so it follows that $\lambda_0 = (\lambda_0\mu_0) \cdot \bar{\mu}_0 \in \sigma_T(b) \cdot \sigma_T(a)$: a contradiction! In this way we have, for a convenient $\varepsilon > 0$, that

$$-\frac{1}{2\pi i} \int_{\Gamma_\varepsilon} a_T \left(\frac{1}{\mu}\right) b_T(\mu\lambda) \frac{d\mu}{\mu}$$

is analytic, as function of λ, for $\lambda \in \omega_{2\varepsilon}$. Now for $\lambda \in \omega_{2\varepsilon} \setminus \omega_\varepsilon$ this function coincides, by (3) and a preceding remark, with $(ab)_T(\lambda)$. This completes our proof.

1.12. *Remark.* If $\mathscr{B} = C(X)$ [or $= L^\infty(S, \Sigma, \mu)$] where X is a compact Hausdorf space [respectively, (S, Σ, μ) is a measure space] and if $Tf(x) = f(\mathscr{T}x)$, where $\mathscr{T}$ is a homomeomorphic mapping of X (respectively an invertible measure preserving the transformation of S) then theorem 1.11 can be directly applied.

2. The Banach Algebra $\mathfrak{A}[\varrho]$

To give classes of $\mathfrak{A}$-unitary operators, larger than those considered in the preceding paragraph, we need to study a certain Banach algebra of functions. To this end, let $\varrho = \{\varrho_n\}_{n \in Z}$ be a sequence of real numbers $\geqslant 1$

verifying

$$\varrho_{n+m} \leqslant \varrho_n \varrho_m, \quad (m, n \in Z) \tag{1}$$

and

$$\lim_{|n| \to \infty} \sqrt[|n|]{\varrho_n} = 1. \tag{2}$$

2.1. Definition. Let $\mathfrak{A}[\varrho]$ be the set of all functions $f: C_1 \to C$ such that

$$f(e^{it}) = \sum_{n \in Z} a_n e^{int}, \quad \sum_{n \in Z} |a_n| \varrho_n < \infty. \tag{3}$$

For $f \in \mathfrak{A}[\varrho]$ put

$$\|f\| = \sum_{n \in Z} |a_n| \varrho_n. \tag{4}$$

Obviously $\mathfrak{A}[\varrho]$ is a linear space with respect to the usual operations of addition and scalar multiplication. It is also obvious that $f \to \|f\|$ is a norm on $\mathfrak{A}[\varrho]$; moreover $\mathfrak{A}[\varrho]$ is a Banach space with respect to this norm.

Actually $\mathfrak{A}[\varrho]$ is *a Banach algebra* if multiplication is defined by the usual multiplication of functions.

Indeed if $f, g \in \mathfrak{A}[\varrho]$, then

$$f(e^{it})\, g(e^{it}) = \sum_{n \in Z} c_n e^{int}, \quad (t \in R)$$

where, for every $n \in Z$,

$$c_n = \sum_{k \in Z} a_{n-k} b_k$$

(a_n and b_n being the Fourier coefficients of f and g, respectively), hence

$$\|fg\| = \sum_{n \in Z} \varrho_n |c_n| \leqslant \sum_{n \in Z} \varrho_{n-k} \varrho_k \sum_{k \in Z} |a_{n-k}| \cdot |b_k|$$

$$= \Big(\sum_{n \in Z} \varrho_n |a_n|\Big) \Big(\sum_{n \in Z} \varrho_n |b_n|\Big) = \|f\| \cdot \|g\|;$$

this shows that $fg \in \mathfrak{A}[\varrho]$ and that

$$\|fg\| \leqslant \|f\| \cdot \|g\|.$$

Denote by Λ the operator defined in $\mathfrak{A}[\varrho]$ by multiplication with the independent variable, i.e.

$$(\Lambda f)(\lambda) = \lambda f(\lambda), \quad (f \in \mathfrak{A}[\varrho]).$$

Evidently

$$(\Lambda^{-1}f)(\lambda) = \lambda^{-1}f = \bar{\lambda}f(\lambda)$$

and

$$(\Lambda^n f)(e^{it}) = e^{int}\sum_{m\in Z} a_m e^{imt} = \sum_{m\in Z} a_m e^{i(n+m)t},$$

hence

$$\|\Lambda^n f\| = \sum_{m\in Z} |a_m|\, \varrho_{n+m} \leqslant \sum_{m\in Z} |a_m|\, \varrho_n\varrho_m = \varrho_n\|f\|,$$

therefore

$$\|\Lambda^n\| \leqslant \varrho_n \quad \text{for any} \quad n\in Z. \tag{5}$$

By (5) and (2) it results that

$$\sigma(\Lambda) \subset C_1. \tag{6}$$

2.2. LEMMA. *The space of maximal ideals of $\mathfrak{A}[\varrho]$ can be identified with C_1. With this identification the Gelfand representation $f \to f\hat{\ }(\xi)$ is given by $f\hat{\ }(\xi) \equiv f(\xi)$, $\xi \in C_1$. Therefore $\mathfrak{A}[\varrho]$ is semisimple.*

Proof. Let $\mathfrak{M}_\varrho$ be the space of maximal ideals of $\mathfrak{A}[\varrho]$ and for every $\xi \in C_1$ set

$$M_\xi = \{f \in \mathfrak{A}[\varrho] \| f(\xi) = 0\}.$$

It is well known that $M_\xi \in \mathfrak{M}_\varrho$ and

$$f\hat{\ }(M_\xi) = f(\xi) \quad \text{for any} \quad f\in \mathfrak{A}[\varrho]. \tag{1}$$

The mapping $\xi \to M_\xi$ $(: C_1 \to \mathfrak{M}_\varrho)$ is *injective*. Indeed, for $\xi, \eta \in C_1$ such that

$$M_\xi = M_\eta$$

we have

$$f\hat{\ }(M_\xi) = f\hat{\ }(M_\eta) \quad \text{for any} \quad f\in \mathfrak{A}[\varrho].$$

In particular for $f = id$ $[id(\mu) = \mu]$, we obtain

$$\xi = id(\xi) = (id)\hat{\ }(M_\xi) = (id)\hat{\ }(M_\eta) = id(\eta) = \eta,$$

which proves our statement.

The mapping $\xi \to M_\xi$ is *surjective*.

For this we need the following result:

$$(id)\hat{\ }(M) \in C_1 \quad \text{for any} \quad M \in \mathfrak{M}_\varrho.$$

Writing

$$(id)^{\wedge}(M) = r\, e^{it},$$

we shall show that $r = 1$. It is clear that

$$r^n = |((id)^{\wedge}(M))^n| = |(id^n)^{\wedge}(M)| \leqslant \|(id)^n\| = \varrho_n,$$

hence

$$r = \lim_{n\to+\infty} \sqrt[n]{r^n} \leqslant \lim_{n\to+\infty} \sqrt[n]{\varrho^n} = 1$$

and

$$\frac{1}{r} = \lim_{n\to+\infty} \sqrt[n]{r^{-n}} \leqslant \lim_{n\to+\infty} \sqrt[n]{\varrho_{-n}} = 1,$$

therefore $r = 1$.

Let now $M \in \mathfrak{M}$ and take $\xi_M = (id)^{\wedge}(M) \in C_1$, then if

$$p(\xi) = \sum_{k=-n}^{n} a_k \xi^k, \quad (\xi \in C_1)$$

we have

$$p(id)^{\wedge}(M_{\xi_M}) = p(\xi_M) = \sum_{k=-n}^{n} a_k \xi_M^k = \sum_{k=-n}^{n} a_k\, ((id)^{\wedge}(M))^k$$

$$= \sum_{k=-n}^{n} a_k\, ((id)^k)^{\wedge}(M) = p(id)^{\wedge}(M).$$

The set of trigonometric polynomials being dense in $\mathfrak{A}[\varrho]$ and the mapping $f \to f^{\wedge}$ being continuous [since $|f^{\wedge}(M)| \leqslant \|f\|$ for any $M \in \mathfrak{M}_\varrho$] it follows that the above equality holds also for any $f \in \mathfrak{A}[\varrho]$, i.e.

$$f^{\wedge}(M_{\xi_M}) = f^{\wedge}(M),$$

therefore

$$M_{\xi_M} = M.$$

This shows that the mapping of ξ is onto M_ξ. Therefore $\xi \to M_\xi$ is bijective and its inverse is the mapping

$$M \to (id)^{\wedge}(M) = \xi_M.$$

It is well known that if $\mathfrak{A}$ is a commutative Banach algebra with unit and $\mathfrak{M}$ the space of its maximal ideals, then the function $x^{\wedge} : \mathfrak{M} \to C$ (the Gelfand transform of x) is continuous for any $x \in \mathfrak{A}$. Therefore the function $M \to \xi_M$ is continuous, hence bicontinuous because it is bijective, its domain of definition $\mathfrak{M}_\varrho$ is compact, and its range is separate. Identifying M_ξ with ξ we can write [by (1)]

$$f^{\wedge}(\xi) = f(\xi). \tag{2}$$

For every f in the radical of $\mathfrak{A}[\varrho]$, we have

$$\sup_{\xi \in C_1} |f(\xi)| = \sup_{\xi \in \mathfrak{M}_\varrho} |f^{\wedge}(\xi)| = \lim_{n \to \infty} \sqrt[n]{\|f^n\|} = 0,$$

hence $f = 0$. Thus $\mathfrak{A}[\varrho]$ is a semisimple algebra.

2.3. COROLLARY. *We have* $\sigma(\Lambda) = C_1$.

Proof. Let $\xi \in C_1 \cap \varrho(\Lambda)$. Then putting

$$f(\lambda) = R(\xi, \Lambda)\, 1(\lambda), \quad [1(\lambda) = 1],$$

we have

$$(\xi - id) f(\lambda) = (\xi I - \Lambda) f(\lambda) = 1(\lambda),$$

hence $R(\xi, id)$ exists as element of $\mathfrak{A}[\varrho]$, therefore $C_1 \cap \varrho(\Lambda) \subset \varrho\,(id)$, i.e.

$$\sigma\,(id) \subset \sigma(\Lambda) \cup \mathbf{C}(C_1).$$

The spectrum of *id* (as element of $\mathfrak{A}[\varrho]$) is given by

$$\sigma\,(id) = (id)^{\wedge}\,(\mathfrak{M})_\varrho = (id)^{\wedge}\,(C_1) = id\,(C_1) = C_1,$$

hence

$$C_1 \subset \sigma(\Lambda);$$

but $\sigma(\Lambda) \subset C_1$ [see relation (6) from beginning of this paragraph] therefore

$$\sigma(\Lambda) = C_1.$$

For any closed set $F \subset C_1$ we put

$$\mathfrak{A}_F = \{f \in \mathfrak{A}[\varrho]\ |\mathrm{supp}\,(f) \subset F\}$$

and

$$\Lambda_F = \Lambda | \mathfrak{A}_F.$$

Evidently $\mathfrak{A}_F$ is a closed ideal invariant with respect to Λ. With these notations, we have the following result:

2.4. PROPOSITION. *If $\mathfrak{A}[\varrho]$ is a regular algebra, then*

$$\sigma(\Lambda_F) \subset F.$$

Proof. Firstly we remark that if $f, g \in \mathfrak{A}[\varrho]$

$$g(\lambda) = \sum_{n \in Z} c_n \lambda^n, \quad (\lambda \in C_1),$$

then

$$(g(\Lambda)f)(\lambda) = \sum_{n \in Z} c_n (\Lambda^n f)(\lambda) = \sum_{n \in Z} c_n \lambda^n f(\lambda)$$

$$= \Big(\sum_{n \in Z} c_n \lambda^n\Big) f(\lambda) = g(\lambda) f(\lambda). \tag{1}$$

Denote by $\mathbf{B}_F$ the commutative Banach algebra generated in $\mathbf{B}(\mathfrak{A}_F)$ by the set

$$\{f(\Lambda_F) | f \in \mathfrak{A}[\varrho]\}.$$

The spectrum of Λ_F as element of $\mathbf{B}_F$ coincides with the spectrum of Λ_F considered as operator on $\mathfrak{A}_F$, therefore

$$\hat{\Lambda_F}(M) \in \hat{\Lambda_F}(\mathfrak{M}_F) = \sigma(\Lambda_F) \subset \sigma(\Lambda) = C_1$$

for any $M \in \mathfrak{M}_F$ (= the space of maximal ideals of $\mathbf{B}_F$).

If we put

$$\xi_M = \hat{\Lambda_F}(M), \quad (M \in \mathfrak{M}_F),$$

then for any polynomial

$$p(\lambda) = \sum_{k=-n}^{n} a_k \lambda^k, \quad (\lambda \in C_1)$$

we have

$$p(\xi_M) = \sum_{k=-n}^{n} a_k (\hat{\Lambda_F^k}(M))^k = p(\Lambda_F)\hat{\ }(M),$$

hence by continuity

$$f(\xi_M) = f(\Lambda_F)\hat{\ }(M) \quad \text{for any} \quad f \in \mathfrak{A}[\varrho]. \tag{2}$$

The mapping $M \to \xi_M (: \mathfrak{M}_F \to C_1)$ is *injective*. Indeed, in the case that $M_1, M_2 \in \mathfrak{M}_F$ such that

$$\xi_{M_1} = \xi_{M_2},$$

then by (2)

$$f(\Lambda_F)\hat{\ }(M_1) = f(\xi_{M_1}) = f(\xi_{M_2}) = f(\Lambda_F)\hat{\ }(M_2) \quad \text{for any} \quad f \in \mathfrak{A}[\varrho],$$

and by continuity

$$T^{\wedge}(M_1) = T^{\wedge}(M_2) \quad \text{for any} \quad T \in \mathbf{B}_F. \tag{3}$$

As the set of the Gelfand transforms of a commutative Banach algebra with unit separates the space of its maximal ideals, from (3) we get $M_1 = M_2$.

$\Lambda_f^{\wedge}: \mathfrak{M}_F \to C_1$ being an injective and continuous mapping from a compact space into a separate (Hausdorff) space, it is bicontinuous. Thus we may identify $\mathfrak{M}_F$ with a closed subset of C_1, hence by (2)

$$f(\Lambda_F)^{\wedge}(\xi) = f(\xi), \quad (\xi \in \mathfrak{M}_F, f \in \mathfrak{A}[\varrho]). \tag{4}$$

On the other hand

$$\sigma(\Lambda_F) = \Lambda_F^{\wedge}(\mathfrak{M}_F) = \mathfrak{M}_F, \tag{5}$$

where on the right $\mathfrak{M}_F$ is considered a subset of C_1.

Since $\mathfrak{A}[\varrho]$ is regular, for every $\mu \notin F$ there exists a $g \in \mathfrak{A}[\varrho]$ such that

$$g(\mu) \neq 0 \quad \text{and}$$

$$g(\xi) = 0 \quad \text{for any} \quad \xi \in F,$$

hence $\operatorname{supp}(g) \cap F = \varnothing$, therefore

$$\operatorname{supp}(g) \cap \operatorname{supp}(f) = \varnothing \quad \text{for any} \quad f \in \mathfrak{A}_F,$$

whence

$$g(\Lambda_F)f = gf = 0 \quad \text{for any} \quad f \in \mathfrak{A}_F,$$

i.e.

$$g(\Lambda_F) = 0. \tag{6}$$

From (4), (5), and (6) it results that

$$g(\xi) = 0 \quad \text{for any} \quad \xi \in \sigma(\Lambda_F),$$

hence [by $g(\mu) \neq 0$] $\mu \notin \sigma(\Lambda_F)$. In this manner

$$\sigma(\Lambda_F) \subset F.$$

2.5. LEMMA. *The operator Λ has the single-valued extension property, and*

$$\operatorname{supp}(f) \subset \sigma_\Lambda(f).$$

Proof: The spectrum of Λ being a nowhere dense set of C [since $\sigma(\Lambda) \subset C_1$] it results immediately (see for instance Ref. 28, § 4, Lemma 1) that Λ has the single-valued extension property.

For every $f \in \mathfrak{A}[\varrho]$ let $\tilde{f}: \varrho_\Lambda(f) \to \mathfrak{A}[\varrho]$ be the unique analytic extension of the resolvent of Λ, that is

$$(\xi I - \Lambda)\tilde{f}(\xi) \equiv f \quad \text{on} \quad \varrho_\Lambda(f),$$

hence

$$(\xi - \lambda)\tilde{f}(\xi)(\lambda) = ((\xi I - \Lambda)\tilde{f}(\xi))(\lambda) = f(\lambda), \quad (\lambda \in C_1, \xi \in \varrho_\Lambda(f)),$$

whence, for $\xi = \lambda \in \varrho_\Lambda(f) \cap C_1$, it results that $f(\lambda) = 0$, hence

$$\operatorname{supp}(f) \subset \sigma_\Lambda(f) \cup (C \setminus C_1),$$

but $\operatorname{supp}(f) \subset C_1$, therefore

$$\operatorname{supp}(f) \subset \sigma_\Lambda(f).$$

2.6. Proposition. *If the algebra $\mathfrak{A}[\varrho]$ is topologically admissible, then there exists a continuous $\mathfrak{A}[\varrho]$-spectral function* **U** *such that*

$$\mathbf{U}_\lambda = \Lambda,$$

i.e. Λ is an $\mathfrak{A}[\varrho]$-unitary operator.

Proof. Define $\mathbf{U}: \mathfrak{A}[\varrho] \to \mathbf{B}(\mathfrak{A}[\varrho])$ by

$$\mathbf{U}_g = g(\Lambda) = \sum_{n \in Z} a_n \Lambda^n$$

for

$$g(\lambda) = \sum_{n \in Z} a_n \lambda^n.$$

We have seen [relation (5) at the beginning of this paragraph] that

$$\|\Lambda^n\| \leqslant \varrho_n \quad \text{for all} \quad n \in Z,$$

therefore

$$\|\mathbf{U}_g\| \leqslant \sum_{n \in Z} |a_n| \cdot \|\Lambda^n\| \leqslant \sum_{n \in Z} |a_n| \cdot \varrho_n = \|g\|,$$

hence $\mathbf{U}_g$ is well defined and $\mathbf{U}$ is continuous.

Since $g(\Lambda)f = gf$ (see proof of Proposition 2.3), it is clear that $\mathbf{U}$ is an algebraic homomorphism, and

$$\mathbf{U}_\lambda = \Lambda.$$

2.7. THEOREM. *The following three propositions are equivalent:*
(i) $\mathfrak{A}[\varrho]$ *is topologically admissible,*
(ii) Λ *is a decomposable operator,*
(iii) $\mathfrak{A}[\varrho]$ *is regular as Banach algebra.*

Proof:

(i) $\Rightarrow$ (ii) Evidently, since for every admissible algebra $\mathfrak{A}$, all $\mathfrak{A}$-scalar operators are decomposable (see Theorem 3.1.16).

(ii) $\Rightarrow$ (iii) Let $F \subset C_1$ be a closed set and $\lambda_0 \in C_1 \setminus F$, then there exists an open G such that $F \subset G \subset \bar{G} \not\ni \lambda_0$. Putting $G_0 = \complement F$ we obtain an open covering $\{G, G_0\}$ of C_1, therefore (since Λ is decomposable) there exist two spectral maximal spaces, $\mathscr{Y}$, $\mathscr{Y}_0$ of $\mathfrak{A}[\varrho]$ such that

$$\sigma(\Lambda|\mathscr{Y}) \subset G, \quad \sigma(\Lambda|\mathscr{Y}_0) \subset G_0, \tag{1}$$

and

$$\mathfrak{A}[\varrho] = \mathscr{Y} + \mathscr{Y}_0. \tag{2}$$

Since $1 \in \mathfrak{A}[\varrho]$, from (2) it results that there exist $f \in \mathscr{Y}$ and $f_0 \in \mathscr{Y}_0$ such that

$$1 = f + f_0. \tag{3}$$

But

$$\mathscr{Y} = \mathfrak{A}[\varrho]_\Lambda(\sigma(\Lambda|\mathscr{Y})),$$

$$\mathscr{Y}_0 = \mathfrak{A}[\varrho]_\Lambda(\sigma(\Lambda|\mathscr{Y}_0)),$$

hence using Lemma 2.5 we get

$$\operatorname{supp}(f) \subset \sigma_\Lambda(f) = \sigma_{\Lambda|\mathscr{Y}}(f) \subset \sigma(\Lambda|\mathscr{Y}) \subset G \tag{4}$$

and analogously

$$\operatorname{supp}(f_0) \subset G_0. \tag{5}$$

Since $F \cap G_0 = \emptyset$, from (5) it results that

$$f_0(\lambda) = 0 \quad \text{for every} \quad \lambda \in F.$$

As $\lambda_0 \in G_0$ and $\lambda_0 \notin G$, from (3) and (4) we get

$$1 = f(\lambda_0) + f_0(\lambda_0) = f_0(\lambda_0).$$

Thus for every closed set $F \subset C_1 = \mathfrak{M}(\mathfrak{A}[\varrho])$ and every $\lambda_0 \in C_1 \setminus F$ there exists a function $f \in \mathfrak{A}[\varrho]$ with

$$f_0(\lambda_0) \neq 0$$

and

$$f_0|F = 0,$$

that is the semisimple algebra $\mathfrak{A}[\varrho]$ is regular.

(iii) ⇒ (i). Condition (i) from Definition 3.5.1 is evidently satisfied.

Since every regular Banach algebra is normal (Ref. 91, § 15, No. 4, Corollary to Theorem 7), also condition (ii) is verified from the same definition.

Denoting by $\mathcal{T}$ the topology of $\mathfrak{A}[\varrho]$ given by the norm

$$\|f\| = \sum_{n \in \mathbf{Z}} |a_n| \varrho_n, \quad (f(\lambda) = \sum_{n \in \mathbf{Z}} a_n \lambda^n)$$

from the inequality

$$|f(\lambda)| \leqslant \sum_{n \in \mathbf{Z}} |a_n| \leqslant \sum_{n \in \mathbf{Z}} |a_n| \varrho_n = \|f\|, \quad (\lambda \in C_1)$$

it results that the topology $\mathcal{T}$ is stronger than the pointwise convergence topology on C_1. On the other hand $\mathfrak{A}[\varrho]$ is $\mathcal{T}$-complete, therefore by Remark 3.5.2(b) condition (iii) of Definition 3.5.1 is verified.

Let $f \in \mathfrak{A}[\varrho]$ and put $F = \operatorname{supp}(f)$. Then by Proposition 2.4 $\sigma(\Lambda_F) \subset F$, hence

$$(\xi I - \Lambda_F)^{-1}$$

exists and is bounded on $\mathfrak{A}_F$ for every $\xi \notin F$, therefore

$$g_\xi = (\xi I - \Lambda_F)^{-1} f \in \mathfrak{A}_F \subset \mathfrak{A}[\varrho]$$

exists for every $\xi \notin F$, being a vector-valued analytic function of ξ. Moreover, we have

$$f(\lambda) = ((\xi I - \Lambda_F)\, g_\xi)\, (\lambda) = (\xi - \lambda)\, g_\xi(\lambda),$$

consequently

$$g_\xi(\lambda) = f(\lambda)/(\xi - \lambda) \quad \text{for} \quad \lambda \in C_1 \setminus \{\xi\}.$$

Since $\xi \notin \text{supp}(f)$ there is a neighborhood V of ξ such that $V \cap \text{supp}(f) = \emptyset$. We have $g_\xi(\lambda) = 0$ for $\xi \neq \lambda \in V \cap C_1$, thus, since $g_\xi(\lambda)$ is continuous as function of λ we must have also $g_\xi(\xi) = 0$. Thus $g_\xi(\lambda)$ coincides with the function $f_\xi(\lambda)$ as defined in the condition (iv) in the Definition 3.5.1 of a topologically admissible algebra.

2.8. *Remark. In the hypothesis of the preceding theorem, for every $f \in \mathfrak{A}[\varrho]$ we have*

$$\sigma_\Lambda(f) = \text{supp}(f).$$

Since in what follows we shall not use this fact, we let its proof to the reader as an exercise. Hint: use the fact that $\xi \to f_\xi$ is the analytic extension of $\xi \to R(\xi, \Lambda) f$ for $|\xi| \neq 1$.

2.9. COROLLARY. *If $\mathfrak{A}[\varrho]$ is regular, then there exists $\mathfrak{A}[\varrho]$-unitary operators.*

Namely, Λ.

The effectiveness of Theorem 2.7 is due to the fact that there exists a concrete sufficient condition for the regularity of $\mathfrak{A}[\varrho]$.

Such a condition, which in a certain sense is also necessary, is here given.

2.10. LEMMA. *If the sequence $\{\varrho_n\}_{n \in Z}$ verifies the Beurling's* condition

$$\text{(B)} \qquad \sum_{n \in Z} \frac{\log \varrho_n}{1 + n^2} < \infty,$$

then for every $\varepsilon \in (0, \pi)$ there exists a function $f: (-\pi, \pi) \to C$ such that

$$f(x) = \sum_{n \in Z} a_n e^{inx},$$

$$f(0) \neq 0, \quad f(x) = 0 \quad \textit{for} \quad |x| \geqslant \varepsilon$$

and

$$|a_n| \leqslant M/\varrho^n, \quad \left(M = \sqrt{\pi/2}, \quad n \in Z\right).$$

Proof. Define the function $\varphi : R \to R$ by

$$\varphi(x) = \frac{1}{\varrho_n (1 + x^2)} \quad \text{if} \quad x \in \left(n - \frac{1}{2}, n + \frac{1}{2}\right), \; (n \in Z)$$

whence

$$\varphi(x) \leqslant 1/(1 + x^2),$$

therefore $\varphi \in L^2(R)$ (R = the real line) and

$$\int_{-\infty}^{\infty} \frac{|\log \varphi(x)|}{1 + x^2}\, dx \leqslant \sum_{n \in Z} \int_{n-1/2}^{n+1/2} \frac{\log \varrho_n}{1 + x^2}\, dx + \sum_{n \in Z} \int_{n-1/2}^{n+1/2} \frac{\log (1 + x^2)}{1 + x^2}\, dx$$

$$\leqslant \int_{-\infty}^{\infty} \frac{\log (1 + x^2)}{1 + x^2}\, dx + \sum_{n \in Z} \frac{\log \varrho_n}{1 + n^2} \max \left\{(1 + n^2) \int_{n-1/2}^{n+1/2} \frac{dx}{1 + x^2}\right\}$$

$$\leqslant M_1 + M_2 \max_{n \in Z} \left\{(1 + n^2) \int_{n-1/2}^{n+1/2} \frac{dx}{1 + x^2}\right\} = M_1 + M_3 < \infty.$$

In this manner we may apply Theorem XII of the classical monograph[94] of Paley and Wiener. Thus there exists a function $F \in L^2(R)$ such that

$$F(x) = 0 \quad \text{for} \quad x \geqslant 0$$

and its Fourier transform $\hat{F}$ verifies

$$|\hat{F}(x)| = \varphi(x) \quad \text{a.e.}$$

F being the inverse Fourier transform of $\hat{F} \in L^1(R)$, and since $\varphi \in L^1(R)$ it results that F is continuous. On the other hand $F(x) \not\equiv 0$ since $\hat{F}(x) \not\equiv 0$ a.e. Thus there exists an $\alpha < 0$ such that

$$\alpha = \sup \{x | x \in \operatorname{supp}(F)\},$$

and hence there exists also a $\beta > \alpha - \varepsilon$ with $F(\beta) \neq 0$.

Denoting by $F_1 : R \to C$ the function defined by

$$F_1(x) = F(x + \beta), \quad (x \in R),$$

we obtain

$$F_1(0) \neq 0, \quad F_1(x) = 0 \quad \text{for} \quad x \geqslant \varepsilon$$

and

$$\hat{F}_1(x) = \frac{1}{\sqrt{2\pi}} \int_{-\infty}^{\infty} e^{-ixy} F_1(y)\, dy = \frac{1}{\sqrt{2\pi}} \int_{-\infty}^{\infty} e^{-ixy} F(y + \beta)\, dy$$

$$= e^{ix\beta} \frac{1}{\sqrt{2\pi}} \int_{-\infty}^{\infty} e^{-ixt} F(t)\, dt = e^{ix\beta} \hat{F}(x),$$

hence

$$|\hat{F}_1(x)| = \varphi(x), \quad (x \in R).$$

Apply now the same argument to the function $\psi(x) = \varphi(-x)$ $(x \in R)$ and let Φ_1 be the functions corresponding to ψ as F_1 corresponds to φ. Put $F_2(x) = \Phi(-x)$ $(x \in R)$. Then

$$F_2(0) \neq 0, \quad F_2(x) = 0 \quad \text{for} \quad x \leqslant -\varepsilon$$

and

$$\hat{F}_2(x) = \frac{1}{\sqrt{2\pi}} \int_{-\infty}^{\infty} e^{-ixy} F(-y)\, dy = \hat{\Phi}_1(-x),$$

thus

$$|\hat{F}_2(x)| = \varphi(x).$$

Let $H(x) = F_1(x)\, F_2(x)$. Then

$$H(0) \neq 0, \quad H(x) = 0 \quad \text{for} \quad |x| \geqslant \varepsilon.$$

Moreover, for the Fourier transform $\hat{H}$ of H we have

$$\hat{H}(x) = (\hat{F}_1 * \hat{F}_2)(x) = \int_{-\infty}^{\infty} F_1(x - y)\, F_2(y)\, dy,$$

thus

$$|\hat{H}(n)| \leqq \int_{-\infty}^{\infty} |\hat{F}_1(n - y)| \cdot |\hat{F}_2(y)|\, dy$$

$$\leqq \sum_{m \in Z} \int_{m-1/2}^{m+1/2} \frac{dy}{\varrho_{n-m} \varrho_m [1 + (x - y)^2](1 + y^2)}$$

$$= \sum_{m \in Z} \frac{1}{\varrho_{n-m} \varrho_m} \int_{m-1/2}^{m+1/2} \frac{dy}{[1 + (x - y)^2](1 + y^2)}$$

$$\leqq \frac{1}{\varrho_n} \int_{-\infty}^{\infty} \frac{dy}{[1 + (x - y)^2](1 + y^2)}$$

$$\leqslant \frac{1}{\varrho_n} \int_{-\infty}^{\infty} \frac{dy}{1 + y^2} = \frac{\pi}{\varrho_n}.$$

Or putting

$$f(x) = H(x) \quad \text{for} \quad |x| < \pi,$$

we have for the Fourier coefficients of f:

$$|a_n| = \left|\frac{1}{2\pi}\int_{-\pi}^{\pi} e^{-inx} f(x)\, dx\right| = \left|\frac{1}{2\pi}\int_{-\infty}^{\infty} e^{-inx} H(x)\, dx\right| = \frac{1}{\sqrt{2\pi}} |\hat{H}(n)|$$

$$\leqslant \sqrt{\frac{\pi}{2}} \cdot \frac{1}{\varrho_n}$$

and this completes the proof.

2.11. Lemma. *In the same conditions as in the preceding lemma, for every* $\eta \in (0, \pi)$ *there exists a function* $f: (-\pi, \pi) \to 0$ *such that*

$$f(x) = \sum_{n \in Z} a_n e^{inx},$$

$$f(0) \neq 0, \quad f(x) = 0 \quad for \quad |x| \geqslant \eta$$

and

$$\sum_{n \in Z} |a_n| \varrho_n < \infty.$$

Proof. Take in the preceding lemma $\varepsilon = \eta/2$ and denote by g the function whose existence is assured by this lemma. Let h be an infinitely differentiable function defined on the real line and having the following properties:

$$h(x) \geqslant 0 \quad \text{for all} \quad x \in R,$$

$$h(x) = 0 \quad \text{for} \quad 1 \leqslant |x| < \infty,$$

and

$$\int_{-\pi}^{\pi} h(x)\, dx = 1.$$

For every $\delta > 0$ we put $h_\delta(k) = 1/\delta\, h\,(x/\delta)$ and

$$g_\delta(x) = \int_{-\pi}^{\pi} g(x)\, h_\delta\,(x - y)\, dy.$$

Then

$$g_\delta(x) = 0 \quad \text{for} \quad |x| \geqslant \varepsilon + \delta = \eta/2 + \delta$$

and

$$\lim_{\delta \to 0} g_\delta(x) = g(x).$$

Thus for δ small enough $g_\delta(0) \neq 0$, and $g_\delta(x) = 0$ for $|x| \geqslant \eta$. Putting $f(x) = g_\delta(x)$ for such a small $\delta > 0$, and denoting by $a_n(f)$, $a_n(g)$, and $a_n(h_\delta)$ the nth Fourier coefficient of f, g, and h_δ respectively, we obtain

$$|a_n(f)| = |a_n(g)|\,|a_n(h_\delta)| \leqslant \frac{M}{\varrho_n}\frac{M_1}{n^2+1},$$

since h_δ is infinitely differentiable and therefore

$$|a_n(h_\delta)| = O\,(1/|n|^k) \quad \text{for all} \quad k \geqslant 1$$

(this is obtained integrating by parts). This completes the proof.

2.12. THEOREM. *If the sequence* $\{\varrho_n\}_{n\in Z}$, *with the properties* (1) *and* (2) *stated at the beginning of this paragraph, verifies the Beurling's condition*

$$\text{(B)} \qquad \sum_{n\in Z} \frac{\log \varrho_n}{1+n^2} < \infty,$$

then the Banach algebra $\mathfrak{A}[\varrho]$ *is regular.*

Proof. We recall that $\mathfrak{A}[\varrho]$ is a set of functions

$$f(x) = f_1(e^{ix}) = \sum_{n\in Z} a_n\, e^{inx}, \quad (x \in R)$$

such that

$$\|f\| = \sum_{n\in Z} |a_n|\, \varrho_n < \infty.$$

Let $F \subset C_1 = \{\lambda \in C \,|\, |\lambda| = 1\}$ be any closed set, and let $e^{ix_0} \notin F$. There exists an $\eta \in (0, \pi)$ such that

$$e^{i(x-x_0)} \notin F \quad \text{for every} \quad |x - x_0| < \eta. \tag{1}$$

Let

$$f(x) = f_1(e^{ix}) = \sum_{n\in Z} a_n\, e^{inx}, \quad (x \in R)$$

be the function constructed in Lemma 2.11. This function verifies $f(0) \neq 0$ and $f(x) = 0$ for $|x| \geqslant \eta$. Therefore, if we put

$$g(x) = f_1(x - x_0) = \sum_{n\in Z} a_n\, e^{-inx_0}\, e^{inx}$$

it results that $g \in \mathfrak{A}[\varrho]$ and

$$g(x_0) = f(0) \neq 0, \quad g(x) = f\,(x - x_0) = 0 \quad \text{for} \quad |x - x_0| \geqslant \eta. \tag{2}$$

From (1), it results that $e^{i(x-x_0)} \in F$ implies $|x - x_0| \geqslant \eta$, hence by (2)

$$g_1(e^{i(x-x_0)}) = g(x) = 0 \quad \text{for every} \quad e^{i(x-x_0)} \in F.$$

Thus $\mathfrak{A}[\varrho]$ is regular.

3. $\mathfrak{A}$-unitary Operators; the $\mathfrak{A}_T$-unitary Operators

Let $\mathscr{X}$ be a Banach space and $T \in \mathbf{B}(\mathscr{X})$ such that $\sigma(T) \subset C_1$. Put

$$\varrho_n = \|T^n\|, \quad (n \in Z). \tag{1}$$

Then $\varrho = \{\varrho_n\}_{n \in Z}$ verifies the conditions (1) and (2) at the beginning of paragraph 2. Thus we may consider the algebra $\mathfrak{A}[\varrho]$; this algebra will be denoted by $\mathfrak{A}_T$.

For $f \in \mathfrak{A}_T$,

$$f(e^{it}) = \sum_{n \in Z} a_n e^{int},$$

et us put

$$\mathbf{U}_f = \sum_{n \in Z} a_n T^n.$$

It is an easy matter to verify that $f \to \mathbf{U}_f$ is a continuous algebraic homomorphism of $\mathfrak{A}_T$ into $\mathbf{B}(\mathscr{X})$. It is also obvious that

$$\mathbf{U}_1 = I, \quad \mathbf{U}_\lambda = T.$$

Thus by Theorem 2.7 we obtain the following basic fact:

3.1. THEOREM. *Let $T \in \mathbf{B}(\mathscr{H})$ be such that $\sigma(T) \subset C_1$. If the Banach algebra $\mathfrak{A}_T$ is regular, then T is $\mathfrak{A}_T$-unitary.*

From Theorem 2.12 and the preceding theorem we obtain the following more precise result:

3.2. THEOREM. *Let $T \in \mathbf{B}(\mathscr{X})$ be such that $\sigma(T) \subset C_1$. If T verifies*

$$\sum_{n \in Z} \frac{\log \|T^n\|}{1 + n^2} < \infty,$$

then T is $\mathfrak{A}_T$-unitary, In particular T is decomposable.

3.3. COROLLARY. *Let $T \in \mathbf{B}(\mathscr{X})$ be such that $\sigma(T) \subset C_1$ and that*

$$\sum_{n \in Z} \frac{\log \|T^n\|}{1 + n^2} < \infty.$$

If $\sigma(T)$ is not reduced to a single point, then T has nontrivial spectral maximal spaces; consequently T has nontrivial ultra-invariant subspaces in $\mathscr{X}$.

3.4. *Remark. Let $T \in \mathbf{B}(\mathscr{X})$ be such that there exists an $\alpha \geqslant 0$ for which*

$$\|T^n\| = O(|n|^\alpha), \quad (n \in Z, |n| \to \infty).$$

Then T is $\mathfrak{A}_T$-unitary.

Indeed,

$$\sum_{n \in Z} \frac{\log \|T^n\|}{1 + n^2} \leqslant M_1 \sum_{n \in Z} \frac{1}{1 + n^2} + M_2 \sum_{n \in Z} \frac{\log |n|}{1 + n^2} < \infty .$$

It is very useful to replace condition (1) of Proposition 1.6 with another growth condition on the resolvent of T. For this purpose we give the following

3.5. Proposition. *Let T be an operator in $\mathscr{X}$ having the spectrum $\sigma(T)$ on the unit circle $\{\lambda | \, |\lambda| = 1\}$, and verifying the following growth relation*

$$\|R(\lambda; T)\| \leqslant M \exp K \big| |\lambda| - 1 \big|^{-\beta}, \quad (|\lambda| \neq 1) \tag{1}$$

for a certain $\beta > 0$; here $0 < M < \infty$, $0 < K < \infty$ are constants. Then

$$\|T^n\| \leqslant M_1 \exp [K_1 |n|^{1 - 1/(1 + \beta)}], \quad (n \in Z), \tag{2}$$

where $0 < M_1 < \infty$, $0 < K_1 < \infty$ are some other constants.

Proof; Let $r > 1$. Then for $n \geqslant 0$ we have

$$T^n = \frac{1}{2\pi i} \int_{|\lambda| = r} \lambda^n R(\lambda; T) \, d\lambda \tag{3}$$

so that by (1)

$$\|T^n\| \leqslant r^{n+1} M \exp [K (r - 1)^{-\beta}],$$

whence, putting $r = 1 + 1/n^\alpha$, we obtain

$$\|T^n\| \leqslant M (1 + 1/n^\alpha)^{n+1} \exp (K n^{\alpha\beta}) \leqslant M_1 \exp (n^{1-\alpha} + K n^{\alpha\beta}).$$

Taking $\alpha = 1/(1 + \beta)$ we obtain directly (2) with $K_1 = 1 + K$ and $n \geqslant 0$. The case $n \leqslant 0$ is deduced in a similar manner.

As an immediate corollary of the preceding proposition and Theorem 3.2 we have the following useful

3.6. THEOREM. *Let* $T \in \mathbf{B}(\mathscr{X})$ *have the spectrum* $\sigma(T)$ *included in the unit circle and verify*

$$\|R(\lambda; T)\| \leqslant M \exp\left(K\big||\lambda| - 1\big|^{-\beta}\right), \quad (|\lambda| \neq 1)$$

for certain $0 < \beta < \infty$, $0 < M < \infty$, $0 < K < \infty$. *Then* T *is an* $\mathfrak{A}_T$*-unitary operator.*

Proof; By the preceding theorem we have

$$\|T^n\| \leqslant M_1 \exp\left[K_1 |n|^{1-1/(1+\beta)}\right], \quad (n \in Z)$$

whence

$$\sum_{n \in Z} \frac{\log \|T^n\|}{1 + n^2} \leqslant M_1 \sum_{n \in Z} \frac{1}{1 + n^2} + K_1 \sum_{n \in Z} \frac{n^{1-1/(\beta+1)}}{1 + n^2} < \infty,$$

therefore by Theorem 3.2, T is $\mathfrak{A}_T$-unitary.

4. $\mathfrak{A}$-self-adjoint Operators

In analogy with the $\mathfrak{A}$-unitary operators we can make the following

4.1. DEFINITION. An operator $T \in \mathbf{B}(\mathscr{X})$ is called $\mathfrak{A}$*-self-adjoint* if it is an $\mathfrak{A}$-scalar operator for an admissible algebra formed by functions defined on the real line R.

Obviously, if T is $\mathfrak{A}$-self-adjoint then it is decomposable and

$$\sigma(T) \subset R.$$

The study of the $\mathfrak{A}$-self-adjoint operators can be reduced to that of the $\mathfrak{A}$-unitary operators by the following

4.2. PROPOSITION. *Let* $T \in \mathbf{B}(\mathscr{X})$ *and let* $r > \|T\|$. *Then* T *is an* $\mathfrak{A}$*-self-adjoint operator if and only if its Cayley transform*

$$S_r = (T - irI)(T + irI)^{-1}$$

is an $\mathfrak{A}$*-unitary operator.* (Note that the two admissible algebras corresponding to T and S_r are different.)

Proof. Suppose that S_r is an $\mathfrak{A}$-unitary operator for a certain admissible algebra $\mathfrak{A}_{C_1}$ of functions defined on C_1. Let $\mathfrak{A}_R$ be the algebra of functions $f(\varrho)$ defined on R which are for $|\varrho| \leqslant \|T\| + 1$ of the form

$$f(\varrho) = \varphi_f\left(\frac{\varrho - ir}{\varrho + ir}\right), \quad \text{with} \quad \varphi_f(\lambda) \in \mathfrak{A}_{C_1}. \tag{1}$$

It is obvious that $\mathfrak{A}_R$ is normal and that $f(\varrho) \equiv 1$ belongs to $\mathfrak{A}_R$. Let now $\varphi(\lambda) \in \mathfrak{A}_{C_1}$ be equal to 1 for λ on an open arc of C_1 containing the arc α obtained from $[-1- \|T\|, \|T\| + 1] \subset R$ by the transformation

$$\varrho \to \frac{\varrho - ir}{\varrho + ir}$$

and equal to 0 in a neighborhood of $\lambda = 1$. Since $\mathfrak{A}_{C_1}$ is admissible and $\lambda = 1 \notin \operatorname{supp}(\varphi)$ we have that

$$\varphi_1(\lambda) = \begin{cases} \dfrac{\varphi(\lambda)}{1 - \lambda} & \text{if} \quad \lambda \in \operatorname{supp}(\varphi), \\ 0 & \text{if} \quad \lambda \notin \operatorname{supp}(\varphi), \end{cases}$$

belongs to $\mathfrak{A}_{C_1}$; consequently $\psi(\lambda) = ir\,(1 + \lambda)\,\varphi_1(\lambda) \in \mathfrak{A}_{C_1}$ too. We have obviously

$$\varrho \equiv \psi\left(\frac{\varrho - ir}{\varrho + ir}\right) \quad \text{for all} \quad |\varrho| \leqslant \|T\| + 1, \tag{2}$$

so that the function $f(\varrho) \equiv \varrho$ belongs to $\mathfrak{A}_R$. It remains to prove that if $f \in \mathfrak{A}_R$ and $\xi \notin \operatorname{supp}(f)$, then $f_\xi \in \mathfrak{A}_R$ too, where as usual f_ξ is defined by

$$f_\xi(\varrho) = \begin{cases} \dfrac{f(\varrho)}{\xi - \varrho} & \text{if} \quad \varrho \in \operatorname{supp}(f), \\ 0 & \text{if} \quad \varrho \notin \operatorname{supp}(f). \end{cases}$$

Let $\eta = (\xi - ir)(\xi + ir)^{-1}$ and let φ_f be the function of $\mathfrak{A}_{C_1}$ verifying (1). If $|\xi| \geqslant \|T\| + 1$, then multiplying φ_f by a function of $\mathfrak{A}_{C_1}$ equal to 1 in a neighborhood of α we may assume that $\eta \notin \operatorname{supp}(\varphi_f)$. We have consequently that for $|\varrho| \leqslant \|T\| + 1$:

$$f_\xi(\varrho) = \begin{cases} \dfrac{1}{\xi + ir}\left(1 - \dfrac{\varrho - ir}{\varrho + ir}\right)(\varphi_f)_\eta\left(\dfrac{\varrho - ir}{\varrho + ir}\right) & \text{for } \xi \neq -ir, \\ -\dfrac{1}{2ir}\left(1 - \dfrac{\varrho - ir}{\varrho + ir}\right)\varphi_f\left(\dfrac{\varrho - ir}{\varrho + ir}\right) & \text{for } \xi = -ir, \end{cases} \tag{3}$$

thus f_ξ verifies also a relation of the type (1), that is $f_\xi \in \mathfrak{A}_R$.

Let now U be a $\mathfrak{A}_{C_1}$-spectral function of S_r. Put, by definition, $V_f = U_{\varphi_f}$, where $\varphi_f \in \mathfrak{A}_{C_1}$ verifies (1). This definition is coherent.

Indeed if φ_f and φ_f' verify (1), then $\varphi_f(\lambda) = \varphi_f'(\lambda)$ for $\lambda \in \alpha$. Now $\sigma(T) \subset [-\|T\| - 1, \|T\| + 1]$ so that

$$\sigma(S_r) = \left\{\frac{\varrho - ir}{\varrho + ir}\,\middle|\, \varrho \in \sigma(T)\right\} \subset \alpha,$$

which implies

$$\mathbf{U}_{\varphi_f} - \mathbf{U}_{\varphi_f'} = \mathbf{U}_{\varphi_f - \varphi_f'} = 0.$$

It is obvious that $f \to \mathbf{V}_f$ is an algebraic homomorphism of $\mathfrak{A}_R$ in $\mathbf{B}(\mathscr{X})$ such that $\mathbf{V}_1 = I$ and $\mathbf{V}_\varrho = T$. This last fact needs a proof. With this aim let us remark that by (2) we have $\mathbf{V}_\varrho = \mathbf{U}_\psi$, hence

$$(I - S_r)\,\mathbf{V}_\varrho = \mathbf{U}_{(1-\lambda)\psi} = \mathbf{U}_{ir\,(1+\lambda)\varphi} = ir\,(I + S_r)\,\mathbf{U}_\varphi = ir\,(I + S_r)$$

[where the last equality follows from the fact that $\varphi(\lambda) \equiv 1$ in a neighborhood of $\sigma(S_r)$]. Taking into account the relation

$$S_r\,(T + irI) = (T + irI)\,S_r = T - irI$$

we can now deduce easily that $\mathbf{V}_\varrho = T$. It then remains only to prove that $\xi \to \mathbf{V}_{f_\xi}$ is an analytic operator-valued function of ξ, for $\xi \notin \operatorname{supp}(f)$. Using (3), this can be proved without any essential difficulty remarking that η is analytic in ξ and $\eta \to \mathbf{U}_{g_\eta}$ is analytic in η for $\eta \notin \operatorname{supp}(g)$, where $g \in \mathfrak{A}_{C_1}$. However, a special attention must be paid to the behaviour of V_{f_ξ} in a neighborhood of $-ir$. Now, since $\sigma(S_r) \subset C_1$, we have for ξ non real that $|\eta| \neq 1$, hence

$$\mathbf{U}_{(\varphi_f)_\eta} = (\eta I - S_r)^{-1}\,\mathbf{U}_\varphi,$$

thus

$$\mathbf{V}_{f_\xi} = [(\xi - ir)\,I - (\xi + ir)\,S_r]^{-1}\,\mathbf{U}_\varphi\,(1 - S_r),$$

where the formula holds as well for $\xi \neq -ir$ as for $\xi = -ir$. Obviously $\mathbf{V}_{f_\xi}$ is analytic in ξ for ξ in a neighborhood of $-ir$. This finishes to prove that T is an $\mathfrak{A}$-self-adjoint operator.

As we shall not use the converse implication and as its proof is quite similar to that just given, we leave it to the reader as an exercise.

Proposition 4.2 has an important consequence.

4.3. THEOREM. *Let $T \in \mathbf{B}(\mathscr{H})$ have the spectrum situated on the real line and suppose that*

$$\|R(\lambda; T)\| \leqslant M \exp(K|\operatorname{Im} \lambda|^{-\beta}) \quad \textit{for} \quad \operatorname{Im} \lambda \neq 0,$$

where $0 < M < \infty$, $0 < K < \infty$ and $0 < \beta < \infty$ are constant. Then T is an $\mathfrak{A}$-self-adjoint operator.

Proof. We have, for $S_r = (T - irI)(T + irI)^{-1}$ and $|\lambda| \neq 1$

$$\begin{aligned} R(\lambda; S_r) &= [\lambda I - (T - irI)(T + irI)^{-1}]^{-1} \\ &= (T + irI)[\lambda(T + irI) - (T - irI)]^{-1} \\ &= (T + irI)[ir(\lambda + 1)I + (\lambda - 1)T]^{-1} \\ &= (T + irI)\left(ir\frac{1 + \lambda}{1 - \lambda} I - T\right)^{-1} \frac{1}{1 - \lambda}, \end{aligned}$$

whence for $|\lambda| \to 1$, $|\lambda| \neq 1$,

$$\begin{aligned} \|R(\lambda; S_r)\| &\leqslant (\|T\| + r)\frac{1}{\big||\lambda| - 1\big|}\left\|\left(ir\frac{1 + \lambda}{1 - \lambda} I - T\right)^{-1}\right\| \\ &\leqslant M_1 \exp\left[\log\big||\lambda| - 1\big|\right] \exp\left[K \operatorname{Im}\left|ir\left(\frac{1 + \lambda}{1 - \lambda}\right)\right|^{-\beta}\right] \\ &\leqslant M_1 \exp\left[\log\big||\lambda| - 1\big|\right] \exp\left[K_1\big||\lambda| - 1\big|^{-\beta}\right] \\ &\leqslant M_1 \exp\left[K_2\big||\lambda| - 1\big|^{-\beta}\right], \end{aligned}$$

where M_1, K_1, K_2 represent different constants. As $\sigma(S_\varrho) \subset C_1$, because $\sigma(T) \subset R$, the above inequalities show that S_ϱ verifies the conditions of Theorem 3.6; hence S_ϱ is an $\mathfrak{A}$-unitary operator so that by Proposition 4.2, T is an $\mathfrak{A}$-self-adjoint operator.

In the case where T is a generalized scalar operator, we can give some precise results analogous to those given in § 1. For this let us introduce the algebra $C^m(a)$ (where $m \geqslant 0$ is an integer and $a > 0$ a real number) of the complex-valued functions $f(\varrho)$ defined on $[-a, a]$ m-times continuously differentiable, endowed with the norm

$$\|f\| = \max_{\substack{|\varrho| \leqslant a \\ 0 \leqslant k \leqslant m}} \left| \left(\frac{d}{d\varrho} \right)^k f(\varrho) \right|.$$

Obviously $C^m(a)$ is a topologically admissible algebra.

4.4. Definition. An operator $T \in \mathbf{B}(\mathscr{X})$ is called *C^m-self-adjoint* if it is a $C^m(a)$-scalar operator having a continuous $C^m(a)$-spectral function, for a certain a.

It is obvious, since we may consider $C^\infty(R)$ as a subalgebra of $C^m(a)$ and the restriction to $C^\infty(R)$ of the continuous $C^m(a)$-spectral function of T as a $C^\infty(R)$-spectral function of T, that if T is a C^m-self-adjoint operator then T is also an $\mathfrak{A}$-self-adjoint operator in the sense of Definition 4.1.

4.5. Theorem. *For an operator $T \in \mathbf{B}(\mathscr{X})$ the following statements are equivalent:*

(i) *T is a generalized scalar operator whose spectrum lies on the real line.*

(ii) *T is, for a certain $m > 0$, a C^m-self-adjoint operator.*

(iii) *T verifies for an integer $n > 0$ and a real number $a > 0$ the following inequalities*

$$\|p(T)\| \leqslant M \sup_{\substack{|\varrho| \leqslant a \\ 0 \leqslant k \leqslant n}} \left| \left(\frac{d}{d\varrho} \right)^k p(\varrho) \right|$$

for every polynomial $p(\varrho)$.

(iv) *The spectrum of T lies on R, and for a certain $\beta \geqslant 1$*

$$\|R(\lambda; T)\| = O(|\operatorname{Im} \lambda|^{-\beta}) \quad \textit{for} \quad \operatorname{Im} \lambda \neq 0, \operatorname{Im} \lambda \to 0.$$

(v) *For a certain $\gamma \geqslant 0$*

$$\|e^{itT}\| = O(|t|^\gamma) \quad \textit{for} \quad |t| \to \infty.$$

(The different relations between the constant m, n, β, and γ which occur in connection with the above equivalence will be specified in the course of the proof.)

Proof. Obviously (ii) implies (iii) with $n = m$ since

$$p(T) = \mathbf{U}_p \tag{1}$$

for every polynomial $p(\varrho)$. Conversely, defining $\mathbf{U}_f$ by (1) for f equal to the polynomial, we may define by continuity [since polynomials are dense in $C^n(a)$] $\mathbf{U}_f$ for every $f \in C^n(a)$, obtaining a continuous $C^n(a)$-spectral function of T. Thus the equivalence

$$\text{(ii)} \Leftrightarrow \text{(iii)} \quad \textit{with} \quad m = n \tag{2}$$

is established. Now if (ii) is valid, then for $\operatorname{Im} \lambda \neq 0$, $\operatorname{Im} \lambda \to 0$

$$\|R(\lambda; T)\| \leqslant M \max_{\substack{|\varrho| \leqslant a \\ 0 \leqslant k \leqslant m}} \left| \left(\frac{d}{d\varrho} \right)^k (\lambda - \varrho)^{-1} \right| \leqslant M_1 \frac{1}{|\operatorname{Im} \lambda|^{m+1}},$$

thus

$$\text{(ii)} \Rightarrow \text{(iv)} \quad \textit{with} \quad \beta = m + 1. \tag{3}$$

Analogously, for $|t| \to \infty$

$$\|e^{itT}\| \leqslant M \max_{\substack{|\varrho| \leqslant a \\ 0 \leqslant k \leqslant m}} \left| \left(\frac{d}{d\varrho} \right)^k e^{it\varrho} \right| \leqslant M_2 |t|^m,$$

thus

$$\text{(ii)} \Rightarrow \text{(v)} \quad \textit{with} \quad \gamma = m. \tag{4}$$

The implication (ii) $\Rightarrow$ (i) is immediate. Indeed, defining for every $f(\lambda) \in C^\infty(C)$,

$$\mathbf{V}_f = \mathbf{U}_{f|[-a,a]},$$

where $\mathbf{U}$ is the $C^m(a)$-spectral function of T, we obtain a spectral distribution of T, thus T is a generalized scalar operator. Obviously $\sigma(T) \subset R$. The converse implication (i) $\Rightarrow$ (ii) results as follows: Let $\mathbf{V}$ be a spectral distribution of T and let q denote the order of $\mathbf{V}$, i.e.

$$\|\mathbf{V}_f\| \leqslant M \sup_{\substack{\alpha+\beta \leqslant q \\ |s+it| \leqslant \|T\|+1}} \left| \frac{\partial^{\alpha+\beta}}{\partial s^\alpha \partial t^\beta} f(s + it) \right|, \quad (f \in C^\infty(C)). \tag{5}$$

Put $S = \mathbf{V}_{\operatorname{Re} \lambda}$ and $Q = T - S$. We have

$$(T - S)^{q+1} = (\mathbf{V}_\lambda - \mathbf{V}_{\operatorname{Re} \lambda})^{q+1} = \mathbf{V}_{(\operatorname{Im} \lambda)^{q+1}}.$$

Now the support of the numerical distribution

$$\mathbf{V}_{x,x^*} : \varphi \to \langle \mathbf{V}_f x, x^* \rangle, \quad (x \in \mathscr{X}, x^* \in \mathscr{X}^*)$$

is contained on the real line and its order is $\leqslant q$, thus by Theorem 1.5.4 in Hörmander,[49] we have $\mathbf{V}_{x,x^*}((\mathrm{Im}\,\lambda)^{q+1}) = 0$, because

$$\frac{\partial^{\alpha+\beta}(\mathrm{Im}\,\lambda)^{q+1}}{\partial(\mathrm{Re}\,\lambda)^{\alpha}\,\partial(\mathrm{Im}\,\lambda)^{\beta}} = 0 \quad \text{for} \quad \mathrm{Im}\,\lambda = 0 \quad \text{and} \quad \alpha + \beta \leqslant q.$$

It results $\mathbf{V}_{(\mathrm{Im}\,\lambda)^{q+1}} = 0$, *i.e.* $Q^{q+1} = 0$. Thus by the commutativity of T and S as well as by Taylor's formula

$$p(\lambda + \mu) = \sum_{k \leqslant 0} \frac{1}{k!}\left(\frac{d^k}{d\lambda^k} p(\lambda)\right)\mu^k,$$

for a polynomial $p(\lambda)$, we obtain

$$p(T) = p(S + Q) = \sum_{k=0}^{q} \frac{1}{k!} p^{(k)}(S)\,Q^k = \sum_{k=0}^{q} \frac{1}{k!} \mathbf{V}_{p^{(k)}(\mathrm{Re}\,\lambda)} Q^k,$$

whence

$$\|p(T)\| \leqslant \sum_{k=0}^{p} \frac{1}{k!} \|\mathbf{V}_{p^{(k)}(\mathrm{Re}\,\lambda)}\| \cdot \|Q^k\|.$$

Using now (5) we deduce

$$\begin{aligned}
\|p(T)\| &\leqslant \sum_{k=0}^{q} \frac{1}{k!} M \sup_{\substack{\alpha+\beta \leqslant q \\ |s+it| \leqslant \|T\|+1}} \left| \frac{\partial^{\alpha+\beta}}{\partial s^{\alpha}\,\partial t^{\beta}} p^{(k)}(s) \right| \|Q^k\| \\
&\leqslant M \sum_{k=0}^{q} \frac{\|Q^k\|}{k!} \sup_{\substack{\alpha \leqslant q \\ |s+it| \leqslant \|T\|+1}} \left| \frac{d^{\alpha}}{ds^{\alpha}} p^{(k)}(s) \right| \\
&\leqslant M_1 \sup_{\substack{k \leq 2q \\ |s| \leqslant \|T\|+1}} |p^{(k)}(s)|,
\end{aligned}$$

which shows that T verifies (iii) with $n = 2q$. Thus the equivalence of the three conditions (i), (ii), (iii) is completely proved.

Suppose now that (v) is valid. Then for $\xi \in C$ with $\mathrm{Re}\,\xi < 0$ we may consider

$$T_{\pm}(\xi) = \int_0^{\infty} e^{\xi t} e^{\pm itT} dt.$$

Obviously for $-1 < \operatorname{Re} \xi < 0$

$$\|T_{\pm}(\xi)\| \leqslant M \int_0^{\infty} \exp[(\operatorname{Re}\xi)t]\,(t^{\gamma} + 1)\,dt \leqslant M_1\,|\operatorname{Re}\xi|^{-\gamma-1}. \tag{6}$$

Moreover

$$(\xi I \pm iT)\,T_{\pm}(\xi) = T_{\pm}(\xi)\,(\xi I \pm iT)$$

$$= \lim_{1+\|T\|<\mathcal{T}\to\infty} \int_0^{\mathcal{T}} e^{\xi t}(\xi I \pm iT)\,e^{\pm itT}dt$$

$$= \lim_{1+\|T\|<\mathcal{T}\to\infty} \int_0^{\mathcal{T}} e^{\xi t}\left(\frac{1}{2\pi i}\int_{|\lambda|=\|T\|+1} (\xi \pm i\lambda)\,e^{\pm it\lambda}\,R(\lambda; T)\,d\lambda\right)dt$$

$$= \lim_{1+\|T\|<\mathcal{T}\to\infty} \frac{1}{2\pi i}\int_{|\lambda|=\|T\|+1} R(\lambda; T)\left(\int_0^{\mathcal{T}} (\xi \pm i\lambda)\,e^{(\xi\pm i\lambda)t}dt\right)d\lambda$$

$$= \lim_{1+\|T\|<\mathcal{T}\to\infty} \frac{1}{2\pi i}\int_{|\lambda|=\|T\|+1} R(\lambda, T)\,[e^{(\xi\pm i\lambda)\mathcal{T}} - 1]\,d\lambda$$

$$= -\frac{1}{2\pi i}\int_{|\lambda|=\|T\|+1} R(\lambda; T)\,d\lambda = -I,$$

therefore

$$T_{\pm}(\xi) = -i\,(\xi iI \mp T)^{-1}.$$

This shows firstly that $\sigma(T)$ lies on R and secondly, by (6), that $R(\lambda; T)$ verifies (iv) with $\beta = \gamma + 1$, i.e.

$$\text{(v)} \Rightarrow \text{(iv)} \quad \textit{with} \quad \beta = \gamma + 1. \tag{7}$$

It remains to prove that (iv) implies one of the conditions (i)–(iii). With this purpose set

$$S = (T - iI)\,(T + iI)^{-1}.$$

Then $\sigma(S)$ lies on the unit circle and $1 \notin \sigma(S)$, in virtue of the spectral mapping formula

$$\sigma(S) = \left\{\frac{\varrho - i}{\varrho + i}\,\middle|\,\varrho \in \sigma(T)\right\}.$$

Moreover for $|\lambda| \neq 1$, $|\lambda| \to 1$

$$\|R(\lambda; S)\| \leqslant \|T + I\| \cdot \frac{1}{|1+\lambda|} \cdot \left\| \left(i \frac{1+\lambda}{1-\lambda} I - T \right)^{-1} \right\|$$

$$\leqslant \frac{M}{|1-\lambda|} \left| \operatorname{Im} i \frac{1+\lambda}{1-\lambda} \right|^{-\beta} \leqslant \frac{M_1}{|1-\lambda|} \left| |\lambda| - 1 \right|^{-\beta}.$$

Since $1 \notin \sigma(S)$ the above inequality can obviously be better written

$$\|R(\lambda; S)\| \leqslant M_2 \left| |\lambda| - 1 \right|^{-\beta} \quad \text{for} \quad |\lambda| \neq 1, |\lambda| \to 1.$$

Therefore we may apply to S Proposition 1.7; it follows that S is a $C^m(C_1)$-unitary operator with $m > [\beta] + 1$. Using again for T and S the same argument as that used in the proof of Proposition 4.2 for T and S_r, we obtain that T is actually a C^m-self-adjoint operator. Thus

$$\text{(iv)} \Rightarrow \text{(ii)} \textit{ with } m > [\beta] + 1. \tag{8}$$

This completes the proof of the theorem.

4.6. Corollary. *If T_1 and T_2 are two commuting C^{m_1}-self-adjoint and C^{m_2}-self-adjoint operators, respectively, then $T_1 + T_2$ is a $C^{m_1+m_2+2}$-self-adjoint operator.*

Proof. By the implication (4) in the above proof we have for $j = 1, 2$

$$\|e^{itT_j}\| = O(|t|^{m_j}) \quad \text{for} \quad |t| \to \infty,$$

thus

$$\|e^{it(T_1+T_2)}\| = \|e^{itT_1} \cdot e^{itT_2}\| \leqslant \|e^{itT_1}\| \cdot \|e^{itT_2}\| = O(|t|^{m_1+m_2})$$

$$\text{for} \quad |t| \to \infty,$$

thus by the implications (7) and (8), $T_1 + T_2$ is a $C^{m_1+m_2+3}$-self-adjoint operator.

5. $\mathfrak{A}$-unitary and $\mathfrak{A}$-self-adjoint Operators in Hilbert Spaces

We need the following results on the von Neumann-Schatten ideals of compact operators, taken from Ref. 30 (Chapter XI, §§ 9–10) or Ref. 112.

5.1. DEFINITION. Let T be a compact operator in a Hilbert space $\mathscr{H}$ and $|T| = (T^*T)^{1/2}$. The operator $|T|$ is a compact non-negative self-adjoint operator. The eigenvalues $\mu_1(T), \mu_2(T), \ldots, \mu_n(T), \ldots$ of $|T|$, arranged in decreasing order and repeated according to multiplicity, form a sequence of non-negative numbers approaching zero. By definition

$$\mathscr{C}_p = \left\{ T \in \mathbf{B}(\mathscr{H}) | T \text{ compact}, |T|_p = \left(\sum_{n=1}^{\infty} (\mu_n(T)^p) \right)^{1/p} < \infty \right\},$$

for $0 < p < \infty$.

Among the properties related to these classes $\mathscr{C}_p$, we shall use the following:

(a) The spaces $\mathscr{C}_p$ $(1 \leqslant p < \infty)$ with the norms $|T|_p$ are Banach spaces.

(b) $|ATB|_p \leqslant \|A\| \cdot |T|_p \cdot \|B\|$.

(c) $|T_q| \leqslant |T|_p$ if $p \leqslant q$; consequently $\mathscr{C}_p \subset \mathscr{C}_q$ for $p \leqslant q$.

(d) If $T \in \mathscr{C}_p$ $(1 \leqslant p < \infty)$ and λ_i are the eigenvalues of T repeated according to multiplicity, then

$$\sum_{i=1}^{\infty} |\lambda_i|^p \leqslant |T|_p^p,$$

and the infinite product

$$\delta_k(T) = \prod_{i=1}^{\infty} \left\{ (1 + \lambda_i) \exp \left(\sum_{j=1}^{k-1} \frac{(-1)^j}{j} \lambda_i^j \right) \right\}$$

converges absolutely for $k \geqslant p$. If $k - 1 \leqslant p \leqslant k$ there exists a finite constant Γ, depending only on k and p, such that

$$|\delta_k(T)| \leqslant \exp (\Gamma |T|_p^p);$$

if $-1 \notin \sigma(T)$ then $\delta_k(T) \neq 0$.

(e) Moreover, the mapping $T \to \delta_k(T)$ is continuous on $\mathscr{C}_p$.

(f) For $1 \leqslant p < \infty, k - 1 \leqslant p \leqslant k$, the mapping $T \to \delta_k(T)(I + T)^{-1}$ of $\mathscr{C}_p$ into $\mathbf{B}(\mathscr{H})$ is continuous and satisfies the inequality

$$\|\delta_k(T)(I + T)^{-1}\| \leqslant \exp (\Gamma_1 |T|_p^p),$$

where Γ_1 is a finite constant depending only on p.

(g) If $R(\lambda) \in \mathbf{B}(\mathscr{H})$ is analytic for $\lambda \in \omega$ and $T \in \mathscr{C}_p$ then $\delta_k(TR(\lambda))$ is analytic in ω.

To verify this assertion, let $\lambda_0 \in \omega$ and let $\omega_0 \subset \omega$ be a compact neighborhood of λ_0. We have $\|R(\lambda)\| \leqslant M_0$ for all $\lambda \in \omega_0$. There exists a sequence T_n of compact operators having finite dimensional ranges such that $|T_n - T|_p \to 0$ as $n \to \infty$ (see Ref. 30, Lemma XI, 9.11). We have

$$\delta_k(T_n R(\lambda)) \to \delta_k(TR(\lambda))$$

by (b) and (e). Moreover, in virtue of (d) and (b)

$$|\delta_k(T_n R(\lambda))| \leqslant \exp(\Gamma |T_n|_p^p M_0) \quad \text{for} \quad \lambda \in \omega_0,$$

which shows that $\{\delta_k(T_n R(\lambda))\}$ is a uniformly bounded (in ω_0) convergent sequence of functions. Since for an operator T_n with finite dimensional range, $\delta_k(T_n R(\lambda))$ is obviously analytic for $\lambda \in \omega$, applying to our sequence of analytic functions the classical Vitali theorem we deduce that the limit $\delta(TR(\lambda))$ is analytic in ω_0; λ_0 being arbitrary in ω, $\delta(TR(\lambda))$ results analytic in ω. Finally let us mention that $\mathscr{C}_1$ is the class of operators with finite trace, while $\mathscr{C}_2$ is that of Hilbert-Schmidt operators.

The main aim of the present paragraph is to prove the following

5.2. THEOREM.

(i) *Let* $T \in \mathbf{B}(\mathscr{H})$ *be such that* $\sigma(T) \subset \{\lambda \mid |\lambda| = 1\}$. *If there exists a* p $(1 \leqslant p < \infty)$, *such that* $T^*T - I \in \mathscr{C}_p$, *then* T *is* $\mathfrak{A}$*-unitary.*

(ii) *Let* $A \in \mathbf{B}(\mathscr{X})$ *be such that* $\sigma(A) \subset R$ (= *the real line*). *If there exists a* p $(1 \leqslant p < \infty)$ *for which* $A - A^* \in \mathscr{C}_p$, *then* A *is* $\mathfrak{A}$*-self-adjoint.*

Proof: The case (ii) reduces to (i) because for $T = (A - iI)(A + iI)^{-1}$ we have

$$T^*T - I = (A^* - iI)^{-1}(A^* + iI)(A - iI)(A + iI)^{-1} - I$$

$$= (A^* - iI)^{-1}[(A^* + iI)(A - iI) - (A^* - iI)(A + iI)](A + iI)^{-1}$$

$$= 2i(A^* - iI)^{-1}(A - A^*)(A + iI)^{-1} \in \mathscr{C}_p$$

owing to (ii) and the inequality (b) at the beginning of this paragraph.

Thus it remains to prove the case (i). To this end let us remark that if we take the polar decomposition of T (see Ref. 30, XII, 7.7) we have

$$T = U|T|,$$

where U is unitary and $|T|^2 - I = T^*T - I \in \mathscr{C}_p$. Or, on account of (b)

$$K = |T| - I = (I + |T|)^{-1} (|T|^2 - I) \in \mathscr{C}_p,$$

thus

$$T = U(I + K) = U + UK = U + L,$$

where $L = UK \in \mathscr{C}_p$ by (b). Hence we have

$$\begin{aligned} R(\lambda, T) &= (\lambda I - T)^{-1} = (\lambda I - U - L)^{-1} \\ &= (\lambda I - U)^{-1} \cdot [I - L(\lambda I - U)^{-1}]^{-1}, \end{aligned}$$

where the operator $I - L(\lambda I - U)^{-1}$ has a bounded inverse for $|\lambda| \neq 1$. So

$$\delta(\lambda) = \delta_k(-L(\lambda I - U)^{-1})$$

exists, and is different from 0 for all $|\lambda| \neq 1$. By (d) we have for $|\lambda| \neq 1$

$$\begin{aligned} |\delta(\lambda)| &= |\delta_k(-L(\lambda I - U)^{-1})| \leqslant \exp(\Gamma |L(\lambda I - U)^{-1}|_p^p) \\ &\leqslant \exp(\Gamma |L|_p^p \, \|R(\lambda, U)\|^p) \leqslant \exp\left(\Gamma |L|_p^p \frac{1}{||\lambda| - 1|^p}\right), \end{aligned}$$

where we have applied the following inequality: $\|R(\lambda; U)\| \leqslant ||\lambda| - 1|^{-1}$.† As $\delta(\lambda) \neq 0$ for $|\lambda| \neq 1$, we may write $\delta(\lambda) = \exp(\alpha(\lambda))$, where $\alpha(\lambda)$ is analytic in $\{\lambda \in C \mid |\lambda| < 1\}$ and in $\{\lambda \in C \mid |\lambda| > 1\}$. Replacing $\alpha(\lambda)$ by $\alpha(1/\lambda)$, we may consider only the first case:

$$\operatorname{Re} \alpha(\lambda) \leqslant M/(1 - |\lambda|)^p \quad \text{for} \quad |\lambda| \leqslant 1.$$

We recall the Caratheodory's inequality: *If f is analytic for $|\lambda| < r$, $f(0) = 0$ and* $\operatorname{Re} f(\lambda) \leqslant M(r)$ *for $|\lambda| < r$, then*

$$|f(\lambda)| < \frac{2M(r)\,|\lambda|}{r - |\lambda|}.$$

---

† Here is an elementary proof of this inequality:
For every $x \in \mathscr{H}$ and $|\lambda| \neq 1$, in virtue of the isometry of U,

$$\|(\lambda I - U)x\| \geqslant \big|\,|\lambda|\,\|x\| - \|Ux\|\,\big| = \big|\,|\lambda| - 1\big| \cdot \|x\|$$

whence, since $R(\lambda; U)$ exists, we obtain

$$\|R(\lambda; U)\| \leqslant \frac{1}{||\lambda| - 1|}.$$

Since by (g), $\delta(\lambda)$ is analytic, $\alpha(\lambda)$ is also analytic. Thus applying this inequality to $\alpha - \alpha(0)$ for $r = 1$, we obtain

$$|\alpha(\lambda)| \leqslant |\alpha(0)| + 2\left(\frac{1}{(1-|\lambda|)^p} + |\alpha(0)|\right)\frac{|\lambda|}{1-|\lambda|},$$

whence

$$|\alpha(\lambda)| \leqslant \frac{M_1}{(1-|\lambda|)^{p+1}}, \quad (|\lambda| < 1).$$

In this way

$$\frac{1}{|\delta(\lambda)|} \leqslant \exp\left(\frac{M_1}{(1-|\lambda|)^{p+1}}\right), \quad (|\lambda| < 1). \tag{1}$$

Now we have

$$R(\lambda, T) = \frac{(\lambda I - U)^{-1}}{\delta(\lambda)} \cdot \delta(\lambda)\,[I - L(\lambda I - U)^{-1}]^{-1}$$

$$= \frac{(\lambda I - U)^{-1}}{\delta(\lambda)} \cdot \delta_k(-L(\lambda I - U)^{-1})\,[I - L(\lambda I - U)^{-1}]^{-1},$$

so that by (f), (1), we obtain

$$\|R(\lambda, T)\| \leqslant \frac{\|R(\lambda, U\|}{|\delta(\lambda)|} \cdot \|\delta_k(-LR(\lambda, U))\,[I - LR(\lambda, U)]^{-1}\|$$

$$\leqslant \frac{1}{1-|\lambda|}\exp\left(\frac{M_1}{(1-|\lambda|)^{p+1}}\right)\exp\left(\Gamma_1|LR(\lambda, U)|_p^p\right)$$

$$\leqslant \frac{1}{1-|\lambda|}\exp\left(\frac{M_1}{(1-|\lambda|)^{p+1}}\right)\exp\left(\frac{|L|_p^p}{(1-|\lambda|)^p}\right)$$

$$\leqslant M_2\exp\left(\frac{M_3}{(1-|\lambda|)^{p+1}}\right), \quad (|\lambda| < 1).$$

Analogously, for $|\lambda| > 1$, we obtain

$$|R(\lambda, T)| \leqslant M_2'\exp\left(\frac{M_3'}{(|\lambda| - 1)^{p+1}}\right).$$

By Theorem 3.6. T is $\mathfrak{A}_T$-unitary.

5.3. COROLLARY. *Let $T \in \mathbf{B}(\mathscr{H})$. If $\sigma(T) \subset C_1$ (respectively, $\sigma(T) \subset R$), and if $T^*T - I \in \mathscr{C}_p$(respectively, $A - A^* \in \mathscr{C}_p$), then T is decomposable. Therefore, if $\sigma(T)$ is not reduced to a single point, then T has nontrivial spectral maximal spaces; consequently T has nontrivial ultra-invariant subspaces in $\mathscr{H}$.*

5.4. *Remark. If $T^*T - I$ (respectively $T^* - T$) has a finite dimensional range and if $\sigma(T) \subset C_1$ (respectively, $\sigma(T) \subset R$), then T is a generalized scalar operator.*

Indeed, reasoning as before [using the fact that $\delta_1(\lambda)$ is now a polynomial] we obtain for T the hypotheses of Proposition 1.7 (respectively, Theorem 4.5).

Let us consider as an application the case of bounded J-unitary or J-self adjoint operators in a Pontreagin space.

5.5. DEFINITION. Let $\mathscr{X}$ be a Hilbert space and let Q be an orthogonal projection of $\mathscr{X}$ with range $Q\mathscr{H}$ of finite dimension $\varkappa < \infty$. $\mathscr{X}$ together with the bilinear form

$$[x, y] = ((I - 2Q)\, x, y), \quad (x, y \in \mathscr{X}),$$

where $(.,.)$ denotes the usual scalar product in $\mathscr{X}$, is called a *Pontreagin space $\Pi_\varkappa$*.

5.6. DEFINITION. *A bounded J-unitary* (respectively, *bounded J-self-adjoint*) operator T is a linear operator of $\mathscr{X}$, bounded with respect to the Hilbert structure of $\mathscr{X}$, and verifying with respect to the Pontreagin structure the condition

$$[Tx, Ty] = [x, y], \quad (\text{respectively, } [Tx, y] = [x, Ty])$$

for every $x, y \in \mathscr{X}$.

These definitions made, Theorem 5.2, has the following

5.7. COROLLARY. *Let T be a bounded J-unitary, (respectively, a bounded J-self-adjoint) operator in a Pontreagin space $\mathscr{X}$ of type $\Pi_\varkappa$, having the spectrum contained in the unit circle (respectively, in the real line); then T is a generalized scalar operator.*

Proof. Let Q be the orthogonal projection occurring in Definition 5.5; if T is J-unitary, then

$$T^* (I - 2Q) T = I - 2Q,$$

so that

$$T^*T - I = 2 (T^*QT - Q)$$

has a finite dimensional range; thus by Remark 5.4, T is a generalized scalar operator. Analogously if T is J-selfadjoint then

$$T^* (I - 2Q) = (I - 2Q) T,$$

so that

$$T^* - T = 2 (T^*Q - QT)$$

has a finite dimensional range; therefore using again Remark 5.4, T is a generalized scalar operator.

6. Triangular Form and Invariant Subspaces for Operators in Hilbert Spaces

The results of the preceding paragraph can be applied to a very interesting question, namely the triangularisation of certain classes of operators. This will be shown in the current paragraph.

6.1. PROPOSITION. *Let* $L^2[0, 1]$ *be the Hilbert space of square-integrable functions on* $[0, 1]$ *and let* $A \in \mathbf{B}(L^2[0, 1])$. *Then there exists a function* $K\colon [0, 1] \times [0, 1] \to C$ *such that*

(i) *the mapping* $x \to K(x,.)$ *of* $[0, 1]$ *into* $L^2[0, 1]$ *is continuous*

(ii) *for every* $f \in L^2[0, 1]$, *the function* $x \to \int_0^1 K(x, t) f(t)\, dt$ *is absolutely continuous*

(iii) $(Af)(x) = d/dx \int_0^1 K(x, t) f(t)\, dt$ *almost everywhere.*

Moreover, if K' *is another function verifying* (i), (ii) *and* (iii), *then*

$$K(x, t) - K'(x, t) = \text{function only of } t.$$

Proof. Denote by e_ξ the characteristic function of the interval $[0, \xi]$. Evidently the mapping $\xi \to A^*e_\xi$ of $[0, 1]$ into $L^2[0, 1]$ is continuous. Put

$$K(x, t) = \overline{A^*e_x(t)},$$

then K verifies (i). On the other hand

$$\int_0^x (Af)(t)\,dt = (Af, e_x) = (f, A^* e_x) = \int_0^1 K(x,t) f(t)\,dt, \quad (f \in L^2[0,1]),$$

which proves (ii) and (iii).

Now if K' is another function verifying (i), (ii) and (iii), we have

$$\int_0^1 K(x,t) f(t)\,dt - \int_0^1 K(0,t) f(t)\,dt$$

$$= \int_0^1 K'(x,t) f(t)\,dt - \int_0^1 K'(0,t) f(t)\,dt,$$

whence, putting $L = K(0,.) - K'(0,.) \in L^2[0,1]$, we get

$$\int_0^1 [K(x,t) - K'(x,t) - L(t)] f(t)\,dt = 0$$

for every $f \in L^2[0,1]$, thus

$$H(x,t) = K(x,t) - K'(x,t) - L(t) = 0 \quad \text{a.e.}$$

6.2. Definition. The operator $A \in \mathbf{B}(L^2[0,1])$ is called *subdiagonal* (respectively, *superdiagonal*) if the K in Proposition 1 can be chosen so that

$$K(x,t) = 0 \quad \text{for} \quad t > x \quad (\text{respectively, } t < x);$$

that is if

$$(Af)(x) = \frac{d}{dx} \int_0^x K(x,t) f(t)\,dt$$

$$\left(\text{respectively, } (Af)(x) = \frac{d}{dx} \int_x^1 K(x,t) f(t)\,dt\right)$$

for every $f \in L^2[0,1]$.

6.3. *Remark. If $A \in \mathbf{B}(L^2[0,1])$ is subdiagonal, then T^* is superdiagonal.* Indeed, if

$$(Af)(x) = \frac{d}{dx} \int_0^x K(x,t) f(t)\,dt,$$

then for $f_\xi = 1 - e_\xi$ we have $(Af_\xi)(x) = 0$ for $x < \xi$, hence

$$\int_\xi^1 (A^*f)(x)\,dx = \overline{(A^*f, f_\xi)} = (f, Af_\xi) = \int_\xi^1 f(t)\,\overline{(Af_\xi)(t)}\,dt.$$

Putting $K_*(\xi, t) = -\overline{(Af_\xi)(t)}$ we deduce

$$(A^*f)(x) = \frac{d}{dx}\int_x^1 K_*(x, t) f(t)\,dt;$$

it is also evident that K_* verifies (i) and (ii).

Let $\mathscr{H} = \bigoplus_{1 \leqslant n < N} L^2[0, 1]$, where N is an integer or ∞. Every operator $T \in \mathbf{B}(\mathscr{H})$ defines uniquely a matrix of operators of $L^2[0, 1]$,

$$T = (T_{nm})_{1 \leqslant n, m < N}$$

with T_{nm} = (orthogonal projection of $\mathscr{H}$ on the n term $L^2[0, 1]$) $\times T$ restricted to the m term $L^2[0, 1]$ of $\mathscr{H}$.

It is obvious that if to two operators T_1 and $T_2 \in \mathbf{B}(\mathscr{H})$ corresponds the same matrix (T_{nm}), then $T_1 = T_2$.

6.5. Definition. Let $\mathscr{H}$ be a (separable) Hilbert space and let $T \in \mathbf{B}(\mathscr{X})$. *$T$ is reducible to a triangular form* if T is unitary equivalent to a matrix $(T_{nm})_{1 \leqslant n,m < N}$ of operators $T_{nm} \in \mathbf{B}(L^2[0, 1])$ which are *subdiagonal.*

The matrix $(T_{n,m})$ is called a *triangular form* of T.

The first main aim of this paragraph is to study the reducibility to a triangular form.

6.6. Definition. An operator T in a Hilbert space $\mathscr{X}$ is said to have the *property (Triang$_1$)* if there exists a spectral scale $\{E_t\}_{0 \leqslant t \leqslant 1}$ of orthogonal projections of $\mathscr{X}$† such that

(i) $\mathbf{E}_t T \mathbf{E}_t = T\mathbf{E}_t$, $(0 \leqslant t \leqslant 1)$;

(ii) $\mathbf{E}_t - \mathbf{E}_{t-0}$ is equal to 0 or it is a one-dimensional projection.

If the spectral scale $\{\mathbf{E}_t\}_{0 \leqslant t \leqslant 1}$ has no point of discontinuity, T is said to have the *property (Triang$_2$)*.

6.7. *Remark.* Using Theorem 3.4.5, and Lemma 4.3.5, one can easily see that if T is a generalized scalar operator in a Hilbert space $\mathscr{X}$, then T has the property (Triang$_1$).

The above two Definitions 6.6 are related by the following

† i.e. $\mathbf{E}_x\mathbf{E}_y = \mathbf{E}_{\min\{x,y\}}$ and $\mathbf{E}_{x+0} = \mathbf{E}_x$, $\mathbf{E}_0 = 0$, $\mathbf{E}_1 = I$.

6.8. PROPOSITION. *Let T be an operator in a (separable) Hilbert space $\mathscr{X}$, having the property (Traing$_1$). Then there exists a normal operator U in a (separable) Hilbert space $\mathscr{Y}$ (perhaps $\mathscr{Y} = \{0\}$) such that:*

(i) *The operator $T \oplus U \in \mathbf{B}(\mathscr{X} \oplus \mathscr{Y})$ has the property (Triang$_2$).*

(ii) *The spectrum $\sigma(U)$ of U is included in the set $\sigma_\infty(T)$ complementary to the unbounded component $\varrho_\infty(T)$ of $\varrho(T)$; in particular if $\sigma(T)$ does not separate the complex plane, then $\sigma(U) \subset \sigma(T)$.*

Proof. Let $\{x_n\}_{1 \leqslant n < N}$ be an orthonormal basis of $\mathscr{X}$. Let $\{\varepsilon_n\}_{1 \leqslant n < N}$ be a sequence of positive numbers such that $\sum \varepsilon_n = 1$; put

$$\tau(t) = \sum_{1 \leqslant n < N} \varepsilon_n (\mathbf{E}_t x_n, x_n),$$

where $\{\mathbf{E}_t\}_{0 \leqslant t \leqslant 1}$ is the spectral scale occurring in the definition of the property (Triang$_1$). Denote by D the set of the points of discontinuity for $\{\mathbf{E}_t\}_{0 \leqslant t \leqslant 1}$. They coincide with the points of discontinuity of the function $\tau(t)$ [this function verifies also the following conditions: $\tau(0) = 0$, $\tau(1) = 1$, $\tau(t + 0) = \tau(t)$]. For $d \in D$ we have

$$(\mathbf{E}_d - \mathbf{E}_{d-0})\,\varphi = (\varphi, \varphi_d)\,\varphi_d, \quad (\varphi \in \mathscr{X})$$

for a certain $\varphi_d \in \mathscr{X}$, $\|\varphi_d\| = 1$; if $d_1 \neq d_2$, then $\varphi_{d_1} \perp \varphi_{d_2}$. On the other hand since $\mathbf{E}_d\mathscr{X}$ is invariant to T we have

$$T_{\varphi_d} = a_d\varphi_d + \psi_d, \quad \text{where} \quad \mathbf{E}_{d-0}\psi_d = \psi_d.$$

Moreover, since $\mathbf{E}_{d-0}\mathscr{X}$ is also invariant with respect to T, we have $(T - a_d I)\,\mathbf{E}_d\mathscr{X} \subset \mathbf{E}_{d-0}\mathscr{X}$ so that $a_d \in \sigma(T_x|\mathbf{E}_d\mathscr{X}) \subset \sigma_\infty(T)$. Putting first

$$\mathscr{Y}_d = \left\{ f | f \in L^2 [\tau(d-0), \tau(d)], \int_{\tau(d-0)}^{\tau(d)} f(t)\, dt = 0 \right\}$$

and

$$U_d f(t) = a_d f(t) \quad \text{for} \quad f \in \mathscr{Y}_d,$$

for every $d \in D$, and then

$$\mathscr{Y} = \bigoplus_{d \in D} \mathscr{Y}_d, \quad U = \bigoplus_{d \in D} U_d$$

we obtain the desired normal operator $U \in \mathbf{B}(\mathscr{Y})$. The last task is to prove that $T \oplus U$ has the property (Triang$_2$). To this end we shall identify every φ_d with the constant function $\equiv [\tau(d) - \tau(d-0)]^{-1/2}$ of

$L^2\,[\tau\,(d-0), \tau(d)]$. Thus $\mathscr{X} \oplus \mathscr{Y}$ becomes the space

$$\mathscr{X} \vee \bigoplus_{d \in D} L^2\,[\tau\,(d-0), \tau(d)].$$

Let us define for $\tau \in [0, 1]$

$$\mathscr{Z}_\tau = (\bigvee_{\tau(t)<\tau} \mathbf{E}_t\mathscr{X}) \vee (\bigoplus_{\tau(d) \leqslant \tau} \mathscr{Y}_d)$$

if τ does not belong to any interval $[\tau\,(d-0), \tau(d)]$ for a $d \in D$, and if $\tau \in [\tau\,(\delta-0), \tau(\delta)]$, then

$$\mathscr{Z}_\tau = \mathscr{Z}_{\tau(\delta-0)} \oplus \{f | f \in L^2\,[\tau\,(\delta-0), \tau(\delta)],\ f(t) = 0 \quad \text{for} \quad \tau < t < \tau(\delta)\}.$$

The spaces $\{\mathscr{Z}_\tau\}_{0 \leqslant \tau \leqslant 1}$ form a continuous nest of invariant subspaces of $T \oplus U$. Moreover $\mathscr{Z}_0 = \{0\}$, $\mathscr{Z}_1 = \mathscr{X} \oplus \mathscr{Y}$. The corresponding scale $\{\mathbf{F}_\tau\}_{0 \leqslant \tau \leqslant 1}$ formed by the orthogonal projections $\mathbf{F}_\tau$ of $\mathscr{X} \oplus \mathscr{Y}$ on $\mathscr{Z}_\tau$ verifies all conditions occurring in the Definition 6.6 of the property (Triang$_2$).

It is easy to see that if an operator T in a (separable) Hilbert space is reducible to a triangular form (see Definition 6.5) then T possesses the property (Triang$_2$). The converse fact is also true but in the following sense.

6.9. THEOREM. *Let T be an operator in a (separable) Hilbert space $\mathscr{X}$, having the property (Triang$_2$). Then there exists a normal operator V in a (separable) Hilbert space $\mathscr{Z}$ (perhaps $\mathscr{Z} = \{0\}$) such that $\sigma(V) \subset \sigma(T)$ and $T \oplus V \in \mathbf{B}\,(\mathscr{X} \oplus \mathscr{Z})$ is reducible to a triangular form.*

Proof. Let $\{\mathbf{E}_t\}_{0 \leqslant t \leqslant 1}$ be the spectral scale occurring in the Definition 6.6 of the property (Triang$_2$). Let $\{x_n\}$ be an orthonormal basis in $\mathscr{X}$ and let us put again as in the preceding proof

$$\tau(t) = \sum_n \varepsilon_n\,(\mathbf{E}_t x_n, x_n),$$

where $\sum_n \varepsilon_n = 1$ and $\varepsilon_n > 0$. Then $\tau(t)$ is a monotone function which, since $\{\mathbf{E}_t\}_{0 \leqslant t \leqslant 1}$ is continuous, is also continuous. Put $\mathbf{F}_\tau = \mathbf{E}_t$, where t is defined by $\tau(t) = \tau$. Then $\{\mathbf{F}_\tau\}_{0 \leqslant \tau \leqslant 1}$ is also a continuous spectral scale verifying

$$\tau = \sum_n \varepsilon_n\,(\mathbf{F}_\tau x_n, x_n), \quad (0 \leqslant \tau \leqslant 1).$$

This relation shows that the spectral measure $\mathbf{F}(\sigma) = \int_\sigma d\mathbf{F}_\tau$ ($\sigma \subset [0, 1]$ is a Borel set) is absolutely continuous with respect to the Lebesgue measure $\mathbf{m}(\sigma)$ since

$$\mathbf{m}(\sigma) = \sum_n \varepsilon_n (\mathbf{F}(\sigma) x_n, x_m).$$

In this manner the ordered spectral representation (see Ref. 30, X.5) of the operator $A = \int_0^1 (1 - \tau)\, d\mathbf{F}_\tau$ has the form

$$\bigoplus_{1 \leqslant k < N} L^2 (e_k, \mathbf{m}), \quad A \bigoplus_{1 \leqslant k < N} f_k(t) = \bigoplus_{1 \leqslant k < N} \tau f_k(t),$$

where $e_1 \supseteq e_2 \supseteq \cdots \supseteq e_k \supseteq \cdots$ are Borel set. By this representation of $\mathscr{X}$ and A, the spectral scale $\{\mathbf{F}_\tau\}_{0 \leqslant \tau \leqslant 1}$ becomes the scale formed by the following multiplication operators:

$$M_\tau\colon \bigoplus_{1 \leqslant k < N} f_k(t) \to \bigoplus_{1 \leqslant k < \infty} \chi_{(1-\tau, 1)}(t) f_k(t) \tag{1}$$

since the spectral scale of $A = \int_0^1 s\, dG_s$ given by $G_s = I - \mathbf{F}_{1-s}$ becomes

$$\bigoplus_{1 \leqslant k < N} f_k(t) \to \bigoplus_{1 \leqslant k < N} \chi_{(0,s)}(t) f_k(t).$$

Let $\mathscr{Z}$ be the following orthogonal sum:

$$\bigoplus_{1 \leqslant k < n} L^2 ([0, 1] \setminus e_k, \mathbf{m})$$

and let V be defined by

$$V\colon \bigoplus_{1 \leqslant k < N} g_k(t) \to \bigoplus_{1 \leqslant k < N} v(t)\, g_k(t),$$

where $v(t)$ is a Borel function with values in $\sigma(T)$. Then V is a normal operator in $\mathscr{Z}$ verifying $\sigma(V) \subset \sigma(T)$. Moreover the representation of $\mathscr{X}$ with respect to A induces an obvious unitary representation of $\mathscr{X} \oplus \mathscr{Z}$ onto

$$\Big(\bigoplus_{1 \leqslant k < \infty} L^2 (e_k; \mathbf{m})\Big) \oplus \Big(\bigoplus_{1 \leqslant k < \infty} L^2 ([0, 1] \setminus e_k; \mathbf{m})\Big) = \bigoplus_{1 \leqslant k < N} L^2 [0, 1],$$

where the equality is understood as an identity up to a unitary transformation. By this representation the operator $T \oplus V$ becomes an operator S of the last orthogonal sum such that

$$M_\tau S M_\tau = S M_\tau, \quad (0 \leqslant \tau \leqslant 1), \tag{2}$$

where this time M_τ represents the same multiplication operator as in (1), but considered in $\bigoplus_{1 \leqslant k < N} L^2[0, 1]$. Since $T \oplus V$ and S are unitary equivalent it remains to prove that the operator $S_{n,m}$ corresponding to the matrix representation

$$S \sim (S_{n,m})_{1 \leqslant n,m < N}$$

of S as operator of $\bigoplus_{1 \leqslant n < N} L^2[0, 1]$ are subdiagonal. To this purpose let $f \in L^2[0, 1]$ be considered as the element $\bigoplus_{1 \leqslant n < N} f_k(t)$, where $f_m = f$ and all the other f_k are 0. Since

$$\bigoplus_{1 \leqslant k < N} S_{k,m} f = S \bigoplus_{1 \leqslant k < N} f_k, \tag{3}$$

we have by (2) and (3) applied to

$$M_\tau \bigoplus_{1 \leqslant k < N} f_k(t) = \oplus\, \chi_{(1-\tau,1)}(t) f_k(t)$$

instead of $\bigoplus_{2 \leqslant k \leqslant N} f_k(t)$,

$$\bigoplus_{1 \leqslant k < N} \chi_{(1-\tau,1)} S_{k,m} \chi_{(1-\tau,1)} f = \bigoplus_{1 \leqslant k < N} S_{k,m} \chi_{(1-\tau,1)} f$$

so that for $k = n$

$$\chi_{(1-\tau,1)}\, S_{n,m}\, \chi_{(1-\tau,1)} f = S_{n,m}\, \chi_{(1-\tau,1)} f \tag{4}$$

for every $0 \leqslant \tau \leqslant 1$ and $f \in L^2[0, 1]$. In virtue of the Definition 6.2 and part of the proof of Proposition 6.1, we have only to show that

$$\overline{S_{n,m}^*\, e_x(t)} = 0 \quad \text{for} \quad t > x, \tag{5}$$

where e_x denotes the characteristic function $\chi_{(0,x)}$ of the interval $(0, x)$. Now by (4) we have, taking the adjoints,

$$\chi_{(1-\tau,1)}\, S_{n,m}^*\, \chi_{(1-\tau,1)}\, g = \chi_{(1-\tau,1)}\, S_{n,m}^*\, g$$

for every $0 \leqslant \tau \leqslant 1$ and $g \in L^2[0, 1]$. Taking into account that $\chi_{(1-\tau,1)} = 1 - e_{1-\tau}$ we have for every $x = 1 - \tau$

$$(1 - e_x)\, S_{n,m}^*\, (1 - e_x)\, g = (1 - e_x)\, S_{n,m}^*\, g,$$

whence

$$S_{n,m}^* e_x g = e_x S_{n,m}^* e_x g.$$

Taking $g = e_x$ we deduce that

$$S^*_{n,m}e_x = e_x S^*_{n,m}e_x,$$

for every $x \in [0, 1]$. Obviously [since $e_x(t) = 0$ for $t > x$], the last relation implies (5). The proof is now complete.

Properties (Triang$_1$) and (Triang$_2$) can not easily be verified in general. Therefore we shall give now the following

6.10. DEFINITION. Let $T \in \mathbf{B}(\mathscr{X})$, where $\mathscr{X}$ is a Banach space. T is said to have the property (Triang$_0$) if for every pair $\mathscr{X}_1 \subsetneqq \mathscr{X}_2$ of (linear closed) invariant subspaces of T, such that $\dim(\mathscr{X}_2/\mathscr{X}_1) > 1$ there exists another (linear closed) invariant subspace $\mathscr{X}_3$ of T verifying

$$\mathscr{X}_1 \subsetneqq \mathscr{X}_3 \subsetneqq \mathscr{X}_2.$$

6.11. PROPOSITION. *Let T be an operator in a (separable) Hilbert space $\mathscr{X}$, possessing the property* (Triang$_0$). *Then T has also the property* (Triang$_1$).

Proof. Let $\mathscr{N} = \{\mathscr{X}_\alpha\}_{\alpha \in A}$ be a maximal nest of invariant subspaces of T. For the existence of such a maximal nest we send the reader to Chapter 3, § 4. Let $\{x_n\}_{n \geqslant 1}$ be an orthonormal basis of $\mathscr{X}$ and as in the preceding proof let

$$t(\alpha) = \sum_n \varepsilon_n (P_\alpha x_n, x_n),$$

where P_α denotes the orthogonal projection of $\mathscr{X}$ on $\mathscr{X}_\alpha$. Obviously $\alpha < \alpha'$ if and only if $t(\alpha) < t(\alpha')$. Denote by $t(A)$ the values of the function $\alpha \to t(\alpha)$. Since $\mathscr{N}$ must contain the spaces $\{0\}$ and $\mathscr{X}$, 0 and 1 belong to $t(A)$. On the other hand if $t_1 \geqslant t_2 \geqslant \cdots t_m \geqslant \cdots \to t$ or $t_1 \leqslant t_2 \leqslant \cdots \leqslant t_m \leqslant \cdots \to t$, and $\{t_m\} \subset t(A)$, then $t \in t(A)$ too. Indeed, if $t_m = t(\alpha_m)$ then we have that

$$\mathscr{Y} = \bigcap_{m=1}^{\infty} \mathscr{X}_{\alpha m}$$

(in the first case, the second one being analogous) is also an invariant subspace and if $\mathscr{Y} \notin \mathscr{N}$, $\mathscr{N} \cup \{\mathscr{Y}\}$ would be another nest larger than $\mathscr{N}$. Thus $\mathscr{Y} \in \mathscr{N}$, i.e. $\mathscr{Y} = \mathscr{X}_\alpha$. Now $P_{\alpha_1} \geqslant P_{\alpha_2} \geqslant \cdots$ converges strongly to P_α, thus $t(\alpha_n) \to t(\alpha)$, i.e. $t_m \to t(\alpha)$, whence $t = t(\alpha) \in t(A)$. In this manner, $t(A)$ is closed and contains the points 0 and 1. Therefore $[0, 1] \setminus t(A)$ is the union of a family $\mathscr{F}$ (at most countable) of open disjoint intervals

$(a, a') \subset [0, 1]$. For $t = t(\alpha) \in t(A)$ put $\mathbf{E}_t = P_\alpha$, while for t belonging to an interval $(a, a') \in \mathscr{F}$ put $\mathbf{E}_t = \mathbf{E}_a$ which makes sense since $a \in t(A)$. Obviously $\mathbf{E}_0 = 0, \mathbf{E}_1 = I, \mathbf{E}_s \leqslant \mathbf{E}_t$ for $s \leqslant t$ and $\mathbf{E}_{t+0} = \mathbf{E}_t$, that is $\{\mathbf{E}_t\}_{0 \leqslant t \leqslant 1}$ is a spectral scale. Since $\mathbf{E}_t\mathscr{X}$ is invariant to T the condition (i) in Definition 6.6 is verified. Concerning the second condition (ii), let us remark that if $\mathbf{E}_d \neq \mathbf{E}_{d-0}$, then there exists an interval $(a, a') \in \mathscr{F}$, $a' = d$ and

$$\mathbf{E}_{d-0} = \mathbf{E}_a, \quad \mathbf{E}_d = \mathbf{E}_{a'}.$$

Let $a = t(\alpha)$, $a' = t(\alpha')$. If

$$\dim (\mathscr{X}_{\alpha'}/\mathscr{X}_\alpha) = \dim (\mathscr{X}_{\alpha'} \ominus \mathscr{X}_\alpha)$$

is $\neq 1$, then by the property (Triang$_0$) of T there exists an invariant subspace $\mathscr{Y}$ of T such that $\mathscr{X}_\alpha \underset{\neq}{\subset} \mathscr{Y} \underset{\neq}{\subset} \mathscr{X}_{\alpha'}$ so that $\mathscr{N}$ is no longer maximal. In this way $\dim (\mathscr{X}_{\alpha'} \ominus \mathscr{X}_\alpha) = 1$, i.e. $\mathbf{E}_d - \mathbf{E}_{d-0}$ has a one-dimensional range (namely $\mathscr{X}_{\alpha'} \ominus \mathscr{X}_\alpha$). This completes our proof.

6.12. COROLLARY. *Let $T \in B(\mathscr{H})$, where $\mathscr{H}$ is a separable Hilbert space, have the property* (Triang$_0$). *Then there exists a normal operator N in a (separable) Hilbert space $\mathscr{N}$ such that $T \oplus N$ is reducible to a triangular form and $\sigma(N) \subset \sigma_\infty(T)$. If $\sigma(T)$ does not separate the plane then $\sigma(N) \subset \sigma(T)$; in particular if T is self-adjoint, N is also self-adjoint.*

With the exception of the last assertion (which follows from the fact that if a normal operator N has a real spectrum then N is self-adjoint) the corollary follows directly from Propositions 6.8 and 6.11 and Theorem 6.9.

In what follows we shall show some operators having the property (Triang$_0$).

6.13. THEOREM. *Let $\mathscr{H}$ be a Hilbert space of dimension > 1 and let $T \in B(\mathscr{H})$ be such that $\sigma(T) = \{0\}$ and that in the closed* [*in $B(\mathscr{H})$*] *algebra generated by T and I there exists a compact operator $A \neq 0$. Then T has nontrivial invariant subspaces.*

(*Remark.* Since $\sigma(T) = \{0\}$ and A is compact it follows easily that actually A belongs to the closed algebra generated only by T).

Proof. We may suppose $\|T\| \leqslant 1$, and $\dim \mathscr{H} = \aleph_0$. Choose $f \in \mathscr{H}$, $\|f\| = 1$, and denote by $\mathscr{H}_n$ the space spanned by $f, Tf, \ldots T^n f$, and by P_n the orthogonal projection of $\mathscr{H}$ on $\mathscr{H}_n$. Obviously

$$P_1 \leqslant P_2 \leqslant \cdots \leqslant P_n \leqslant \cdots$$

If $P_n \nrightarrow I$, $\overline{\bigcup_n \mathscr{H}_n} = \mathscr{L}$ would be an invariant nontrivial subspace of T, hence we have to suppose that $P_n \to I$. Moreover, we may suppose that f, $Tf, \ldots, T^n f$ form a linearly independent system (for every n) since otherwise we would have

$$T^{k+1} f = a_0 f + \cdots + a_k T^k f$$

for a certain k and $\mathscr{H}_k$ would be invariant for T. Now set

$$T_n = P_n T | \mathscr{H}_n, \quad (n = 1, 2, \ldots)$$

and take a maximal system $\{\mathscr{L}_n^{(i)}\}_i$ of invariant subspaces of T_n. Since $\mathscr{H}_n$ is finite dimensional we have

$$\{0\} = \mathscr{L}_n^{(0)} \subsetneqq \mathscr{L}_n^{(1)} \subsetneqq \mathscr{L}_n^{(2)} \subsetneqq \cdots \subsetneqq \mathscr{L}_n^{(n-1)} \subsetneqq \mathscr{L}_n^{(n)} = \mathscr{H}_n,$$

where

$$\dim \mathscr{L}_n^{(i)} = i.$$

Denote by $Q_n^{(i)}$ the orthogonal projection of $\mathscr{H}$ on $\mathscr{L}_n^{(i)}$. We have $Q_n^{(i)} \leqslant P_n$ and

$$Q_n^{(i)} T Q_n^{(i)} = Q_n^{(i)} P_n T P_n Q_n^{(i)} = Q_n^{(i)} T_n Q_n^{(i)} = T_n Q_n^{(i)} = P_n T Q_n^{(i)},$$

i.e. $Q_n = Q_n^{(i)}$ verifies the following conditions

$$Q_n \leqslant P_n \quad \text{and} \quad Q_n T Q_n = P_n T Q_n. \tag{1}$$

Now from (1) we deduce

$$(P_n - Q_n)\, T^* (P_n - Q_n) = P_n T^* P_n - Q_n T^* P_n - P_n T^* Q_n + Q_n T^* Q_n$$
$$= P_n T^* (P_n - Q_n),$$

i.e.

$$(P_n - Q_n)\, T^* (P_n - Q_n) = P_n T^* (P_n - Q_n). \tag{2}$$

Suppose now that $Q_{n_k} \rightharpoonup Q$ (weakly). Then

$$TQT^* \leqslant Q, \quad T^* (I - Q)\, T \leqslant I - Q. \tag{3}$$

Indeed for $h \in \mathscr{H}$ we have, by (1),

$$(P_n T Q_n T^* P_n h, h) = (Q_n T Q_n T^* Q_n h, h) = \|Q_n T^* Q_n h\|^2 \leqslant \|Q_n h\|^2 = (Q_n, h, h).$$

Since $P_{n_k} \to I$ (strongly) and $Q_{n_k} \rightharpoonup Q$ (weakly) we obtain

$$(QT^*h, T^*h) = \lim_{n\to\infty} (Q_{n_k} T^* P_{n_k} h, TP_{n_k} h) \leqslant \lim_{n\to\infty} (Q_{n_k} h, h) = (Qh, h)\,(h \in \mathscr{H});$$

this is the first of relations (3). The second one can be deduced in the same manner, using (2) instead of (1). As $(Q_n^{(i)} f, f)$ is increasing with i from 0 to 1 there exists an i_n such that for a fixed $0 < \alpha < 1$ we have

$$(Q_n^{(i_n)} f, f) \leqslant \alpha < (Q_n^{(i_n+1)} f, f). \tag{4}$$

Since $\dim \mathscr{H}_n = n$, $\dim \mathscr{H}_{n-1} = n - 1$, there exists an element $f_n \in \mathscr{H}_n \ominus \mathscr{H}_{n-1}$ such that $\|f_n\| = 1$ and

$$P_n f = P_{n-1} f + (f, f_n) f_n, \quad (n = 1, 2, \ldots; f \in \mathscr{H}).$$

We may choose $n_k \to \infty$ so that

$$(Tf_{n_k}, f_{n_k+1}) \to 0 \tag{5}$$

and

$$Q_{n_k}^{(-)} = Q_{n_k}^{(i_{n_k})} \to Q^{(-)}, \quad Q_{n_k}^{(+)} = Q_{n_k}^{(i_{n_k}+1)} \to Q^{(+)} \text{ (weakly).} \tag{6}$$

Obviously it is sufficient to prove that one can choose $n_k \to \infty$ so that (5) is valid. With this aim let us remark that

$$(T^n f_0, f_n) = (Tf_0, f_1) \cdots (Tf_{n-1}, f_n), \quad (n = 1, 2, \ldots). \tag{7}$$

Indeed, if $T^n f_0 = \alpha_0 f_0 + \cdots + \alpha_n f_n$, then

$$\begin{aligned}(T^{n+1} f_0, f_{n+1}) &= (T(\alpha_0 f_0 + \cdots + \alpha_n f_n), f_{n+1}) \\ &= \alpha_n (Tf_n, f_{n+1}) = (T^n f_0, f_n)(Tf_n, f_{n+1}) \\ &= (Tf_0, f_1)(Tf_1, f_2) \cdots (Tf_n, f_{n+1}).\end{aligned}$$

If there exists an $\varepsilon > 0$ such that

$$|(Tf_n, f_{n+1})| \geqslant \varepsilon \quad \text{for} \quad n \to \infty,$$

then by (7)

$$\varepsilon^n \leqslant |(T^n f_0, f_n)| \leqslant \|T^n f_0\| \, \|f_n\| \leqslant \|T^n\|,$$

contradicting the fact that $\sigma(T) = \{0\}$, i.e. $\|T^n\|^{1/n} \to 0$.

Thus we may assume that (5) and (6) hold. Taking into account that

$$\|T^j P_n - (P_n T P_n)^j\| \leqslant j \|TP_n - P_n T P_n\|$$

and that

$$\|TP_n - P_n T P_n\| \leqslant |(Tf_n, f_{n+1})|$$

it follows by (5)

$$\|T^j P_{n_k} - (P_{n_k} T P_{n_k})^j\| \to 0 \quad \text{for all} \quad j = 0, 1, 2, \ldots$$

Therefore, using (1),

$$\|T^j Q_{n_k}^{(\pm)} - Q_{n_k}^{(\pm)} T^j Q_{n_k}^{(\pm)}\| = \|(I - Q_{n_k}^{(\pm)}) \, T^j P_{n_k} Q_{n_k}^{(\pm)}\|$$

$$\leqslant \|(I - Q_{n_k}^{(\pm)}) \, (P_{n_k} T P_{n_k})^j Q_{n_k}^{(\pm)}\|$$

$$+ \|T^j P_{n_k} - (P_{n_k} T P_{n_k})^j\| \to 0,$$

that is

$$\|T^j Q_{n_k}^{(\pm)} - Q_{n_k}^{(\pm)} T^j Q_{n_k}^{(\pm)}\| \to 0. \tag{8}$$

Let now $p(\lambda)$ be a polynomial (in λ). Using (8) and the fact that A is compact (hence that $AQ_{n_k}^{(\pm)} \to AQ^{(\pm)}$ strongly and consequenty

$$Q_{n_k}^{(\pm)} \, A Q_{n_k}^{(\pm)} \to Q^{(\pm)} A Q^{(\pm)}$$

weakly) we obtain

$$|((Q^{(\pm)} A Q^{(\pm)} - AQ^{(\pm)}) f, g)| = \lim_{n_k \to \infty} |((Q_{n_k}^{(\pm)} A Q_{n_k}^{(\pm)} - A Q_{n_k}^{(\pm)}) f, g)|$$

$$\leqslant \lim_{n_k \to \infty} \{|([Q_{n_k}^{(\pm)} - I] \, [A - p(T)] \, Q_{n_k}^{(\pm)} f, g)|$$

$$+ \|p(T) \, Q_{n_k}^{(\pm)} - Q_{n_k}^{(\pm)} p(T) \, Q_{n_k}^{(\pm)}\| \, \|f\| \, \|g\|\}$$

$$\leqslant \|A - p(T)\| \, \|f\| \|g\|$$

for all $f, g \in H$, hence

$$\|Q^{(\pm)} \, A Q^{(\pm)} - A Q^{(\pm)} \, \| \leqslant \|A - p(T)\|. \tag{6}$$

Now the norm on the right side of (9) can be made as small as we want, therefore

$$Q^{(\pm)} AQ^{(\pm)} = AQ^{(\pm)}, \quad A \neq 0. \tag{10}$$

Since $Q_{n_k}^{(+)} - Q_{n_k}^{(-)}$ has one-dimensional range, $Q^{(+)} - Q^{(-)}$ has the range of dimension $\leqslant 1$. On the other hand, by (4)

$$(Q^{(-)} f, f) \leqslant \alpha \leqslant (Q^{(+)} f, f),$$

so that at least either $Q^{(+)}$ or $Q^{(-)}$ must be $\neq 0$ and I also. Let Q be this operator. By the second of relations (3) the space $\mathscr{L} = \{h; Qh = h\}$ is invariant with respect to T. Since $Q \neq I$, we have $\mathscr{L} \neq \mathscr{H}$. The only unpleasant case is when $\mathscr{L} = \{0\}$. By (10) this implies $AQ = 0$. Since $A \neq 0$, we have $\overline{Q\mathscr{H}} \neq \mathscr{H}$ and since $Q \neq 0$, we have also $\overline{Q\mathscr{H}} \neq \{0\}$. Now $\mathscr{L}' = \mathscr{H} \ominus \overline{Q\mathscr{H}} = \{h; Qh = 0\}$ so that by the first of relations (3), $\mathscr{L}'$ is invariant with respect to T^*, thus $\overline{Q\mathscr{H}}$ is invariant with respect to T. This completes the proof.

6.14. COROLLARY. *Let $T \in B(\mathscr{H})$ and let $p(T)$ be compact for a certain polynomial $p(\lambda) \not\equiv 0$. Then T has the property* (Triang$_0$).

Proof. Let $\mathscr{H}_1$ and $\mathscr{H}_2$, $\mathscr{H}_1 \subset \mathscr{H}_2$, be two invariant subspaces of T such that $\dim(\mathscr{H}_2 \ominus \mathscr{H}_1) > 1$. Put $T_2 = T|\mathscr{H}_2$. Then $p(T_2) = p(T)|\mathscr{H}_2$, hence $p(T_2)$ is also compact. Putting $p^{\sim}(\lambda) = \overline{p(\bar{\lambda})}$, we have $p^{\sim}(T_2^*) = p(T_2)^*$, hence $p^{\sim}(T_2^*)$ is also compact. Let us now put $U = (T_2^*|\mathscr{H}_2 \ominus \mathscr{H}_1)^*$. Then

$$p(U) = (p^{\sim}(U^*))^* = (p^{\sim}(T_2^*)|\mathscr{H}_2 \ominus \mathscr{H}_1)^*$$

is compact. If $\mathscr{M} \subset \mathscr{H}_2 \ominus \mathscr{H}_1$ is a nontrivial subspace of $\mathscr{H}_2 \ominus \mathscr{H}_1$, invariant with respect to U, it is obvious that $\mathscr{H}_1 \oplus \mathscr{M}$ is the intermediate invariant subspace $\mathscr{H}_3$ occurring in the Definition 6.10 of the property (Triang$_0$). Thus we have only to prove that an operator T verifying the conditions stated in the corollary, has nontrivial invariant subspaces.

If the spectrum of T does not reduce to a point, then the existence of an invariant subspace of T follows by the spectral decomposition corresponding to separate parts of the spectrum, since $\sigma(T)$ contains isolated points. Therefore we may suppose that $\sigma(T)$ reduces to a point which can be taken as 0.

If now $p(T) \neq 0$ the existence of invariant subspaces follows from Theorem 6.13. If $p(T) = 0$, then putting $p(\lambda)$ in the form $a_0 (\lambda - \lambda_1)^{n_1} \cdots (\lambda - \lambda_q)^{n_q}$, we have obviously

$$a_0 (T - \lambda_1 I)^{n_1} \cdots (T - \lambda_q I)^{n_q} = 0,$$

which shows that T has necessarily an eigenvalue, thus also a nontrivial invariant subspace.

6.15. LEMMA. *Let $T = N + K \in B(\mathscr{H})$, where $\mathscr{H}$ is a Hilbert space, N is a normal operator and K a compact operator in $\mathscr{H}$. Suppose that $\sigma(T) = \{\lambda_0\}$. Then $T - \lambda_0 I$ is a compact operator.*

Proof. Since $N = T - K$ we have

$$(\lambda I - N)^{-1} = (\lambda I - T)^{-1} [I - K(\lambda I - T)^{-1}]^{-1},$$

where the operator in [...] has an inverse except for a discrete closed set of points converging to α (this on account of a classical result in perturbation theory; see Ref. 30, Lemma VII.6.13). Thus the normal operator $N - \alpha I$ has for its spectrum a discrete set of points λ_n converging to 0 if this set is infinite. Since λ_n is an isolated point in the spectrum of the normal operator $N - \alpha I$, λ_n must be an eigenvalue of this operator. If the multiplicity of λ_n were not finite, there would exist an orthonormal system $\{h_n\}_{n=1}^{\infty}$ of eigenvectors $(N - \alpha I) h_n = \lambda_n h_n$, i.e. $Nh_n = \mu h_n$ where $\mu \neq \alpha$. Therefore

$$h_n = (T - \mu I)^{-1} K h_n \to 0$$

strongly, since $h_n \rightharpoonup 0$ weakly; a contradiction. Accordingly, every eigenvalue λ_n of $N - \alpha I$ is of finite multiplicity. All this implies that $N - \alpha I$ is a compact operator, thus $T - \alpha I = N - \alpha I + K$ is compact too.

6.16. THEOREM. *Let T be an operator in a Hilbert space $\mathscr{H}$ such that $T^* - T \in \mathscr{C}_p$ for $1 \leqslant p < \infty$. Then T has the property* (Triang$_0$).

Proof. Let us firstly reduce the problem to an easier one. With this aim let $\mathscr{H}_1 \subset \mathscr{H}_2$ be two invariant subspaces of T and let $\mathscr{L} = \mathscr{H}_2 \ominus \mathscr{H}_1$. Put $U = PT|\mathscr{L}$ where P denotes the orthogonal projection of $\mathscr{H}$ on $\mathscr{L}$.

The existence of a nontrivial invariant subspace $\mathscr{M}$ of U implies the existence of an invariant subspace $\mathscr{H}_3 = \mathscr{H}_1 \oplus \mathscr{M}$ of T verifying $\mathscr{H}_1$

$\subsetneqq \mathscr{H}_3 \subsetneqq \mathscr{H}_2$. Since $U^* - U = P(T^* - T)|\mathscr{L} \in \mathscr{C}_p$ too, we have only to verify that the conditions stated in the theorem are sufficient for the existence of a nontrivial subspace of T whenever $\dim \mathscr{H} > 1$.

We have to consider three cases.

(a) The spectrum $\sigma(T) \subset R$ (= the real line) and does not reduce to a point. It suffices to apply Corollary 5.3.

(b) The spectrum of T contains a point $\alpha + i\beta$, with $\beta \neq 0$, but does not reduce to a point. Since $T = A + K$, where $A = A^*$ and K is compact, we have

$$T - (\alpha + i\beta) I = [A - (\alpha + i\beta) I]^{-1} \{I + [A - (\alpha + i\beta) I]^{-1} K\},$$

so that the operator

$$I + \bar{K} = I + [A - (\alpha + i\beta) I]^{-1} K$$

has no inverse bounded everywhere defined operator. Now $\bar{K}$ is compact, hence by the well-known Fredholm-Riesz theory (see for instance Ref. 30, VII.4) there exists an $h \neq 0$, $h \in \mathscr{H}$, such that $(I + \bar{K}) h = 0$. It follows that $Th = (\alpha + i\beta) h$. The space spanned by h is invariant for T and it is nontrivial since otherwise $\sigma(T) = \{\alpha + i\beta\}$.

(c) The spectrum of T contains only one point α. Then by Lemma 6.15, $T - \alpha I$ is compact so that by the Corollary 6.14, T has a nontrivial invariant subspace, if $\dim \mathscr{H} > 1$.

The proof of the theorem is now complete.

Notes and Remarks

The operators with increasing polynomials, that is

$$(P) \quad \|T^n\| = O(|n|^\alpha), \quad (\alpha \geqslant 0 \text{ fixed}, \quad n \in Z, |n| \to \infty)$$

have been studied by E. R. Lorch[77] in the case of reflexive Banach spaces and $\alpha = 0$. On the case of the Hilbert spaces these last operators were already considered by B. Sz.-Nagy[135] who showed that they are similar to unitary operators.

Later F. Wolf[130] introduced the class of all operators verifying (P) and studied it in a detailed manner. Proposition 1.4, 1.6, and 1.7 belong to F. Wolf.[130] Recently G. K. Leaf[69,70], brought new informations on the class of operators satisfying (P) with $\alpha \leqslant 1$. The first application, namely Lemma 1.8, Theorem 1.9, and Corollary 1.10, belongs essentially to B. Sz.-Nagy and the second author. The second application, namely Theorem 1.11 and Remark 1.12, was suggested by Proposition 3 in Ref. 43. However, the proof given here is quite different: the argument used in this proof is taken from the classical proof of Hadamard's multiplication theorem (see Bieberbach[10]).

The algebras $\mathfrak{A}[\varrho]$ were firstly considered by A. Beurling in Ref. 9. The basic Theorem 2.7 seems to be new. The important Theorem 2.12 is believed due to A. Beurling. Its proof, which is given here, is inspired by a paper of Wermer[128] in which the continuous analogue of $\mathfrak{A}[\varrho]$ is studied. Theorem 3.2 is new although the possibility of using the algebra $\mathfrak{A}[\varrho]$ for the construction of a functional calculus for operators was already suggested by A. Beurling (see for instance Ref. 127, p. 616); however, Theorem 3.2 (see for instance its Corollary 3.3) constitutes an improvement on the known result[127] of J. Wermer.

These results should be compared also with previous results of Yu. I. Lyubic and V. I. Mačaev. These authors considered a class of operators which have certain generalized spectral decompositions (called by them S-operators[136,137]).

In our terminology an operator $T \in B(\mathscr{X})$ is an S-operator if

(i) The spectrum $\sigma(T)$ of T lies on the real axis R (or even on a regular Jordan curve),

(ii) for every closed arc Δ of R, there exists the maximal spectral space $\mathscr{X}_T(\Delta)$,

(iii) for every finite covering $\{\Delta_i\}_{i=1}^n$ of $\sigma(T)$ with arcs Δ_i, we have

$$\mathscr{X} = \overline{\mathscr{X}_T(\bar{\Delta}_1) + \mathscr{X}_T(\bar{\Delta}_2) + \cdots + \mathscr{X}_T(\bar{\Delta}_n)}.$$

It seems difficult to determine the precise relationships between the class of the S-operators and the class of decomposable operators with real spectrum; however, some remarks can be made. Lyubic and Mačaev proved that if an operator T has real spectrum and if for a sufficiently small $\varepsilon > 0$ the integral

$$\int_0^{\varepsilon} \log \log \sup_{|\operatorname{Im}\lambda| \geqslant \delta} \|R(\lambda; T)\| \, d\delta$$

is convergent, then T is an S-operator. Actually, T is also decomposable, since it can be seen that the Cayley transform T' of T verifies

$$\sum_{n \in Z} \frac{\log \|T'^n\|}{1 + n^2} < \infty$$

and therefore T' is $\mathfrak{A}$-unitary, thus T is $\mathfrak{A}$-self-adjoint.

Theorem 4.3 seems new, while Theorem 4.5 synthetizes results of Tillmann,[121] Smart, [116] and Sh. Kantorowitz.[55] Corollary 4.6 belongs to Sh. Kantorowitz.[55] For further results concerning the operators considered in Theorem 4.5 we refer to the papers (Refs. 121, 122, 116, 54, 55, 56, etc.) of the above authors. The results of § 5 were suggested by an argument used by Sahnovič in Ref. 104 and by the paper[112] of J. Schwartz. A great part of the exposition and of the proofs given in § 5 are taken from this paper of J. Schwartz. However, the results of the preceding § 4 made it possible for us to deduce the new Theorem 5.2. Corollary 5.3 is a slight improvement of a result of J. Schwartz in Ref. 112 for p arbitrary and of a previous result of Sahnovič[105] for $p = 2$. The applications given in sections 5.5–5.7 are only illustrative. The structure theorems of J-self-adjoint operators or J-unitary operators (see for instance I. S. Iohvidov and M. G. Krein,[50] H. Langer,[69] or M. A. Naimark[92]) are very strong and provide also Corollary 5.7 in a much more precise form.

The first part of § 6 (namely Sections 6.1–6.12), as presented here, is due essentially to Sahnovič.[104] Theorem 6.13 was announced without proof by J. Feldman in Notices Amer. Math. Soc. **12**, No. 4 (81), 470 (1965). Corollary 6.14 is due to A. R. Bernstein and A. Robinson,[131] being antecedent to Feldman's Theorem 6.13. Its proof, here given, was suggested by Halmos's proof[132] of Theorem 6.14. Lemma 6.15 and Theorem 6.16 seem to have been obtained independently by J. Schwartz[112] and I. C. Gohberg and M. G. Krein.[44]

Chapter 6

Some Examples and Some Open Questions

Multiplication Operators in Banach Spaces of Differentiable Functions

For the sake of unity we shall introduce the following

1.1. DEFINITION. Let Ω be a domain in R^n and Ξ a Banach space of (classes of) Borel functions $\xi(x)$ defined on Ω, such that

(i) $\xi = 0$ in Ξ if and only if $\xi(x) = 0$ a.e. (i.e. almost everywhere with respect to the Lebesgue measure) in Ω.

(ii) for all functions $\varphi \in C^\infty(R^n)$ verifying for a certain m $(= 0, 1, 2, \ldots)$

$$\|\varphi\|_m = \sup_{\substack{|\alpha| \leqslant m \\ x \in \Omega}} |D^\alpha \varphi(x)| < \infty \tag{1}$$

(where $D_\alpha = \partial^{\alpha_1 + \cdots + \alpha_n}/\partial x_1^{\alpha_1} \cdots \partial x_n^{\alpha_n}$, $|\alpha| = \alpha_1 + \cdots + \alpha_n$) we have

$$\varphi \Xi \subset \Xi \quad \text{and} \quad \|\varphi \xi\| \leqslant K \|\varphi\|_m \cdot \|\xi\|, \tag{2}$$

where K is a constant $< \infty$ independent of $\varphi \in C^\infty(\Omega)$ and $\xi \in \Xi$. *Ξ will be called a Banach space with differentiable multipliers of order $\leqslant m$.*

1.2. EXAMPLE

(1) If $1 \leqslant p \leqslant \infty$ and $r = 0, 1, 2, \ldots$ the Sobolev's spaces $W_p^r(\Omega)$ [in particular the Lebesgue spaces $L_p(\Omega) = W_p^0(\Omega)$] are Banach spaces with differentiable multipliers of order $\leqslant r$.

(2) If $m = 0, 1, 2, \ldots$ and $\overline{C^m}(\Omega)$ denotes the Banach space obtained by completing $\{\varphi \in C^\infty(\Omega) | \; \|\varphi\|_m < \infty\} \subset C^\infty(\Omega)$ with respect to the norm (1), then $\overline{C^m}(\Omega)$ is also a Banach space with differentiable multipliers of order $\leqslant m$.

(3) If $C^m(\overline{\Omega})$ denotes the closure of $C^\infty(R^n) \cap \overline{C^m}(\Omega)$ in $\overline{C^m}(\Omega)$ then obviously $C^m(\overline{\Omega})$ is also a Banach space with differentiable multipliers of order $\leqslant m$.

(4) If Ω is relatively compact, then the subspace

$$\mathscr{D}^m(\overline{\Omega}) = \{\xi \in \overline{C^m}(R^n) |\ \operatorname{supp} \xi \subset \overline{\Omega}\}$$

is also a Banach space with differentiable multipliers of order m.

(5) If $a \leqslant 1$ and Ξ is the subspace of $\overline{C^m}(\Omega)$ formed by the functions ξ whose mth derivates $D^\alpha \xi(x)$ satisfy a Lipschitz condition of order a, then Ξ is a Banach space with differentiable multipliers of order $\leqslant m + 1$, etc.

1.3. *Remark.* It is obvious that if Ξ is a Banach space with differentiable multipliers of order $\leqslant m$ then the multiplication $\varphi\xi$ is defined and continuous [actually (2) holds] from $C^m(\overline{\Omega}) \times \Xi$ into Ξ.

1.4. DEFINITION. Let Ξ be a Banach space with differentiable multipliers of order $\leqslant m$. A multiplication operator T in Ξ is an operator defined by

$$T\xi\,(x) = T(x)\,\xi(x), \quad \xi \in \Xi, \tag{1}$$

where $T(x) \in C^m(\overline{\Omega})$ is fixed.

We shall say that T corresponds to $T(x)$ and vice-versa.

1.5. PROPOSITION. *Let T be a multiplication operator in Ξ corresponding to $T(x)$. Then T is a generalized scalar operator, a spectral distribution of T is given by*

$$\mathbf{U}_\varphi \xi\,(x) = (\varphi \circ T)\,(x)\,\xi(x) = \varphi\,[T(x)]\,\xi(x), \quad \varphi \in C^\infty, \xi \in \Xi, \tag{1}$$

and finally

$$\Xi_T(F) = \{\xi | \xi \in \Xi, \operatorname{supp}(\xi) \subset T^{-1}(F)\} \tag{2}$$

for every closed $F \subset C$.

(Here the supp (ξ) is defined as the smallest subset ω of Ω closed in Ω, such that $\xi(x) = 0$, a.e. in $\Omega \setminus \omega$.)

Proof. Since it is evident that there exists a constant k such that for all $\varphi \in C^\infty$

$$\|\varphi \circ T\|_m \leqslant k|\varphi|_m\,\|T\|_m,$$

where

$$|\varphi|_m = \sup_{\substack{|\lambda| \leqslant \|T\|_m + 1 \\ \alpha+\beta \leqslant m}} \left| \frac{\partial^{\alpha+\beta}\varphi(\lambda)}{\partial\,(\text{Re}\,\lambda)^\alpha\,\partial\,(\text{Im}\,\lambda)^\beta} \right|,$$

$\mathbf{U}_\varphi$ is a multiplication operator in Ξ. In virtue of the Definition 1.1 (ii) we have

$$\|\mathbf{U}_\varphi\| \leqslant Kk\|T\|_m\,|\varphi|_m.$$

Thus $\varphi \to \mathbf{U}_\varphi$ is an operator-valued distribution of order $\leqslant m$. Since it is evident that $\varphi \to \mathbf{U}_\varphi$ is multiplicative and that $\mathbf{U}_\lambda = T$, $\mathbf{U}_1 = I$, $\mathbf{U}$ is a spectral distribution of T; consequently T is a generalized scalar operator. It remains to prove (2). With this aim let $\xi \in \Xi_T(F)$ and take an open set $G \subset \Omega$, relatively compact in Ω, such that $\bar{G} \cap T^{-1}(F) = 0$. Choose a $\psi \in C^\infty$, $\psi = 1$ in a neighborhood of $T(G)$ and $\psi = 0$ in a neighborhood of F [this choice is possible since by the continuity of $T(x)$ on $\bar{G}$, $T(\bar{G})$ is compact and disjoint of F]. Consequently since $\sigma_T(\xi) \subset F$ and supp (ψ) $\cap F = \varnothing$ we have (see Proposition 3.1.12) $\mathbf{U}_\psi\xi = 0$, i.e. $\psi\,(T(x))\,\xi(x)$ $= 0$ a.e. in Ω. In particular $\xi(x) = 0$ a.e. in G, therefore $G \cap$ supp (ξ) $= \varnothing$; whence it easily follows that supp $(\xi) \subset T^{-1}(F)$.

Conversely, if supp $(\xi) \subset T^{-1}(F)$ and H is an arbitrary neighborhood of F, then choosing a $\psi \in C^\infty$ such that $\psi = 1$ in a neighborhood of F and $\psi = 0$ outside of H, we have $\psi\,[T(x)]\,\xi(x) - \xi(x) = 0$ a.e. in Ω, i.e. $U_\psi\xi$ $- \xi = 0$. Thus

$$\xi = U_\psi\xi \in \Xi_T\,(\text{supp}\,(\psi)) \subset \Xi_T(\bar{H}).$$

As

$$\bigcap_{\substack{H \supset F \\ H \text{ open}}} \Xi_T(\bar{H}) = \Xi_T(F),$$

it results $\xi \in \Xi_T(F)$. Thus (2) is demonstrated.

1.6. Corollary. *In the hypothesis of the preceding proposition we have*

$$\sigma(T) \subset \overline{T(\Omega)}.$$

Indeed, by the relation (2) of the preceding proposition we have $\Xi_T\,(\overline{T(\Omega)}) = \Xi$, whence by the property $\sigma\,(T|\Xi_T(F)) \subset F \cap \sigma(T)$ (see Proposition 1.3.8) we deduce $\sigma(T) \subset \overline{T(\Omega)}$.

A basic spectral property of the multiplication operators is given by the following

1.7. THEOREM. *Let S and T be two multiplication operators in a Banach space Ξ with differential multipliers of order $\leqslant m$. The following properties are equivalent*

(i) $S \overset{q}{\sim} T$;
(ii) $(S - T)^{[n]} = 0 = (T - S)^{[n]} = 0$ *for a certain* $n = 1, 2, \ldots$;
(iii) $\Xi_S(F) = \Xi_T(F)$ *for every closed* $F \subset C$; *and finally*
(iv) $S = T$.

Proof. The equivalence of properties (i), (ii), and (iii) is a consequence of the fact that by Proposition 1.5, S and T are generalized scalar operators (see Theorem 4.4.5). The implication (iv) $\Rightarrow$ (i) or (ii) or (iii) is obvious. It remains to prove that (iii) implies (iv).

For this purpose let $S(x)$ and $T(x)$ be the functions corresponding to S, respectively T. Let $x_0 \in \Omega$ be such that $S(x_0) \neq T(x_0)$ and choose $\varepsilon > 0$ small enough for the disks

$$\alpha = \{\lambda | \, |\lambda - S(x_0)| \leqslant \varepsilon\} \quad \text{and} \quad \beta = \{\lambda | \, |\lambda - T(x_0)| \leqslant \varepsilon\}$$

to be disjoint. Using Proposition 1.5 (2), we have, since (iii) is supposed to be valid,

$$\begin{aligned} \{\xi \in \Xi | \operatorname{supp} \xi \subset S^{-1}(\alpha)\} &= \Xi_S(\alpha) = \Xi_T(\alpha) \\ &= \{\xi \in \Xi | \operatorname{supp} \xi \subset T^{-1}(\alpha)\}. \end{aligned} \tag{1}$$

By the continuity of S, S^{-1} (Int α) is open and thus a neighborhood of x_0. We can therefore take a $\eta_0 \in C^\infty(R^n)$ with compact support in $S^{-1}(\alpha)$ such that $\eta_0 = 1$ in a neighborhood ω_0 of x_0. By (1) we have

$$\eta\eta_0 \in \{\xi \in \Xi | \operatorname{supp} \xi \subset T^{-1}(\alpha)\}, \tag{2}$$

for all $\eta \in \Xi$. Consequently, since $T^{-1}(\beta) \cap T^{-1}(\alpha) = \varnothing$ and $\eta_0 = 1$ on ω_0, we have

$$\eta(x) = 0 \quad \text{a.e. in} \quad \omega_1 = \omega_0 \cap T^{-1}(\text{Int}\, \beta).$$

Now ω_1 is a neighborhood of x_0, so that if ω is the largest open subset of Ω on which all $\eta \in \Xi$ vanish a.e., we have

$$\{x_0 \in \Omega | T(x_0) \neq S(x_0)\} \subset \omega.$$

In this way, $S(x)\,\eta(x) = T(x)\,\eta(x)$ a.e. in Ω, thus $S\eta = T\eta$ for all $\eta \in \Xi$, i.e. $S = T$.

1.8. COROLLARY. *A multiplication operator T has a single spectral distribution U for which* U_φ *are also multiplication operators, namely that given by formula* (1) *in Proposition* 1.5.

Indeed if V is another such spectral distribution of T, then by Corollary 3.2.5, we have $V_\varphi \overset{q}{\sim} U_\varphi$ for all $\varphi \in C^\infty$, thus, by Theorem 1.7, $U_\varphi = V_\varphi$.

From now on let us introduce a new condition on Ξ.

1.9. DEFINITION. A Banach space Ξ with differentiable multipliers of order $\leqslant m$, will be called *regular* if every $\xi \in \Xi$ belongs to $C(\Omega)$ (i.e. is continuous on Ω) and the applications $\varepsilon_x : \xi \to \xi(x)$ is continuous and $\neq 0$ on Ξ for every $x \in \Omega$.

1.10. EXAMPLES. Case (1) in section 1.2 is regular if $p > n$. This is a direct consequence of Sobolev's imbedding theorem for the spaces $W_p^r(\Omega)$ (see Ref. 30, Theorem XIV.4.5). The other cases are all regular!

1.11. THEOREM. *Let Ξ be a regular Banach space with differentiable multipliers of order $\leqslant n$ and let T be a multiplication operator of Ξ. Then T is not spectral (in Dunford's sense) except for the case $T = cI$ (where c is a constant and I the identity operator of Ξ).*

Proof. Suppose that T is spectral and let $\mathbf{E}$ be its spectral measure. Let $T(x)$ be the corresponding function of T. We have, for every closed set $F \subset C$:

$$\mathbf{E}(F)\,\Xi = \Xi_T(F) = \{\xi \in \Xi \mid \operatorname{supp} \xi \subset T^{-1}(F)\}. \tag{1}$$

Put $G = C \setminus F$ and let $\{F_n\}_1^\infty$ be an increasing sequence of closed sets such that $G = \bigcup_1^\infty F_n$. We have $\mathbf{E}(F_n) \to \mathbf{E}(G) = I - \mathbf{E}(F)$ strongly. Hence for every $\xi \in \Xi$ we have

$$\eta_n = \mathbf{E}(F_n)\,\xi \to [I - \mathbf{E}(F)]\,\xi = \eta.$$

Now by (1)

$$\operatorname{supp} \eta_n \subset T^{-1}(F_n),$$

so that $\eta_n(x) = 0$ for $x \in T^{-1}(F)$. We have, using the regularity of Ξ,

$$0 = \eta_n(x) = \langle \eta_n, \varepsilon_x \rangle \to \langle \eta, \varepsilon_x \rangle = \eta(x), \quad x \in T^{-1}(F);$$

accordingly

$$\eta(x) = 0 \quad \text{on} \quad T^{-1}(F),$$

thus

$$\xi(x) = (\mathbf{E}(F)\,\xi)\,(x) \quad \text{on} \quad T^{-1}(F). \tag{2}$$

On the other hand by (1) we have

$$(\mathbf{E}(F)\,\xi)\,(x) = 0 \quad \text{on} \quad \Omega \setminus T^{-1}(F). \tag{2'}$$

Consequently if ψ_F denotes the function

$$\psi_F(x) = \begin{cases} 0 & \text{if} \quad x \in \Omega \setminus T^{-1}(F), \\ 1 & \text{if} \quad x \in T^{-1}(F), \end{cases}$$

we infer from (2) and (2')

$$\psi_F \xi = \mathbf{E}(F)\,\xi.$$

In this manner the multiplication by ψ_F is an operator of Ξ. In particular $\chi_F \Xi \subset \Xi \subset C(\Omega)$. Let $\xi_0(x_0) \neq 0$ for a certain $x_0 \in \Omega$ and a suitable choosen $\xi_0 \in \Xi$. Put $F = \{T(x_0)\}$. Then if $T(x)$ is not constant in a neighborhood of x_0, x_0 is not an interior point of $T^{-1}(F)$, thus by continuity we must have

$$\xi_0(x_0) = \psi_F(x_0)\,\xi_0(x_0) = \lim_{\substack{x_n \to x_0 \\ x_n \notin T^{-1}(F)}} \chi_F(x_n)\,\xi(x_n) = 0.$$

Contradiction! Therefore $T(x)$ must be constant in a neighborhood of x_0. Now, obviously, the continuous function $T(x)$ being locally constant in the domain Ω must be constant in Ω, i.e. $T(x) \equiv c$, thus $T = cI$.

1.12. *Remark*. Theorem 1.11 shows that the operator of multiplication with a nonconstant function in any of the spaces indicated in No. 1.10 is not spectral in Dunford's sense, though it is a generalized scalar operator.

1.13 Proposition. *Let Ξ be a regular Banach space with differentiable multipliers of order $\leqslant n$. Suppose moreover that $C_0^\infty(\Omega)$ (the space of infinitely differentiable functions with compact support in Ω) is contained in*

Ξ, and that its closure in Ξ contains every $\xi \in \Xi$ with compact support in Ω. Let T be a multiplication operator in Ξ.

Then, if T is regular as generalized scalar operator, the spectral distribution **U** *defined in Proposition* 1.5 (1) *commutes with every operator $X \in \mathbf{B}(\Xi)$ commuting with T, and moreover* **U** *is uniquely determined by this condition.*

Proof. Let **V** denote a spectral distribution of T commuting with every operator $X \in \mathbf{B}(\Xi)$ which commutes with T. In view of Lemma 4.1.4 it suffices to show that $\mathbf{V}_{\bar{\lambda}} = \mathbf{U}_{\bar{\lambda}}$, i.e. that $\mathbf{V}_{\bar{\lambda}}$ is the multiplication operator corresponding to the complex conjugate function $\overline{T(x)}$ of the function $T(x)$ corresponding to T.

Since the multiplication operator by $\varphi \in C^{\infty}(R^n)$ commutes with T we have

$$\mathbf{V}_{\bar{\lambda}}(\varphi \cdot \xi) = \varphi \cdot \mathbf{V}_{\bar{\lambda}}(\xi), \quad \xi \in \Xi. \tag{1}$$

Fix a point $a \in \Omega$ and put $a^* = \mathbf{V}^*_{\bar{\lambda}}\varepsilon_a$, i.e.

$$a^*(\xi) = \mathbf{V}_{\bar{\lambda}}\xi\,(a), \quad \xi \in \Xi.$$

By (1) we have

$$a^*(\varphi \cdot \xi) = \varphi(a) \cdot a^*(\xi), \quad \varphi \in C^{\infty}(R^n), \quad \xi \in \Xi. \tag{2}$$

Consequently, if $\xi \in \Xi$ is 0 in a neighborhood G of a we have

$$a^*(\xi) = \varphi(a) \cdot a^*(\xi) = a^*(\varphi \cdot \xi) = a^*(0) = 0,$$

for every function $\varphi \in C^{\infty}(R^n)$ such that $\varphi(a) = 1$ and $\varphi(x) = 0$ for $x \notin G$. This shows that if ξ and η coincide in a neighborhood of a then $a^*(\xi) = a^*(\eta)$. Let now φ_0 be a fixed function of $C_0^{\infty}(\Omega)$ such that $\varphi_0 = 1$ in a neighborhood of a. Then by the preceding remark $a^*(\xi) = a^*(\xi \cdot \varphi_0)$. Since $\xi \cdot \varphi_0 \in \Xi$ and supp $(\xi\varphi_0)$ is compact in Ω, by the assumption in the statement of the proposition there exists a $\psi_n \in C_0^{\infty}(\Omega)$ such that $\psi_n \to \xi\varphi_0$ in Ξ. Obviously we have $\psi_n\varphi_0 \to \xi\varphi_0^2$ in Ξ. Thus by (2)

$$a^*(\psi_n\varphi_0) = \psi_n(a)\, a^*(\varphi_0) \to \xi(a)\, \varphi_0(a)\, a^*(\varphi_0) = \xi(a)\, a^*(\varphi_0),$$

and since $a^*(\psi_n\varphi_0) \to a^*(\xi\varphi_0^2) = a^*(\xi)$ (because $\xi = \xi\varphi_0^2$ in a neighborhood of a) we obtain

$$a^*(\xi) = \xi(a)\, a^*(\varphi_0) = \xi(a)\, \alpha(a).$$

Concluding, we obtained a function $\alpha : a \to \alpha(a)$ such that

$$\mathbf{V}_{\bar{\lambda}}(a) = \alpha(a)\,\xi(a) \quad (\xi \in \Xi,\ a \in \Omega). \tag{3}$$

Now $V_{\bar{\lambda}}$ and $U_{\bar{\lambda}}$ are generalized scalar operators having spectral maximal spaces, namely

$$\Xi(F) = \Xi_T(F^*) \quad \text{where} \quad F^* = \{\lambda | \bar{\lambda} \in F\},$$

and $F \subset C$ is an arbitrary closed set.

By Theorem 4.4.5 it results that $(\mathbf{U}_{\bar{\lambda}} - \mathbf{V}_{\bar{\lambda}})^{[n]} = 0$ for a certain integer $n \geqslant 1$. Now, if we put $\beta(x) = \overline{T(x)} - \alpha(x)$, $x \in \Omega$, it is obvious that

$$\beta(x)^n\, \xi(a) = ((\mathbf{U}_{\bar{\lambda}} - \mathbf{V}_{\bar{\lambda}})^{[n]}\xi)\,(x) = 0,$$

from which it follows $\beta(x)^n \equiv 0$, thus $\beta(x) \equiv 0$. In view of (3) this shows that $\mathbf{V}_{\bar{\lambda}} = \mathbf{U}_{\bar{\lambda}}$. The proof is now complete.

1.14. *Remark*. It is obvious that the examples (2)–(4) of section 1.2 satisfy all the assumptions of the preceding theorem. Moreover all these spaces are subspace of $\overline{C^m}(\Omega)$ with the inferred topology. We shall call, for convenience, a subspace of $\overline{C^m}(\Omega)$ veryfying the conditions of the preceding proposition, a *regular Banach subspace* of $\overline{C^m}(\Omega)$. We shall finish this paragraph with the following

1.15. THEOREM. *Let $\Omega \subset R^2$ which is identified as usual with the complex plane C. Let Ξ be a regular Banach subspace of $\overline{C^m}(\Omega)$ and let T be the multiplication operator corresponding to the function $T(\lambda) \equiv \lambda$. Then the following statements are equivalent:*

(i) $\|C_T(X)\|^{1/n} \to 0$;
(ii) $C_T^n(X) = 0$ *for a certain* $n = 1, 2, \ldots$;
(iii) $X\Xi_T(F) \subset \Xi_T(F)$ *for every closed set* $F \subset C$;
(iv) $XT = TX$;

and finally

(v) $(X\xi)(\lambda) = X(\lambda)\,\xi(\lambda)$ *for all* $\xi \in \Xi$, *where* $X(\lambda) \in C^m(\Omega)$

is fixed.

[Here $C^m(\Omega)$ denotes the space of all functions m-times continuously differentiable in Ω.]

Proof. Since (i), (ii) and (iii) are equivalent properties of every generalized scalar operator (see Theorem 4.4.5), hence in particular also of T, and since the implications (v) $\Rightarrow$ (iv) $\Rightarrow$ (ii) are obvious, it suffices to prove that (iii) $\Rightarrow$ (v). With this purpose let us consider the functional

$$u_\omega : \varphi \to X\varphi(\omega)$$

where $\varphi \in C_0^\infty(\Omega) \subset \Xi$ is arbitrary and $\omega \in \Omega$ is fixed. Obviously it is a distribution of order $\leqslant m$. Let $\operatorname{supp} \varphi \not\ni \omega$. Then, since in view of Proposition 1.5 (2) and the fact that $T(\lambda) \equiv \lambda$ we have

$$X\{\xi |\ \operatorname{supp}(\xi) \subset F\} \subset \{\xi |\ \operatorname{supp}(\xi) \subset F\},$$

hence

$$\operatorname{supp}(X\xi) \subset \operatorname{supp}(\xi),$$

it results that $X\varphi(\omega) = 0$. This signifies that the support of the distribution u_ω reduces to $\{\omega\}$, thus

$$u_\omega(\varphi) = \sum_{|\alpha| \leqslant m} a_\alpha(\omega)\, D^\alpha \varphi(\omega).$$

In this way we have

$$X\varphi(\lambda) = \sum_{|\alpha| \leqslant m} a_\alpha(\lambda)\, D^\alpha \varphi(\lambda) = P(\lambda; D)\,\varphi(\lambda)$$

for all $\varphi \in C_0^\infty(\Omega)$ and $\lambda \in \Omega$. By continuity, and by the fact that the closure $\overline{C_0^\infty(\Omega)}$ of $C_0^\infty(\Omega)$ in $\overline{C^m}(\Omega)$ belongs to Ξ, we obtain

$$P(\lambda; D)\,\varphi(\lambda) = X\varphi(\lambda) \in \Xi \subset \overline{C^m}(\Omega) \tag{1}$$

for all $\varphi \in \overline{C_0^\infty(\Omega)}$. Let $\psi(\lambda) \in C^m(\Omega)$. Take $\omega \in \Omega$ and a function $\varphi \in C_0^\infty(\Omega)$ such that $\varphi(\lambda) = 1$ in a neighborhood G of ω. Then $\varphi\psi \in \overline{C_0^\infty(\Omega)}$, thus by (1)

$$P(\lambda; D)\,\psi(\lambda) = P(\lambda; D)\,\varphi(\lambda)\,\psi(\lambda) = (X\varphi\psi)(\lambda) \quad \text{in} \quad G$$

implies that $P(\lambda; D)\,\psi(\lambda)$ is m-times continuously differentiable in G. It results

$$P(\lambda; D)\, C^m(\Omega) \subset C^m(\Omega). \tag{2}$$

Now it is evident that the differential operator $P(\lambda; D)$, which maps $C^m(\Omega)$ into itself, must be of order 0 (however this obvious fact necessitates a proof. We leave this proof to the reader as an exercise, though it is not quite as immediate as it looks!) Taking into account the preceding remark we have hence

$$X\varphi\ (\lambda) \equiv X(\lambda)\,\varphi(\lambda),$$

where $X(\lambda) = a_1(\lambda)$ is fixed and $\varphi \in \overline{C_0^\infty(\Omega)}$. Using now the density property of $C_0^\infty(\Omega)$ with respect to Ξ one deduces readily that

$$X\xi(\lambda) \equiv X(\lambda)\,\xi(\lambda), \quad (\xi \in \Xi).$$

The fact that $X(\lambda) \in \overline{C^m}(\Omega)$ follows easily; indeed if $G \subset \Omega$ is a relatively compact open set in Ω and $\varphi \in C_0^\infty(\Omega)$ verifies $\varphi = 1$ on G, then we have

$$X(\lambda) = X\psi\ (\lambda) \quad \text{on} \quad G,$$

which shows that $X(\lambda)$ is m-times continuously differentiable in G, thus also in the whole Ω. This completes the proof.

1.16. COROLLARY. *Under the conditions of Proposition* 1.5, *the following properties hold*

(i) *T is a regular generalized scalar operator.*
(ii) *T has a single spectral distribution, namely that defined by Proposition* 1.5 (2).
(iii) *Every quasi-nilpotent operator X commuting with T is equal to* 0.

Proof. In virtue of Theorem 4.2.6 it suffices to prove (iii). Suppose thus that $\|X^n\|^{1/n} \to 0$ and that X commutes with T. By the preceding theorem we have

$$X\xi\ (\lambda) = X(\lambda)\,\xi(\lambda), \quad (\xi \in \Xi),$$

where $X(\lambda) \in C^m(\Omega)$. Consequently

$$X^n\xi\ (\lambda) = X(\lambda)^n\,\xi(\lambda),$$

whence

$$|X(\lambda)|\ |\xi(\lambda)|^{1/n} \leqq \|X^n\xi\|^{1/n} \leqq \|X^n\|^{1/n}\ \|\xi\|^{1/n}.$$

Making $n \to \infty$ it results $|X(\lambda)| = 0$, therefore $X = 0$.

1.17. *Remark*. The conclusion of the corollary does not conserve its validity if T is replaced with another operator of multiplication. For instance let $\Omega = \{\lambda \mid |\lambda| < 1\}$, let $\Xi = \overline{C^m}(\Omega)$ and $T\varphi\,(\lambda) = \lambda^2\varphi\,(\lambda)$. Then if a

$a(\lambda) \in C^m(\Omega)$ is such that $a(\lambda) \not\equiv 0$ except that $a(\lambda) = 0$ for $\operatorname{Im} \lambda \leqslant 0$, the operator X defined by

$$X\varphi\,(\lambda) = a(\lambda)\,\varphi(-\lambda), \quad \varphi \in \overline{C^m}(\Omega),$$

is permutable with T, $X^2 = 0$ and $X \neq 0$.

2. Multiplication Operators in Banach Algebras

Let $\mathscr{B}$ be a commutative Banach algebra, let $\mathfrak{M}$ denote the space of (regular if $\mathscr{B}$ has no unity) maximal ideals of $\mathscr{B}$ endowed with Gelfand's topology, and let $x \to \hat{x}$ be the Gelfand's representation of $\mathscr{B}$ into $C_0(\mathfrak{M})$, i.e. into the space of all complex valued continuous functions which are null at infinity; if $\mathfrak{M}$ is compact (that is if $\mathscr{B}$ has unity), then $C_0(\mathfrak{M}) = C(\mathfrak{M})$.

Let us recall that $\mathscr{B}$ is said *regular* if for every $M_0 \in \mathfrak{M}$ and every closed set $\mathfrak{N} \subset \mathfrak{M}$ such that $M_0 \notin \mathfrak{N}$, there exists a $x \in \mathscr{B}$ verifying $\hat{x}(M_0) \neq 0$, $\hat{x}(M) = 0$ on $\mathfrak{N}$; moreover recall also that $\mathscr{B}$ is said *semisimple* if $x = 0$ implies $\hat{x} = 0$, that is if $x \to \hat{x}$ *is injective.*

In what follows $\mathscr{B}$ *will be considered regular and semisimple.*

2.1. Definition. An operator $\mathbf{B}(\mathscr{B})$ is called a multiplier of $\mathscr{B}$ if

$$T\,(xy) = x \cdot Ty = (Tx) \cdot y \quad \text{for all} \quad x, y \in \mathscr{B}.$$

If for an $a \in \mathscr{B}$, we denote by T_a *the multiplication operator by a in* $\mathscr{B}$, i.e.

$$T_a x = ax \quad \text{for all} \quad x \in \mathscr{B},$$

then obviously T_a is a multiplier of $\mathscr{B}$.

2.2. Proposition. *For every multiplier T of* $\mathscr{B}$ *there exists one (and only one) complex valued function* $\hat{T}(M)$ *defined on* $\mathfrak{M}$ *such that*

$$\widehat{Tx}(M) = \hat{T}(M)\,\hat{x}(M) \quad \textit{for all} \quad x \in \mathscr{B}, M \in \mathfrak{M}. \tag{1}$$

This function has the following additional properties

(i) $\hat{T}(M)$ *is continuous on* $\mathfrak{M}$;
(ii) $\hat{T}(M)$ *is bounded, precisely*

$$|\hat{T}(M)| \leqq \lim_{n \to \infty} \|T^n\|^{1/n}, \quad \textit{for all} \quad M \in \mathfrak{M};$$

(iii) $\hat{T}_a(M) = \hat{a}(M)$, *for all* $a \in \mathscr{B}$ *and* $M \in \mathfrak{M}$.

Proof. Apply to the definition of the multiplier T the Gelfand's representation:

$$\hat{x}(M) \cdot \widehat{Ty}(M) = \widehat{Tx}(M) \cdot \hat{y}(M) \tag{2}$$

for all $x, y \in \mathscr{B}$ and $M \in \mathfrak{M}$. If $\hat{x}(M) \neq 0 \neq \hat{y}(M)$, (2) shows that

$$\widehat{Tx}(M)/\hat{x}(M) = \widehat{Ty}(M)/\hat{y}(M),$$

thus denoting by $T(M)$ this value independent of x and y [whose existence is assumed for the fact that for every $M \in \mathfrak{M}$ there exists a $y \in \mathscr{B}$ such that $\hat{y}(M) \neq 0$] we obtain from (2)

$$\widehat{Tx}(M) = \hat{T}(M)\, \hat{x}(M),$$

thus formula (1). Obviously this formula determines $\hat{T}(M)$ uniquely. Now if $M_0 \in \mathfrak{M}$ is fixed, choosing an $y_0 \in \mathscr{B}$ such that $\hat{y}_0(M_0) \neq 0$ we have also $\hat{y}_0(M) \neq 0$ for M in a neighborhood U of M_0. Therefore we have in U, that

$$\hat{T}(M) = \widehat{Ty}(M)/\hat{y}(M)$$

is continuous, hence $\hat{T}(M)$ is continuous in M_0. This for every $M_0 \in \mathfrak{M}$, so $\hat{T}(M)$ is continuous in $\mathfrak{M}$. Concerning (iii) we have only to remark that

$$\hat{a}(M)\, \hat{x}(M) = \widehat{ax}(M) = \widehat{T_a x}(M) = \hat{T}_a(M)\, \hat{x}(M),$$

and this for all $x \in \mathscr{B}$ and $M \in \mathfrak{M}$.

It remains to prove (ii). With this aim, let us begin with the following remark:

$$(Tx)^{n+1} = x^n \cdot T^{n+1}x \quad \text{for all} \quad x \in \mathscr{B}, n = 0, 1 \ldots \tag{3}$$

Indeed, for $n = 0$ (3) becomes $Tx = Tx$, while if (3) is valid for $n = m - 1 \geqslant 0$, then

$$(Tx)^{m+1} = Tx \cdot (Tx)^m = Tx \cdot x^{m-1}T^m x = (Tx \cdot x^{m-1}) \cdot T^m x$$

$$= Tx^m \cdot T^m x = T(x^m \cdot T^m x) = x^m \cdot T^{m+1}x,$$

i.e. (3) is valid for $n = m$ too.

Now from (3) we deduce

$$(\hat{T}(M)\,\hat{x}(M))^{n+1} = \widehat{(Tx)^{n+1}}\,(M) = \widehat{x^n T^{n+1}\,x}(M) = \hat{x}(M)^n \cdot \widehat{T^{n+1}\,x}(M),$$

$$|\hat{T}(M)^{n+1}| \cdot |\hat{x}(M)| \leqq \left|\widehat{T^{n+1}x}(M)\right| \leqq \|T^{n+1}x\| \leqq \|T^{n+1}\| \cdot \|x\|,$$

Taking a $x \in \mathscr{B}$ such that $\hat{x}(M) \neq 0$ and dividing by $\hat{x}(M)$ we obtain

$$|\hat{T}(M)| \leqq \left(\frac{\|x\|}{|\hat{x}(M)|}\right)^{1/n+1} \|T^{n+1}\|^{1/n+1},$$

whence, letting $n \to \infty$, we deduce (iii).

2.3. Proposition. *Let T be a multiplier of $\mathscr{B}$. Then T has the single-valued extension property.*

Proof. If $b_\lambda \in \mathscr{B}$ is analytic in an open set $G \subset C$ and $(\lambda I - T)\,b_\lambda \equiv 0$ on G, then $[\lambda - \hat{T}(M)]\,\hat{b}_\lambda(M) \equiv 0$ on G for every $M \in \mathfrak{M}$. Set $M \in \mathfrak{M}$. Then on $G \setminus \{\hat{T}(M)\}$ we have $\hat{b}_\lambda(M) = 0$, thus by continuity $\hat{b}_\lambda(M) \equiv 0$ on G, and this for all $M \in \mathfrak{M}$. The semisimplicity of $\mathscr{B}$ implies $\hat{b}_\lambda \equiv 0$ on G.

In virtue of Proposition 2.3 we may consider the linear manifold

$$\mathscr{B}_T(F) = \{x | \sigma_T(x) \subset F\},$$

where F is a closed subset of C.

2.4. Proposition. *Let T be a multiplier of $\mathscr{B}$. Then*

$$\mathscr{B}_T(F) \subset \{x \in \mathscr{B} | \operatorname{supp} \hat{x} \subset \hat{T}^{-1}(F)\}.$$

Proof. Let $x \in \mathscr{B}_T(F)$. There exists an analytic function $x_\lambda \in \mathscr{B}$ defined on $G = C \setminus F$ such that

$$(\lambda I - T)\,x_\lambda = x \quad \text{for} \quad \lambda \in G,$$

whence

$$[\lambda - \hat{T}(M)]\,\hat{x}_\lambda(M) = \hat{x}(M), \quad \text{for all} \quad M \in \mathfrak{M} \quad \text{and} \quad \lambda \in G. \tag{1}$$

Let $M_0 \notin \hat{T}^{-1}(F)$. Then $\hat{T}(M_0) \in G$, thus taking in (1)

$$\lambda = \hat{T}(M_0) \quad \text{and} \quad M = M_0,$$

we get $\hat{x}(M_0) = 0$. Since $\hat{T}^{-1}(G)$ is open it results that $\operatorname{supp} \hat{x} \subset \mathfrak{M} \setminus \hat{T}^{-1}(G) = \hat{T}^{-1}(F)$.

2.5. THEOREM. *Let $T = T_a$ be a multiplication operator of $\mathscr{B}$. Then for every closed subset F of C the set*

$$\{x \in \mathscr{B} | \operatorname{supp} \hat{x} \subset \hat{a}^{-1}(F)\}$$

is a spectral maximal subspace of T_a, namely it coincides with $\mathscr{B}_{T_a}(F)$.

Proof. In virtue of Propositions 2.2(iii) and 2.4 we have

$$\mathscr{B}_{T_a}(F) \subset \{x | x \in \mathscr{B}, \operatorname{supp} \hat{x} \subset \hat{a}^{-1}(F)\} \stackrel{\text{def}}{=} \mathscr{B}_a(F).$$

It remains to prove the converse inclusion. Now obviously $\mathscr{B}_a(F)$ is a closed linear manifold of $\mathscr{B}$, i.e. a subspace of $\mathscr{B}$; moreover $\mathscr{B}_a(F)$ is invariant to T_a, since

$$\operatorname{supp} \left(\widehat{T_a x}\right) = \operatorname{supp} (\hat{a}\hat{x}) \subset \operatorname{supp} (\hat{x}).$$

Consequently it is sufficient to prove that the spectrum of $T | \mathscr{B}_a(F)$ is contained in F. For this purpose let $\lambda \notin F$ be fixed. We have to show that

$$(\lambda I - T) x = 0, \quad \text{with} \quad x \in \mathscr{B}_a(F), \quad \text{implies} \quad x = 0, \tag{1}$$

$$(\lambda I - T) \mathscr{B}_a(F) = \mathscr{B}_a(F). \tag{2}$$

The implication (1) can be proved easily. Indeed, taking the Gelfand's representation of the first relation of (1) we obtain

$$[\lambda - \hat{T}(M)] \hat{x}(M) = 0 \quad \text{for all} \quad M \in \mathfrak{M};$$

but here if $M \in \hat{T}^{-1}(F)$ we have $\lambda \neq \hat{T}(M)$, thus necessarily $\hat{x}(M) = 0$. Since $\operatorname{supp} (\hat{x}) \subset \hat{T}^{-1}(F)$, we have obtained in fact that $\hat{x}(M) = 0$ for all $M \in \mathfrak{M}$, hence $x = 0$.

It remains to prove (2). Let $x \in \mathscr{B}_a(F)$ be arbitrary but fixed. Put

$$y(M) = \begin{cases} 0 & \text{for} \quad M \notin \hat{a}^{-1}(F), \\ \dfrac{\hat{x}(M)}{\lambda - \hat{a}(M)} & \text{for} \quad M \in \hat{a}^{-1}(F). \end{cases}$$

It is an easy matter to verify that $y(M)$ is continuous on $\mathfrak{M}$. We shall show that $y(M)$ belongs locally to $\hat{\mathscr{B}}$ [i.e. that for every $M_0 \in \mathfrak{M}$, and also for ∞ if $\mathfrak{M}$ is not compact, there exists a neighborhood U and an $x_0 \in \mathscr{B}$ such that $\hat{x}_0(M) = y(M)$ on U_0], thus by the fact that $\mathscr{B}$ is a regular Banach algebra it will result that $y(M) \in \hat{\mathscr{B}}$, i.e. that there exists a $y \in \mathscr{B}$ such that $\hat{y}(M)$

$\equiv y(M)$. (For this property of the regular Banach algebras we refer to Ref. 91, § 15, no.4, Theorem 3, or to Ref. 75, 25.E.)

For the sake of simplicity we may consider, if $\mathscr{B}$ is without unity, the algebra obtained adjointing the unity to $\mathscr{B}$. This algebra $\mathscr{B}_1$ has its space of maximal ideals $\mathfrak{M}_1 = \mathfrak{M} \cup \{\infty\}$ and $\hat{\mathscr{B}}$ is formed by those functions f of $\mathscr{B}_1$ for which $f(\infty) = 0$. In virtue of the definition of $y(M)$ it is evident that if $\hat{x}(M) = 0$ then $y(M) = 0$, so that it is sufficient to show that $y(M)$ belongs locally to $\hat{\mathscr{B}}_1$. It is also evident that if $\lambda \notin F$ then $\lambda - \hat{a} \neq 0$ on $\mathfrak{N}_1 = \{M \in \mathfrak{M}_1 | \, \hat{a}(M) \in F\}$. If $M_1 \notin \mathfrak{N}_1$, then $y(M)$, being 0 in a neighborhood of M_1, belongs locally to $\hat{\mathscr{B}}_1$. If $M_1 \in \mathfrak{N}_1$ then $\lambda \neq \hat{a}(M_1)$, thus there exists a θ_1 such that

$$\operatorname{Re}\{e^{i\theta_1}[\lambda - \hat{a}(M_1)]\} > 0.$$

By continuity there exists a neighborhood V_1 of M_1 such that

$$\operatorname{Re}\{e^{i\theta_1}[\lambda - \hat{a}(M)]\} > 0 \quad \text{for all} \quad M \in V_1.$$

Take a $x_1 \in \mathscr{B}_1$ such that $0 \leqq \hat{x}_1 \leqq 1$, $\hat{x}_1 = 0$ outside of V_1 and $\hat{x}_1 = 1$ in a neighborhood $U_1 \subset V_1$ of M_1. Then the function

$$f(M) = e^{-i\theta_1}[1 - \hat{x}_1(M)] + [\lambda - \hat{a}(M)]\,\hat{x}_1(M), \quad M \in \mathfrak{M}_1,$$

belongs obviously to $\hat{\mathscr{B}}_1$. Now

$$\operatorname{Re}[e^{i\theta_1}f(M)] = \begin{cases} 1 & \text{if} \quad M \notin V_1, \\ 1 - \hat{x}_1(M) + \operatorname{Re}\{e^{i\theta_1}[\lambda - \hat{a}(M)]\}\,\hat{x}_1(M) > 0 & \text{if } M \in V_1. \end{cases}$$

Thus $f(M) \neq 0$ for $M \in \mathfrak{M}_1$, hence if $z \in \mathscr{B}_1$ is such that $\hat{z} \equiv f$ we have that $z^{-1} \in \mathscr{B}_1$ exists, and $\hat{z}^{-1}(M) = 1/f(M)$. Consequently $y_1 = xz^{-1} \in \mathscr{B}_1$. Now for $M \in U_1$

$$\hat{y}_1(M) = \hat{x}(M)/f(M) = \hat{x}(M)/[\lambda - \hat{a}(M)] = y(M),$$

which completes the proof.

2.6. THEOREM. *Every multiplication operator in $\mathscr{B}$ is a decomposable operator.*

Before proving this theorem we shall prove first the following

2.7. LEMMA. *The spectrum of a multiplication operator T_a of $\mathscr{B}$,* in $\mathbf{B}(\mathscr{B})$, *coincides with the spectrum of a as element of $\mathscr{B}$,* i.e. *with $\sigma(a) = \{\hat{a}(M) | M \in \mathfrak{M}\}$.*

Proof. We may, if $\mathscr{B}$ has no unity, consider $\mathscr{B}_1$ and $\mathfrak{M}_1 = \mathfrak{M} \cup \{\infty\}$ as in the proof of Theorem 2.5. Then

$$\sigma(a) = \{\hat{a}(M) | M \in \mathfrak{M}_1\}.$$

If $\lambda \notin \sigma(a)$, then $(\lambda e - a)^{-1}$ exists as element in $\mathscr{B}_1$, and obviously the operator

$$T: x \to (\lambda e - a)^{-1} x, \quad x \in \mathscr{B},$$

of $\mathscr{B}$ verifies $T(\lambda I - T_a) = (\lambda I - T_a) T = I$, thus $\lambda \notin \sigma(T_a)$.

Conversely if $\lambda \notin \sigma(T_a)$ then $T = (\lambda I - T_a)^{-1}$ commutes with every operator commuting with T_a, in particular with all multiplication operators of $\mathscr{B}$, which signifies that T is a multiplier of $\mathscr{B}$.

We have

$$(\lambda I - T_a) Tb = b \quad \text{for all} \quad b \in \mathscr{B}.$$

Taking the Gelfand's representation of this relation we have by Proposition 1.2

$$[\lambda - \hat{a}(M)] \hat{T}(M) \hat{b}(M) \equiv \hat{b}(M) \quad \text{for all} \quad b \in \mathscr{B} \quad \text{and} \quad M \in \mathfrak{M}. \quad (1)$$

If $0 \neq \lambda \in \sigma(a)$, then there exists an $M_0 \in \mathfrak{M}$ such that $\lambda = \hat{a}(M_0)$. It follows $\hat{b}(M_0) = 0$ for all $b \in \mathscr{B}$, which is impossible. Therefore if $\lambda \notin \sigma(T_a)$ then either $\lambda = 0$ or $\lambda \notin \sigma(a)$. It remains to show that $\lambda \neq 0$. With this aim suppose that $\lambda = 0$. Then we deduce from (1) that

$$|\hat{T}(M)| = 1/|\hat{a}(M)|,$$

for all $M \in \mathfrak{M}$. Now if $M \to \infty$ it follows $|\hat{T}(M)| \to \infty$, in contradiction with Proposition 2.2 (ii).

Proof of Theorem 2.6. Let $\{G_i\}_{i=1}^n$ be an open covering of $\sigma(T_a) = \sigma(a)$, and let $\mathfrak{M}_i = \hat{a}^{-1}(G_i)$. Then $\{\mathfrak{M}_i\}_{i=1}^n$ is an open covering of $\mathfrak{M}$, such that if $\mathscr{B}$ is without unity, a set $\mathfrak{M}_{i_0}$ is a neighborhood of ∞, i.e. $\mathfrak{M} \setminus \mathfrak{M}_{i_0}$ is a compact set $\mathfrak{N}$. Using the regularity of $\mathscr{B}$ we may construct (see Ref. 91, § 15, No. 4, Corollary to Theorem 2) a sequence of elements x_i, $i \neq i_0$, $1 \leqq i \leqq n$, of $\mathscr{B}$ such that $0 \leqq \hat{x}_i \leqq 1$, $\operatorname{supp} \hat{x}_i \subset \mathfrak{M}_i$, $\sum_{i \neq i_0} \hat{x}_i = 1$ on a compact neighborhood $\mathfrak{N}'$ of $\mathfrak{N}$. Denote by F_i the set of the values $\hat{a}(M)$ for $M \in \operatorname{supp}(\hat{x}_i)$ for $i \neq i_0$, and by F_{i_0} the set of the values of $\hat{a}(M)$ for

$M \in \mathfrak{M} \setminus \operatorname{Int} \mathfrak{N}'$. It is obvious that F_i is closed and $\subset G_i$ for all i, $1 \leqq i \leqq n$, and that for every $x \in \mathscr{B}$

$$y_i = xx_i \in \{y \in \mathscr{B} \mid \operatorname{supp}(\hat{y}) \subset \hat{a}^{-1}(F_i)\} \quad \text{if} \quad i \neq i_0,$$

$$y_{i_0} = x - \sum_{i \neq i_0} xx_i \in \{y \in \mathscr{B} \mid \operatorname{supp}(\hat{y}) \subset \hat{a}^{-1}(F_{i_0})\},$$

thus by Theorem 2.5 we have for all i, $1 \leqq i \leqq n$,

$$y_i \in \mathscr{B}_{T_a}(F_i).$$

Now $x = \sum_{i=1}^{n} y_i$, so that

$$x \in \mathscr{B}_{T_a}(F_1) + \mathscr{B}_{T_a}(F_2) + \cdots + \mathscr{B}_{T_a}(F_n);$$

this shows that

$$\mathscr{B} = \sum_{i=1}^{n} \mathscr{B}_{T_a}(F_i),$$

thus T_a is decomposable.

We shall study now the possibility that all multiplication operators T_a of $\mathscr{B}$ be $\mathfrak{A}$-scalar operators. It seems rather difficult to infer something without any additional assumptions. Therefore we shall restrict ourselves to the case when: (α) $\mathfrak{A}$ is an admissible algebra of continuous functions defined on the whole complex plane, inverse closed, and (β) every T_a has an $\mathfrak{A}$-spectral function $f \to U_{a,f}$ ($f \in \mathfrak{A}$) such that $U_{a,f}$ commutes, for every $f \in \mathfrak{A}$, with every operator commuting with T_a. In virtue of this last property $U_{a,f}$ commutes with every multiplication operator of $\mathscr{B}$, thus $U_{a,f}$ is a multiplier of $\mathscr{B}$. Applying to $U_{a,f}$ Theorem 3.2.4, we obtain that $U_{a,f}$ is a decomposable operator, and that

$$\mathscr{B}_{U_{a,f}}(F) = \mathscr{B}_{T_a}(f^{-1}(F)), \tag{*}$$

for every closed set F of C.

Using Proposition 2.4 and Theorem 2.5 we deduce from (*) the following inclusion

$$\{x \in \mathscr{B} \mid \operatorname{supp}(\hat{x}) \subset \hat{a}^{-1}(f^{-1}(F)) = (f \circ \hat{a})^{-1}(F)\}$$
$$\subset \{x \in \mathscr{B} \mid \operatorname{supp}(\hat{x}) \subset \hat{U}_{a,f}^{-1}(F)\}, \tag{**}$$

again for every closed set F of C. Let $M_0 \in \mathfrak{M}$ be fixed and let

$$\lambda_0 = (f \circ \hat{a})(M_0) = f[\hat{a}(M_0)].$$

Take for F in (**) the closure $\bar{\delta}_\varepsilon$ of the disk

$$\delta_\varepsilon = \{\lambda \,|\, |\lambda - \lambda_0| < \varepsilon\}, \quad \text{where} \quad \varepsilon > 0.$$

Then, $(f \circ \hat{a})^{-1}(\bar{\delta}_\varepsilon)$ having M_0 as interior point, we may choose a $x \in \mathscr{B}$ such that $x(M_0) \neq 0$ and $\text{supp}\,(\hat{x}) \subset (f \circ \hat{a})^{-1}(\bar{\delta}_\varepsilon)$. By (**) it results that

$$M_0 \in \text{supp}\,(\hat{x}) \subset \hat{U}_{a,f}^{-1}(\bar{\delta}_\varepsilon), \quad \text{i.e.} \quad \hat{U}_{a,f}(M_0) \in \bar{\delta}_\varepsilon;$$

this last relation being valid for every $\varepsilon > 0$, it follows $\hat{U}_{a,f}(M) = \lambda_0 = (f \circ \hat{a})(M_0)$, and this for every $M_0 \in \mathfrak{M}$. Thus we have obtained that

$$\hat{U}_{a,f}(M) = f \circ \hat{a}(M) \quad \text{for all} \quad M \in \mathfrak{M}.$$

We introduce the following

2.8. Definition. A function f defined on C is by definition *operating* on $\mathscr{B}$ if for every $a \in \mathscr{B}$ there exists a multiplier A of $\mathscr{B}$ such that

$$\hat{A}(M) = f \circ \hat{a}(M) \quad \text{for all} \quad M \in \mathfrak{M}. \tag{1}$$

It is obvious that A is uniquely determined by f and a (this is virtue of the semisimplicity of $\mathscr{B}$ and of Proposition 2.2.)

2.9. Definition. In an analogous manner to the case of the generalized scalar operators, an $\mathfrak{A}$-scalar operator T will be called *regular* if it has an $\mathfrak{A}$-spectral function commuting with every operator which commutes with T.

With these definitions, we may sum the above remarks in the following

2.10. Theorem. *Let $\mathfrak{A}$ be an admissible inverse closed algebra of continuous functions defined on the whole complex plane. Then, if every multiplication operator of $\mathscr{B}$ is a regular $\mathfrak{A}$-scalar operator, the algebra $\mathfrak{A}$ is operating on $\mathscr{B}$.*

Here it is obviously understood by the statement that $\mathfrak{A}$ is operating on $\mathscr{B}$ that every $f \in \mathfrak{A}$ is operating on $\mathscr{B}$.

Let G be a locally compact Abelian group, and let $\mathscr{B} = L^1(G)$ be the space of the complex valued functions integrable with respect to the Haar measure on G. Then $\mathscr{B}$ is a regular semisimple algebra, and the multipliers

T of $\mathscr{B}$ correspond to the bounded Borel measures μ on G in the following manner:

$$Tx(s) = \int_G x(st^{-1})\, d\mu(t), \quad x \in L^1(G), \; s \in G.$$

(About this see for instance Ref. 91, Chap. IV or Ref. 75, Chap. VI). The multiplication operators of $\mathscr{B}$ are the convolution operators in $L^1(G)$, thus we deduce readily from the above results the following

2.11. THEOREM. *Let G be a locally compact Abelian group, then for every $f \in L^1(G)$ the convolution operator*

$$T_f : g \to g * f, \quad \text{where} \quad (g * f)(s) = \int_G f(st^{-1})\, g(t)\, dt, \qquad (1)$$

in $L^1(G)$ is a decomposable operator.

[Let us remark that obviously the equality in (1) holds almost everywhere with respect to the Haar measure.]

2.12. THEOREM. *Under the same conditions as in Theorem 2.11, suppose moreover that G is not compact. Then for any admissible inverse closed algebra $\mathfrak{A}$ of continuous functions defined on the whole complex plane there exist convolution operators T_f, $f \in L^1(G)$, of $L^1(G)$ which are not regular $\mathfrak{A}$-scalar operators.*

Proof. Let us recall to the reader that the space of maximal ideals of $L^1(G)$ can be identified with the dual group Γ of G, and that by this identification the Gelfand representation of $f \in L^1(G)$ coincides with the Fourier transform

$$\hat{f}(\gamma) = \int_G (-x, \gamma) f(\gamma)\, dx, \quad \gamma \in \Gamma.$$

For a multiplier

$$T_\mu g(x) = \int_G g(xy^{-1})\, d\mu(y), \quad x \in G, g \in L^1(G),$$

the Gelfand representation coincides with the Fourier-Stieltjes transform of μ:

$$\hat{\mu}(\gamma) = \int_G (-x, \gamma)\, d\mu(x), \quad \gamma \in \Gamma.$$

Suppose now that every convolution operator T_f of $L^1(G)$ is regular $\mathfrak{A}$-scalar. Then, by Theorem 2.11 every $\varphi \in \mathfrak{A}$ is operating on $\mathscr{B} = L^1(G)$. Take a $\varphi \in \mathfrak{A}$, $\varphi \neq 0$ such that $\varphi = 0$ in a neighborhood of 0. Then for every $f \in \mathscr{B} = L^1(G)$ we have that $\varphi(\hat{f})$, which is (on account of the above remarks) a Fourier-Stietljes transform, is 0 in a neighborhood of ∞ (since "$\hat{f}(\gamma) \to 0$ for $\gamma \to \infty$ in" Γ). Thus $\varphi(\hat{f})$ belongs locally (on $\Gamma \cup \{\infty\}$) to the algebra $\mathbf{A}(\Gamma)$ of the Fourier transforms $\hat{f}, f \in L^1(G)$. It results that $\varphi(\hat{f}) \in \mathbf{A}(\Gamma)$. In this way for all $f \in \mathbf{A}(\Gamma)$ we have $\varphi(\hat{f}) \in \mathbf{A}(\Gamma)$. Since G is not compact, Γ is not discrete, thus by a profound theorem of Helson, Kahane, Katznelson, and Rudin (see Ref. 103, Theorem 6.9.2), $\varphi(\lambda)$ is real analytic in the whole complex plane, that is $\varphi(\lambda)$ as function of $s = \operatorname{Re} \lambda$ and $t = \operatorname{Im} \lambda$ has an expansion with complex coefficients

$$\varphi(\lambda) = \sum_{n,m=0}^{\infty} a_{nm} (s - s_0)^n (t - t_0)^m,$$

which converges absolutely for all $\lambda = s + it$ in some neighborhood of $\lambda_0 = s_0 + it_0$, and this for all λ_0. But $\varphi(\lambda) \equiv 0$ in a neighborhood of 0, thus by analyticity $\varphi(\lambda) \equiv 0$ in the whole complex plane. This contradicts the choice of φ. The contradiction is due to the assumption that every T_f, $f \in L^1(G)$, is a regular $\mathfrak{A}$-scalar operator, so that the theorem is now proved.

From theorems 2.11 and 2.12 it follows obviously:

2.13. Corollary. *For every admissible algebra, inverse closed, $\mathfrak{A}$ of continuous functions defined on the whole complex plane, there exists decomposable operators which are not regular $\mathfrak{A}$-scalar operators.*

3. Krabbe's Functional Calculus for Certain Multipliers in $L^p(R)$

Let $f \in L^\infty(R)$, i.e. an essentially bounded measurable function defined on the real line. The multiplication operator M_f: $g \to fg$ on $L^2(R)$ is obviously a normal operator of $\mathbf{B}(L^2(R))$. Denote by F the Fourier-Plancherel unitary transformation of $L^2(R)$ and denote by T_f the operator

$$g \to F^{-1}(f \cdot Fg), \quad [g \in L^2(R)] \tag{*}$$

of $\mathbf{B}(L^2(R))$. Since $T_f = F^{-1} M_f F$, T_f is also a normal operator of $L^2(R)$.

3.1. DEFINITION. An operator $T \in \mathbf{B}(L^2(R))$ is said to belong to the class $\mathscr{E}$ if

$$|Tg|_p \leqslant C_p |g|_p$$

for every $g \in L^2(R) \cap L^p(R)$, where $1 < p < \infty$ and

$$|g|_p = \left[\int_R |g(x)|^p \, dx\right]^{1/p}.$$

If $T \in \mathscr{E}$, then T defines by continuity an operator of $\mathbf{B}(L^p(R))$, denoted $T^{(p)}$. Obviously $T^{(2)} = T$.

3.2. PROPOSITION. *Let $T_k \in \mathscr{E}$ for a certain bounded Borel function k, and let μ be a bounded measure on R. Then for $f = k * \mu$, defined by*

$$f(x) = \int_R k(x - y) \, d\mu(y), \quad (x \in R),$$

the operator T_f belongs also to $\mathscr{E}$, and

$$\|T_f^{(p)}\| \leqslant \|\mu\| \, \|T_k^{(p)}\|, \quad (1 < p < \infty). \tag{1}$$

[Here $\|\mu\|$ denotes the total variation of μ, and $\|T_f^{(p)}\|$ and $\|T_k^{(p)}\|$ the norms of the operators $T_f^{(p)}$ and $T_k^{(p)}$ of $\mathbf{B}(L^p(R))$.]

Proof. Let $g \in C^\infty(R)$ be with compact support, and let

$$G(y) = \frac{1}{\sqrt{2\pi}} \int_R e^{-iyx} g(x) \, dx = Fg(y), \quad (y \in R).$$

Then

$$T_f g(x) = \frac{1}{\sqrt{2\pi}} \int_R e^{iyx} f(y) \, G(y) \, dy, \quad (x \in R),$$

whence

$$\begin{aligned} |T_f g|_p^p &= \int_R \left| \frac{1}{\sqrt{2\pi}} \int_R e^{iyx} f(y) \, G(y) \, dy \right|^p dx \\ &= \int_R \left| \frac{1}{\sqrt{2\pi}} \int_R e^{iyx} \left(\int_R k(y - z) \, d\mu(z) \right) G(y) \, dy \right|^p dx \\ &= \int_R \left| \int_R \frac{1}{\sqrt{2\pi}} \left(\int_R e^{iyx} G(y + z) \, k(y) \, dy \right) e^{ixz} d\mu(z) \right|^p dx \\ &= \int_R \left| \int_R T_k g_z(x) \, e^{ixz} \, d\mu(z) \right|^p dx, \end{aligned}$$

where

$$g_z(x) = e^{-izy} g(x).$$

Applying Hölder's inequality we obtain

$$|T_f g|_p^p \leqslant \int_R \left(\int_R |T_k g_z(x)|^p \, d|\mu|(z) \right) \|\mu\|^{p-1} \, dx$$

$$= \left(\int_R |T_k g_z|_p^p \, d|\mu|(z) \right) \|\mu\|^{p-1} \leqslant \|T_k^{(p)}\|^p \cdot |g|_p^p \cdot \|\mu\|^p;$$

thus we have $|T_f g|_p \leqslant \|T_k^{(p)}\| \cdot \|\mu\| \cdot |g|_p$ for $f \in C^\infty(R)$ with compact support. By continuity this inequality conserves its validity for all $g \in L^2(R) \cap L^p(R)$, therefore $T_f \in \mathscr{E}$. Moreover, from the established inequality it follows directly also the inequality (1).

Let $h(x) = \pi i \operatorname{sgn} x$ ($= -\pi i$ if $x < 0$, $= 0$ if $x = 0$, and $= \pi i$ if $x > 0$). Then (see Ref. 30, XI.7, Lemma 7)

$$T_h g(x) = \mathscr{P} \int_{-\infty}^{\infty} \frac{g(y)}{x - y} \, dy = \lim_{\epsilon \to 0} \int_{|y-x| > \epsilon} \frac{g(y)}{x - y} \, dy = Hg(x)$$

is the Hilbert transform H which on account of a theorem of M. Riesz (see again Ref. 30, XI.7, Theorem 8) belongs to $\mathscr{E}$.

Put $k(x) \doteq \frac{1}{2} - (1/2\pi i)\, h(x)$. Then $T_k g = \frac{1}{2} g - (1/2\pi i)\, Hg$ $[g \in L^2(R)]$, thus $T_k \in \mathscr{E}$ too. This remark will be used in the proof of the following

3.3. Theorem. *Let $BV(R)$ denote the Banach space of all complex valued bounded functions f defined on R with bounded variation, endowed with the norm*

$$\|f\|_{BV} = \operatorname*{ess.\,max}_{x \in R} |f(x)| + \operatorname*{Var}_R f.$$

Then $T_f \in \mathscr{E}$ for every $f \in BV(R)$ and there exist constants K_p $(1 < p < \infty)$ such that

$$\|T_f^{(p)}\| \leqslant K_p \, \|f\|_{BV}$$

for every $f \in BV(R)$ and $1 < p < \infty$.

Proof. Since f is bounded and has finite total variation on R, the limit $\lim_{x \to -\infty} f(x) = f(-\infty)$ must exist and

$$f(x) = f(-\infty) + \int_{-\infty}^{x} df(y) = f(-\infty) + k * \mu(x),$$

where μ is the bounded measure generated by $df(x)$, and $k(x)$ is the function considered at the end of the remark preceding Theorem 3.3. Then

$$T_f = f(\infty)\, I + T_{k*\mu}.$$

By Proposition 3.2, T_f belongs to $\mathscr{E}$, and

$$\|T_f^{(p)}\| \leqslant |f(\infty)| + \|T_{k*\mu}^{(p)}\| \leqslant |f(\infty)| + \|T_k^{(p)}\|\ \|\mu\|$$

$$\leqslant \operatorname*{ess.\,max}_{x\in R} |f(x)| + \|T_k^{(p)}\| \operatorname*{Var}_R (f) \leqslant K_p \|f\|_{BV},$$

where $K_p = \max\{1, \|T_k^{(p)}\|\}$.

3.4. *Remark. Actually $BV(R)$ is a Banach algebra,* since for $f, g \in BV(R)$

$$\|fg\|_{BV} \leqslant \operatorname*{ess.\,max}_{x\in R} |f(x)| \times \operatorname*{ess.\,max}_{x\in R} |g(x)| + \operatorname*{Var}_R (fg)$$

$$\leqslant \operatorname*{ess.\,max}_{x\in R} |f(x)| \times \operatorname*{ess.\,max}_{x\in R} |g(x)| + \operatorname*{ess.\,max}_{x\in R} |f| \times \operatorname*{Var}_R (g)$$

$$+ \operatorname*{Var}_R (f) \times \operatorname*{ess.\,max}_{x\in R} |g| \leqslant \|f\|_{BV}\ \|g\|_{BV} < \infty.$$

Therefore Theorem 3.3 has the following

3.5. COROLLARY. *For every p, $1 \leqslant p < \infty$, there exists a continuous algebraic homomorphism $f \to T_f^{(p)}$ of $BV(R)$ into $\mathbf{B}(L^p(R))$, where $T_f^{(p)}$ is defined by continuity from the application at the beginning of this paragraph in which $g \in L^2(R) \cap L^p(R)$.*

The only fact remaining to be verified is that

$$T_{f_1}^{(p)} T_{f_2}^{(p)} = T_{f_1 f_2}^{(p)}, \quad [\text{for } f_1, f_2 \in BV(R)].$$

Now if $g \in L^2(R) \cap L^p(R)$, then also

$$g' = T_{f_2}^{(p)} g \in L^2(R) \cap L^p(R),$$

and

$$g' = F^{-1}(f_2 \cdot Fg), \quad Fg' = f_2 \cdot Fg,$$

so that

$$T_{f_1}^{(p)} T_{f_2}^{(p)} g = T_{f_1}^{(p)} g' = F^{-1}(f_1 \cdot Fg') = F^{-1}(f_1 f_2 \cdot Fg) = T_{f_1 f_2}^{(p)} g.$$

We are now able to pass to the basic spectral property of the operators T_f, with $f \in BV(R)$. These operators are usually called multipliers in $L^p(R)$, in virtue of their definition (*) which is analogous to that of the multipliers in $L^1(G)$ (see preceding paragraph).

3.6. DEFINITION. Denote by $BL(C)$ the set of all complex-valued functions φ defined on the complex plane C verifying

$$\|\varphi\|_{BL} = \max_{\lambda \in C} |\varphi(\lambda)| + \sup_{\substack{\lambda \neq \mu \\ \lambda, \mu \in C}} \left| \frac{\varphi(\lambda) - \varphi(\mu)}{\lambda - \mu} \right| < \infty .$$

It is an easy matter to verify that $BL(C)$, *endowed with the norm* $\|\varphi\|_{BL}$, *is a topologically admissible algebra such that if* $f \in BV(R)$ *and* $\varphi \in BL(R)$ *then* $\varphi \circ f$, *defined by* $\varphi \circ f(x) = \varphi(f(x))$, $x \in R$, *belongs to* $BV(R)$ *and*

$$\|\varphi \circ f\|_{BV} \leqslant \|\varphi\|_{BL} \|f\|_{BV} . \tag{**}$$

Using this remark and Theorem 3.3, with its Corollary 3.5, we obtain directly the following

3.7. THEOREM. *For every* $f \in BV(R)$ *and* $1 < p < \infty$, *the multiplier* $T_f^{(p)} \in \mathbf{B}(L^p(R))$ *is a* $BL(C)$*-scalar operator having* $\varphi \to T_{\varphi \circ f}$ $[\varphi \in BL(C)]$ *as a continuous* $BL(C)$*-spectral function.*

Moreover, every such multiplier $T_f^{(p)}$ *is a generalized scalar operator.*

It remains only to prove this last assertion. Now the inequality (**) can be obviously replaced by another one:

$$\|\varphi \circ f\| \leqq \|f\|_{BV} \cdot \max_{|\lambda| \leqslant \|f\|_{BV}} \left\{ |\varphi(\lambda)| + \left| \frac{\partial}{\partial \operatorname{Re} \lambda} \varphi(\lambda) \right| + \left| \frac{\partial}{\partial \operatorname{Im} \lambda} \varphi(\lambda) \right| \right\}.$$

From here we infer (again by Theorem 3.3) that $\varphi \to T_{\varphi \circ f}^{(p)}$, where now $\varphi \in C^\infty(C)$ is an operator valued distribution, thus a spectral distribution of $T_f^{(p)}$.

Take now a function $f \in BV(R)$. The classes $BL(C)$ and $C^\infty(R)$ are much smaller than *the class* $\mathscr{K}(f)$ *formed by the complex-valued functions* $\varphi(\lambda)$ *defined on* C *and verifying* $\varphi \circ f \in BV(R)$.

3.8. THEOREM. *Let* $f \in BV(R)$ *be fixed. Then the class* $\mathscr{K}(f)$ *is an admissible algebra and* $T_f^{(p)}$ *(for* $1 < p < \infty$*) is a* $\mathscr{K}(f)$*-scalar operator having* $\varphi \to T_{\varphi \circ f}^{(p)}$ $[\varphi \in \mathscr{K}(f)]$ *as a* $\mathscr{K}(f)$*-spectral function.*

Proof. That $\mathscr{K}(f)$ is a normal algebra is obvious. Let now $\varphi \in \mathscr{K}(f)$ be fixed and let ω be a closed disk such that $\omega \cap \operatorname{supp}(\varphi) = \varnothing$. Let $\nu(\lambda) \in C^\infty(C)$ be such that $\nu(\lambda) = 0$ on ω and $= 1$ in a neighborhood of $\operatorname{supp}(\varphi)$. Let

$$\nu_\xi(\lambda) = \begin{cases} 0 \quad \text{for} \quad \lambda = \xi, \\ \nu(\lambda)\,(\xi - \lambda)^{-1} \quad \text{for} \quad \lambda \neq \xi, \end{cases}$$

where $\xi \in \omega$. Let us now consider

$$\varphi_\xi(\lambda) = \begin{cases} 0 \quad \text{for} \quad \lambda \notin \operatorname{supp}(\varphi), \\ \dfrac{\varphi(\lambda)}{\xi - \lambda} \quad \text{for} \quad \lambda \in \operatorname{supp}(\varphi). \end{cases}$$

The functions $\varphi_\xi(\lambda)$ and $\nu_\xi(\lambda)$ are related by

$$\varphi_\xi(\lambda) = \nu_\xi(\lambda)\,\varphi(\lambda),$$

hence

$$\varphi_\xi \circ f = \nu_\xi \circ f \cdot \varphi \circ f \in BV(R) \tag{1}$$

since $\nu_\xi \in BL(C)$. Thus $\mathscr{K}(f)$ is an admissible algebra. Moreover, since it is an easy matter to verify that the application $\xi \to \nu_\xi$ from $\operatorname{Int}\omega = \mathring{\omega}$ to $BL(C)$ is analytic, so is also $\xi \to \nu_\xi \circ f$ from $\mathring{\omega}$ to $BV(R)$, and finally

$$\xi \to T^{(p)}_{\nu_\xi \circ f}$$

from $\mathring{\omega}$ to $\mathbf{B}(L^p(R))$ is also analytic. Thus, by (1),

$$\xi \to T^{(p)}_{\varphi_\xi \circ f} = T^{(p)}_{\varphi \circ f} T^{(p)}_{\nu_\xi \circ f}$$

is analytic from $\mathring{\omega}$ to $\mathbf{B}(L^p(R))$. This shows that $\varphi \to T^{(p)}_{\varphi \circ f}$ [for $\varphi \in \mathscr{K}(f)$] is a $\mathscr{K}(f)$-spectral function, obviously belonging to $T^{(p)}_f$.

3.9. Proposition. *Let $f \in BV(R)$ be fixed and let $\varkappa(f)$ be the Boolean algebra of Borel sets $\omega \subset C$ such that χ_ω ($=$ the characteristic function of ω) belongs to $\mathscr{K}(f)$. Then there exists a homomorphic mapping $\omega \to \mathbf{E}(\omega)$ of $\varkappa(f)$ in the family of projectors (idempotents) commuting with $T^{(p)}_f$, of $\mathbf{B}(L^p(R))$, such that $\sigma(T^{(p)}_f | \mathbf{E}(\omega) L^p(R)) \subset \bar{\omega}$.*

Proof. Since $\mathscr{K}(f)$ is an algebra, $\varkappa(f)$ is obviously a Boolean algebra of sets. Putting

$$\mathbf{E}(\omega) = T^{(p)}_{\chi_\omega \circ f}$$

we obtain a projector of $\mathbf{B}(L^p(R))$ [i.e. $\mathbf{E}(\omega)^2 = \mathbf{E}(\omega)$] such that $\omega \to \mathbf{E}(\omega)$ is homomorphic from $\varkappa(f)$ in the family of projectors (commuting with $T_f^{(p)}$) of $\mathbf{B}(L^p(R))$. Obviously $\mathbf{E}(\omega) L^p(R)$ is invariant to $T_f^{(p)}$ and also to every $T_{\varphi \circ f}^{(p)}$. The application

$$\varphi \to \mathbf{U}_\varphi = T_{\varphi \circ f}^{(p)} | \mathbf{E}(\omega) L^p(R)$$

is a $\mathscr{K}(f)$-spectral function of $\mathbf{U}_\lambda = T_f^{(p)} | E_f^{(p)} L^p(R)$; since for every $\varphi = 1$ in a neighborhood of $\bar{\omega}$ and $g \in \mathbf{E}(\omega) L^p(R)$ we have

$$\mathbf{U}_\varphi g = T_{\varphi \circ f}^{(p)} T_{\chi_\omega \circ f} g = T_{\varphi \circ f \cdot \chi_\omega \circ f}^{(p)} g = T_{\chi_\omega \circ f}^{(p)} g = g,$$

it follows, in virtue of Theorem 3.1.6, that the spectrum of $\mathbf{U}_\lambda$ is included in $\bar{\omega}$.

3.10. *Remark*. Let $f \in BV(R)$ have its real and imaginary parts piecewise monotone. Then $\varkappa(f)$ contains every square $\omega = \alpha \times \beta$, where α and β are two intervals. Thus Proposition 3.9 concerns in this case a wide class of projectors.

4. A Remark on a Class of Operators Related to Matrix-functions

Let $\mathscr{H}$ be a Hilbert space and let $\{M, \Sigma, E(\sigma)\}$ be a spectral measure in $\mathscr{H}$, i.e. a function $\sigma \to \mathbf{E}(\sigma)$ defined on a σ-algebra Σ of sets $\sigma \subset M$, with values orthogonal projections of $\mathscr{H}$, verifying

(i) $\mathbf{E}(\sigma_1 \cap \sigma_2) = \mathbf{E}(\sigma_1)\mathbf{E}(\sigma_2)$, $\sigma_1, \sigma_2 \in \Sigma$;

(ii) $\mathbf{E}\left(\bigcup_{n=1}^{\infty} \sigma_n\right) h = \sum_{n=1}^{\infty} \mathbf{E}(\sigma_n)\, h$ for every countable family $\{\sigma_n\}_{n=1}^{\infty}$ of mutually disjoint sets, and for every $h \in \mathscr{H}$; the convergence of the series being in the strong topology of $\mathscr{H}$;

(iii) $\mathbf{E}(\varnothing) = 0$, $\mathbf{E}(M) = 0$.

Let $\mathscr{H}^p$ denote the orthogonal sum of p spaces $\mathscr{H}$.

4.1. Definition. $\mathbf{A}^p$ denotes the algebra of operators A of $\mathscr{H}^p$ which can be represented under the form

$$A = \left(\int_M a_{ij}(m)\, dE(m)\right)_{i,j=1}^{p}$$

for certain Σ-measurable functions $a_{ij}(m)$, $i, j = 1, 2, \ldots, p$.

Introducing the matrix-valued function

$$A(m) = (a_{ij}(m))_{i,j=1}^{p}$$

we may write A under a condensed heuristic form

$$A = \int_M A(m)\, d\mathbf{E}(m). \tag{*}$$

The matrix $A(m)$ can be considered, for every $m \in M$, as an operator of the Euclidian complex space E^p of dimension p. Therefore we may consider the norm $\|A(m)\|$ of $A(m)$ as the norm of an element of $\mathbf{B}(E^p)$.

4.2. PROPOSITION. *For an operator $A \in \mathbf{A}^p$, given by* (*), *we have*

$$\mathbf{E}(\{m \mid \|A(m)\| > \|A\|\}) = 0.$$

Proof. For $h \in \mathscr{H}$ and $\xi = (\xi_k)_{k=1}^{p} \in E^p$ denote by $h\xi$ the vector $(h\xi_k)_{k=1}^{p} \in \mathscr{H}^p$. Then for $h \in \mathscr{H}$, ξ and $\eta \in E^p$ we have

$$\begin{aligned}(A(h\xi), h\eta)_{\mathscr{H}^p} &= \sum_{i,j=1}^{p} (A_{ij}h, h)_{\mathscr{H}}\, \xi_j \bar{\eta}_i \\ &= \sum_{i,j=1}^{p} \xi_j \bar{\eta}_i \int_M a_{ij}(m)\, d(\mathbf{E}(m)h, h)_{\mathscr{H}} \\ &= \int_M (A(m)\xi, \eta)_{E^p}\, d(\mathbf{E}(m)h, h)_{\mathscr{H}},\end{aligned}$$

that is

$$\int_M (A(m)\xi, \eta)_{E^p}\, d(\mathbf{E}(m)h, h)_{\mathscr{H}} = (A(h\xi), h\eta)_{\mathscr{H}^p}. \tag{1}$$

Let now $\sigma \in \Sigma$ be arbitrary and take $h = \mathbf{E}(\sigma)\, l$, where $l \in \mathscr{H}$. Then we obtain, from (1),

$$\left| \int_\sigma (A(m)\xi, \eta)_{E^p}\, d(\mathbf{E}(m)\, l, l)_{\mathscr{H}} \right| \leqslant \|A\|\, \|\xi\|_{E^p}\, \|\eta\|_{E^p}\, (\mathbf{E}(\sigma)\, l, l)_{\mathscr{H}}. \tag{2}$$

The validity of (2), for every $\sigma \in \Sigma$, implies

$$|(A(m)\xi, \eta)_{E^p}| \leqslant \|A\|\, \|\xi\|_{E^p}\, \|\eta\|_{E^p}$$

except for a set $\omega = \omega(l; \xi, \eta)$ of measure zero with respect to $\sigma \to (\mathbf{E}(\sigma) l, l)$. Since E^p is separable we deduce

$$\|(A(m))\| \leqslant \|A\|,$$

except for a set $\omega' = \omega'(l)$ of measure zero with respect to the same measure $\sigma \to (\mathbf{E}(\sigma)\, l, l)$. In this way, since

$$\Omega = \{m |\ \|A(m)\| > \|A\|\} \subset \omega'(l),$$

we obtain $(\mathbf{E}(\Omega)\, l, l)_{\mathscr{H}} = 0$ for all $l \in \mathscr{H}$, i.e. $\mathbf{E}(\Omega) = 0$.

4.3. *Remark*. In virtue of Proposition 4.2 we may always suppose that if

$$A = \int_M A(m)\, d\,\mathbf{E}(m) \in \mathbf{A}^p$$

then

$$\|A(m)\| \leqslant \|A\| \quad \text{for all} \quad m \in M.$$

This supposition will always be assumed in what follows.

Let us now pay attention to the operators of $\mathbf{B}(E^p)$. The Jordan form of every matrix shows that every operator $T \in \mathbf{B}(E^p)$ is a spectral operator (in Dunford's sense) of finite type $\leqslant p - 1$, whose canonical decomposition is of the form

$$T = \sum_{\lambda \in \sigma(T)} \lambda\, \mathbf{E}_\lambda + N,$$

where $N^p = 0$, $\mathbf{E}_\lambda \mathbf{E}_\mu = 0$ for $\lambda \neq \mu$, $\mathbf{E}_\lambda^2 = \mathbf{E}_\lambda$ and $\mathbf{E}_\lambda N = N \mathbf{E}_\lambda$. Let now $f(\lambda)$ be a complex-valued $(p - 1)$-times continuously differentiable function defined in the complex plane. Put

$$f(T) = \sum_{k=0}^{p-1} \frac{N^k}{k!} \sum_{\lambda \in \sigma(T)} \frac{\partial^k}{\partial \lambda^k} f(\lambda) \cdot \mathbf{E}_\lambda,$$

where $\partial/\partial\lambda = (\frac{1}{2})\,[(\partial/\partial \operatorname{Re} \lambda) - i\,(\partial/\partial \operatorname{Im} \lambda)]$. The application $f(\lambda) \to f(T)$ is a spectral distribution of T. We use another notation now, since this spectral distribution is in a certain sense a canonical one. Indeed if

$$\Delta(\lambda) = (\lambda - \lambda_1)^{k_1} \cdots (\lambda - \lambda_m)^{k_m} \qquad (k_1 + \cdots + k_m = p)$$

denotes the determinant of the matrix corresponding in E^p to the operator $\lambda I - T$, and if $\Delta_f(\lambda)$ denotes the polynomial of degree $p - 1$ verifying

$$\left(\frac{d}{d\lambda}\right)^k \Delta_f(\lambda)\bigg|_{\lambda=\lambda_j} = \left(\frac{\partial^k}{\partial\lambda^k} f\right)(\lambda_j) \tag{1}$$

for all

$$0 \leqslant k \leqslant k_j - 1, \quad j = 1, 2, \ldots, m, \tag{1'}$$

then

$$f(T) = \Delta_f(T). \tag{2}$$

(Compare this assertion with Ref. 30, VII.1.)

In order to avoid complicated computations we shall consider only the simplest nontrivial case, namely $p = 2$. In this case $\Delta(\lambda)$ can have the forms

$$\Delta(\lambda) = (\lambda - \lambda_1)^2 \quad \text{or} \quad \Delta(\lambda) = (\lambda - \lambda_1)(\lambda - \lambda_2) \quad \text{if} \quad \lambda_2 \neq \lambda_1 .$$

Thus

$$\Delta_f(\lambda) = f(\lambda_1) + \frac{\partial}{\partial\lambda} f(\lambda_1) \cdot (\lambda - \lambda_1),$$

$$\text{respectively } \Delta_f(\lambda) = f(\lambda_1) + \frac{f(\lambda_2) - f(\lambda_1)}{\lambda_2 - \lambda_1}(\lambda - \lambda_1)$$

[which obviously verify (1) and (1′)]. Using (2) we deduce

$$f(T) = f(\lambda_1) I + \frac{\partial}{\partial\lambda} f(\lambda_1)(T - \lambda_1 I),$$

$$\text{respectively } f(T) = f(\lambda_1) I + \frac{f(\lambda_2) - f(\lambda_1)}{\lambda_2 - \lambda_1}(T - \lambda_1 I),$$

whence in both cases

$$\|f(T)\| \leqslant (2\|T\| + 1) \max_{|\lambda| \leqslant \|T\|} \left\{ |f(\lambda)|, \left|\frac{\partial f(\lambda)}{\partial \operatorname{Re} \lambda}\right|, \left|\frac{\partial f(\lambda)}{\partial \operatorname{Im} \lambda}\right| \right\}. \tag{3}$$

We are now able to prove the following

4.4. THEOREM. *Every $A \in \mathbf{A}^2$ is a generalized scalar operator possessing a spectral distribution of order $\leqslant 1$.*

Proof. Let

$$A = \int_M A(m)\, d\mathbf{E}\,(m).$$

Since the computation of the idempotents $\mathbf{E}_\lambda(m)$ as well as of the nilpotent $N(m)$ involves algebraic operations, these matrices have Σ-measurable entries, thus the matrix $f\,(A(m))$ has also Σ-measurable entries, for every function $f \in C^1(C)$, i.e. for every complex-valued continuously differentiable function. Taking into account the Remark 4.3. and the inequality (3) of the preceding section, we obtain

$$\|f(A(m))\| \leqslant (2\,\|A\| + 1) \max_{|\lambda| \leqslant \|A\|} \left\{ |f(\lambda)|, \left|\frac{\partial f(\lambda)}{\partial \operatorname{Re} \lambda}\right|, \left|\frac{\partial f(\lambda)}{\partial \operatorname{Im} \lambda}\right| \right\}, \tag{1}$$

thus the entries $f_{ij}(m)$ of the matrix

$$f(A(m)) = (f_{ij}(m))_{i,j=1}^2$$

are bounded, hence

$$\left(\int_M f_{ij}(m)\, d\mathbf{E}(m) \right)_{i,j=1}^2$$

defines an operator $\mathbf{U}_f \in \mathbf{B}(\mathscr{H}^2)$ verifying, in virtue of (1),

$$\|\mathbf{U}_f\| \leqslant k(\|A\|) \max_{|\lambda| \leq \|A\|} \left\{ |f(\lambda)|, \left|\frac{\partial f(\lambda)}{\partial \operatorname{Re} \lambda}\right|, \left|\frac{\partial f(\lambda)}{\partial \operatorname{Im} \lambda}\right| \right\}. \tag{2}$$

The application $f \to \mathbf{U}_f$ is obviously linear [since so is $f \to f(A(m))$] and its restriction to $C^\infty(C)$ is, by (2), continuous, hence it is an operator-valued distribution of order $\leqslant 1$. Since it is obvious that $\mathbf{U}_1 = I$, $\mathbf{U}_\lambda = A$, it remains to prove the multiplication property of the distribution $f \to \mathbf{U}_f$. With this aim let $f, g \in C^1(C)$, and let $h = f \cdot g$. Put

$$h\,(A(m)) = (h_{ij}(m))_{i,j=1}^2 \quad \text{and} \quad g(A(m)) = (g_{ij}(m))_{i,j=1}^2.$$

Since $f \to f\,(A(m))$ is multiplicative, we have

$$h\,(A(m)) = f\,(A(m))\, g\,(A(m)),$$

i.e.

$$h_{ij}(m) = \sum_{k=1}^{2} f_{ik}(m)\, g_{kj}(m), \quad (i, j = 1, 2).$$

By the usual functional calculus with spectral measures in $\mathscr{H}$ (see for instance Ref. 30, X.2) we have

$$\int_M h_{ij}(m)\, d\mathbf{E}(m) = \sum_{k=1}^{2} \int_M f_{ik}(m)\, d\mathbf{E}(m) \cdot \int_M g_{kj}(m)\, d\mathbf{E}(m), \quad (i, j = 1, 2)$$

which just shows that

$$\mathbf{U}_{fg} = \mathbf{U}_h = \mathbf{U}_f \mathbf{U}_g.$$

Thus $f \to \mathbf{U}_f$ [for $f \in C^\infty(C)$] is a spectral distribution of A. Recalling that, in virtue of (2), this spectral distribution is of order $\leqslant 1$, we end the proof.

4.5. *Remark*. Except for the inequality (3) of section 4.3 all the other arguments in the proof above are not dependent on the fact that $p = 2$.

5. Some Open Questions

Finally let us list some open problems related to the topics presented in this book.

(a) In the theory of decomposable operators one can replace the condition of Definition 2.1.1 by the following weaker one:

To every finite open covering $\{G_i\}_{i=1}^n$ of the spectrum $\sigma(T)$ there exists a system $\mathscr{Y}_1, \mathscr{Y}_2, \ldots \mathscr{Y}_n$ of maximal spectral spaces of T such that $\sigma(T|\mathscr{Y}_j) \subset G_j$ (for $j = 1, 2, \ldots n$) and $\mathscr{X}$ is the linear closed space spanned by the space $\mathscr{Y}_1 + \mathscr{Y}_2 + \cdots + \mathscr{Y}_n$, i.e.

$$\mathscr{X} = \overline{\mathscr{Y}_1 + \mathscr{Y}_2 + \cdots + \mathscr{Y}_n}.$$

(Recall that for a decomposable operator one must have $\mathscr{X} = \mathscr{Y}_1 + \mathscr{Y}_2 + \cdots + \mathscr{Y}_n$.)

Which of the results given in Chap. 2 for decomposable operators are still valid for the operators satisfying the above weaker condition of decomposability?

(b) Let $T \in \mathbf{B}(\mathscr{X})$ be a decomposable operator and let $\mathscr{Y} \subset \mathscr{X}$ be a maximal spectral space of T. Are then the operators $T|\mathscr{Y} \in \mathbf{B}(\mathscr{Y})$ and $\dot{T} \in \mathbf{B}(\mathscr{X}|\mathscr{Y})$ also decomposable?

(c) Is every decomposable operator also an $\mathfrak{A}$-decomposable operator for a suitable admissible algebra $\mathfrak{A}$? Is every $\mathfrak{A}$-decomposable operator also a $\mathfrak{A}$-spectral operator, at least if $\mathfrak{A} = C^\infty(C)$?

(d) Is every generalized scalar operator a regular one? If not, are the generalized scalar operators, considered in the paragraphs 1 and 3 of this chapter, regular or not?

(e) If $T \in \mathbf{B}(\mathscr{H})$, where $\mathscr{H}$ is a Hilbert space, and if $T^* - T \in \mathscr{C}_p$ for $1 \leqslant p < \infty$, is T a decomposable operator?

(f) Is the convolution operator

$$T_\mu f = \mu * f, \quad [f \in L^1(G)]$$

decomposable for every measure $\mu \in \mathscr{M}(G)$, where G is a locally compact Abelian group?

(g) Is every operator $A \in \mathbf{A}^p$ a generalized scalar operator even if $p > 2$? If yes the definition

$$f \to U_f = \int_M f(A(m)) \, d\mathbf{E}(m), \quad [f \in C^\infty(C)]$$

yields a spectral distribution of order $\leqslant p - 1$ of

$$A = \int_M A(m) \, d\mathbf{E}\,(m)$$

Notes and Remarks

A systematic study of multiplication operators in spaces of differentiable functions is not known to have yet been made. Except for the essay given in § 1, let us mention the introduction by Deal[20,21] of a certain class of operators (which are all decomposable operators) suggested by such multiplication operators. The results of § 2, though very natural, do not seem to have been explicitly stated in the literature. Theorem 3.3 and Corollary 3.5 belong to G.L.Krabbe.[61] A more general result than Theorem 3.3 can be found in I.I.Hirschman, Jr.[48]. Theorems 3.7 and 3.8 especially are new since they are not in connection with Krabbe's theory. Actually Krabbe studies the case mentioned in Remark 3.10, and for this case he shows that in a certain generalized sense

$$T_f = \int \lambda \, dE(\lambda) = \lim \sum_i \lambda_i \mathbf{E}\,(\omega_i),$$

where $E(\omega_i)$ are the projectors considered in the Proposition 3.9, $\lambda_i \in \omega_i$ and ω_i are rectangles.

The class $\mathbf{A}^p$ was recently considered by N.Dunford,[29] where rich information on the spectral properties of the operators of $\mathbf{A}^p$ can be found. This class $\mathbf{A}^p$ extends a former class considered by Foguel in Ref. 38. Theorem 4.4 was known by us in the case of Foguel along time ago; it is related to Theorem 8, § 3 of Dunford's paper.[29]

In connection with Problem (e) of § 5 let us remark that if $T^* - T \in \mathscr{C}_1$, then in virtue of Ref. 120, T is decomposable in the weakened sense given in Problem (a) of § 5.

Bibliography

1. APOSTOL, C., "Sur l'équivalence asymptotique des opérateurs", Rev. Roumaine Math. Pures Appl. (to be published).
2. ARONSZAJN, N. and SMITH, K. R., "Invariant subspaces of completely continuous operators", Ann. Math. **60**, 345–350 (1954).
3. BADE, W. G., "An operational calculus for operators with spectrum in a strip", Pacific J. Math. **3**, 257–290 (1953).
4. BADE, W. G., "Unbounded spectral operators", Pacific J. Math. **4**, 373–392 (1954).
5. BADE, W. G., "Weak and strong limits of spectral operators", Pacific J. Math. **4**, 393–413 (1954).
6. BADE, W. G., "On Boolean algebras of projections and algebras of operators", Trans. Amer. Math. Soc. **80**, 345–360 (1955).
7. BARTLE, R. G., "Spectral localization of operators in Banach spaces", Math. Ann. **153**, 261–269 (1964).
8. BERKSON, E., "A characterisation on scalar type operators on reflexive Banach spaces", Pacific J. Math. **13**, 365–373 (1963).
9. BEURLING, A., "Sur les intégrales de Fourier absolument convergentes et leur application à une transformation fonctionnelle", *Neuvième congrès des mathématiciens scandinaves tenu à Helsingfors, 1938* (Helsingfors, 1939), pp. 345–366.
10. BIEBERBACH, L., *Lehrbuch der Funktionen-Theorie. Band II* (Chelsea Publ. Comp. New York, 1945).
11. BISHOP, E., "Spectral theory for operators on a Banach space", Trans. Amer. Math. Soc. **86**, 414–445 (1957).
12. BISHOP, E., "A duality theorem for an arbitrary operator", Pacific J. Math. **9**, 379–397 (1959).
13. BOURBAKI, N., *Topologie générale* (Herman, Paris, 1958), Chap. IX.
14. BRODSKII, M.S. and LIVSIC, M.S., "Spectral analysis of non-self-adjoint operators", Uspehi Mat. Nauk. **13**, 1–85 (1958).
15. COLOJOARĂ, I., "Generalized spectral operators", Rev. Math. Pures Appl. **7**, 459–465 (1962).
16. COLOJOARĂ, I., "Operatori spectrali generalizati, II", Com. Acad. R.P. Română **12**, 973–977 (1962).
17. COLOJOARĂ, I., "Operatori spectrali generalizati", Stud. Cerc. Mat. **15**, 499–536 (1964).
18. COLOJOARĂ, I., "Logarithms of generalized spectral operators", Rev. Roum. Math. Pures et Appl. **10** 319–322 (1965).
19. COLOJOARĂ, I. and FOIAŞ, C., "Quasi-nilpotent equivalence of not necessarily commuting operators", J. Math. Mech. **15**, 521–540 (1965).

20. DEAL, E.R., "Quasi-spectral theory", Math. Scand. **13**, 188–198 (1963).
21. DEAL, E.R., "A quasi-spectral operator", Math. Scand. **16**, 29–32 (1965).
22. DIEUDONNÉ, J., "Sur la théorie spectrale", J. Math. Pures Appl. **35**, (9), 175–187 (1956).
23. DOMAR, Y., "Harmonic analysis based on certain commutative Banach algebras", Acta Math. **9**, 1–66 (1956).
24. DOWSON, H.R., "Restriction of spectral operators", Proc. London Math. Soc. **15**, 437–457 (1965).
25. DUNFORD, N., "Spectral theory. I. Convergence to projection", Trans. Amer. Math. Soc. **54**, 185–217 (1943).
26. DUNFORD, N., "Spectral theory. II. Resolutions of the identity", Pacific J. Math. **2**, 559–614 (1952).
27. DUNFORD, N., "Spectral operators", Pacific J. Math. **4**, 321–354 (1954).
28. DUNFORD, N., "A survey of the theory of spectral operators", Bull. Am. Math. Soc. **64**, 217–274 (1958).
29. DUNFORD, N., "A spectral theory for certain operators on a direct sum of Hilbert spaces", Math. Ann. **162**, 294–330 (1966).
30. DUNFORD, N. and SCHWARTZ, J.T., *Linear Operators. Part I* (1958), *Part II* (1963) (Interscience Publishers, New York).
31. EDWARDS, D.A. and IONESCU TULCEA, C.T., "Some remarks on commutative algebras of operators on Banach spaces", Trans. Amer. Math. Soc. **93**, 541–551 (1959).
32. ETIENNE, J., "Opérateurs scalaires dans un espace linéaire semi-norme". Bull. Soc. Roy. Sci. Liège **325-6** (supplément), 419–429 (1963).
33. FELDZAMEN, A.N., "Semi-similarity invariants for spectral operators on Hilbert spaces", Trans. Am. Math. Soc. **100**, 277–324 (1961).
34. FIXMAN, U., "Problems in spectral operators," Pacific J. Math. **9**, 1029–1051 (1959).
35. FOGUEL, S.R., "Sums and products of commuting spectral operators", Ark. Mat. **3**, **5**, 449–461 (1958).
36. FOGUEL, S.R., "The relations between a spectral operator and its scalar part", Pacific J. Math. **8**, 51–65 (1958).
37. FOGUEL, S.R., "A perturbation theorem for scalar operators", Comm. Pure Appl. Math. **11**, 293–295 (1958).
38. FOGUEL, S.R., "Normal operators of finite multiplicity", Comm. Pure Appl. Math. **11**, 297–313 (1958).
39. FOIAȘ, C., "Une application des distributions vectorielles à la théorie spectrale", Bull. Sci. Math. **84**, 147–158 (1960).
40. FOIAȘ, C., "Relatia dintre operatorii spectrali si scalari generalizati", Com. Acad. R.P. Române **11**, 1427–1430 (1961).
41. FOIAȘ, C., "Spectral maximal spaces and decomposable operators in Banach spaces", Archiv der Math. **14**, 341–349 (1963).
42. FOIAȘ, C., "Asupra unei probleme de teoria spectrală", Stud. Cercet. Mat. **17**, 921–923 (1965).
43. FOIAȘ, C., "Sur les mesures spectrales qui interviennent dans la théorie ergodique", J. Math. Mech. **13**, 639–658 (1964).
44. GOHBERG, I.C. and KREIN, M.G., "Introduction to the theory of linear non-self-

adjoint operators", Izdat "Nauka" (Glavnaja-Redakcija Fiz-Mat. Lit., Moscow, 1965) (Russian).

45. Grothendieck, A., "Produits tensoriels topologiques et espaces nucléaires", Mémoires Am. Math. Soc., No. 16 (1955).
46. Halmos, P.R., "Commutators of operators", Am. J. Math. **76**, 191–198 (1954).
47. Hille, E. and Phillips, R., *Functional analysis and semi-groups* (Amer. Math. Soc. Colloq. Publ., Providence, 1957), Vol. 31.
48. Hirschman, I.I., Jr., "On multiplier transformations", Duke Math. J. **26**, 221–242 (1959).
49. Hörmander, L., *Linear partial differential operators* (Springer-Verlag, Berlin, 1963).
50. Iohvidov, I.S. and Krein, M.G., "Spectral theory in space with indefinite metric. I", Trudy Moscov. Mat. Obšč. **5**, 367–432 (1956) (Russian).
51. Ionescu Tulcea, C.T., "Spectral operators on locally convex spaces", Bull. Am. Math. Soc. **67**, 125–128 (1961).
52. Ionescu Tulcea, C.T., "Scalar dilations and scalar extension of operators on Banach spaces (I)", J. Math. Mech. **14**, 841–856 (1965).
53. Kakutani, S., "An example concerning uniform boundedness of spectral operators", Pacific J. Math. **4**, 363–372 (1954).
54. Kantorovitz, S., "On the characterization of spectral operators", Trans. Am. Math. Soc. **111**, 152–181 (1964).
55. Kantorovitz, S., "Classification of operators by means of their operational calculus", Trans. Am. Math. Soc. **115**, 194–224 (1965).
56. Kantorovitz, S., "A Jordan decomposition for operators in Banach spaces", Trans. Am. Math. Soc. **120**, 526–550 (1965).
57. Kaplanski, I., "Derivations of Banach algebras", *Seminars on Analytic Functions* (Institute for Advanced Study, Princeton), Vol.II, pp. 254–258.
58. Kesel'man, G.M., "On the single-valued analytic extension of the resolvent of a bounded linear operator", Usp. Mat. Nauk. **17**, 4 (106), 131–139 (1962).
59. Kleinecke, D.C., "On operator commutators", Proc. Am. Math. Soc. **8**, 535–536 (1957).
60. Krabbe, G.L., "Convolution operators that satisfy the spectral theorem", Math. Zeitschr. **70**, 446–462 (1959).
61. Krabbe, G.L., "A space of multipliers of type $L^p(-\infty, \infty)$", Pacif. J. Math. **9**, 729–737 (1959).
62. Krabbe, G.L., "Normal operators on the Banach space $L^p(-\infty, \infty)$, I", Can. J. Math. **13**, 505–518 (1961).
63. Krabbe, G.L., "Normal operators on the Banach space $L^p(-\infty, \infty)$, II. Unbounded operators", J. Math. Mech. **10**, 111–133 (1961).
64. Krabbe, G.L., "Spectral permanence of scalar operators", Pacific J. Math. **13**, 1289–1303 (1963).
65. Krabbe, G.L., "Stieltjes integration, spectral analysis and the locally convex algebra (BV)", Bull. Am. Math. Soc. **71**, 184–185 (1965).
66. Kurepa, S., "On n-th roots of normal operators", Math. Zeitschr. **78**, 285–292 (1962).

67. KUREPA, S., "Logarithms of spectral type operators", Glasnik Mat. Fiz. Astronom. Ser. II. Društvo Mat. Fiz. Hrvastke **18**, 1–2, 53–57 (1963).
68. LANGER, H., "Spektraltheorie linearer Operatoren in J-Räumen und einige Anwendungen auf die Schar $L(\lambda^2) = \lambda^2 I + \lambda B + C$", Habilitationschrift (Technische Univ. Dresden, 1964).
69. LEAF, G.K., "A spectral theory for a class of linear operators", Pacific J. Math. **13**, 141–155 (1963).
70. LEAF, G.K., "An approximation theorem for a class of operators", Proc. Am. Math. Soc. **16**, 991–995 (1965).
71. LJANCE, V.E., "A generalization of the concept of spectral measure", Mat. Sb. **61** (103), 80–120 (1963) (Russian).
72. LJANCE, V.E., "Unbounded operators commuting with the resolution of the identity", Ukrain. Mat. Z. **15**, 376–384 (1963) (Russian).
73. LJANCE, V.E., "On a differential operator with spectral singularities", I, Mat. Sb. **64** (106), 521–561 (1964); II, Mat. Sb. **65** (107), 47–103 (1964) (Russian).
74. LIVSIC, M.S., "On the spectral resolution of non-self-adjoint operators", Mat. Sb. **34** (76), 145–198 (1954) (Russian).
75. LOOMIS, L.H., *An introduction to abstract harmonic analysis* (D. Van Nostrand Comp., New York, 1953).
76. LORCH, E.R., "Bicontinuous linear transformation in certain vector spaces", Bull. Am. Math. Soc. **45**, 564–569 (1939).
77. LORCH, E.R., "The integral representation of weakly almost-periodic transformations in reflexive vector spaces", Trans. Am. Math. Soc. **49**, 18–40 (1941).
78. LUMER, G., "Spectral operators, hermitian operators and bounded groups", Acta Sci. Math. (Szeged) **25**, 75–85 (1964).
79. MACAEV, V.I., "A method of estimation for resilvents of non-self-adjoint operator", Dokl. Akad. Nauk. SSSR **154**, 1034–1037 (1964) (Russian).
80. MAEDA, F.-Y., "A characterisation of spectral operators on locally convex spaces", Math. Ann. **143**, 59–74 (1961).
81. MAEDA, F.-Y., "Generalized spectral operators on locally convex spaces", Pacific J. Math. **13**, 177–192 (1963).
82. MAEDA, F.-Y., "Functions of generalized scalar operators", J. Sci. Hiroshima Univ. Ser. A.-I. Math. **26**, 71–76 (1962).
83. MAEDA, F.-Y., "On spectral representations of generalized spectral operators", J. Sci. Hiroshima Univ. Ser. A.-I, Math. **27**, 137–149 (1963).
84. MAEDA, F.-Y., "Generalized unitary operators", Bull. Am. Math. Soc. **71**, 631–633 (1965).
85. MAEDA, F.-Y., "Generalized scalar operators whose spectra are contained in a Jordan curve", Illinois J. Math. (to be published).
86. MARCENKO, V.A. and ROFE–BEKETOV, F.S., "Expansion in characterisic functions of non-self-adjoint singular differential operators", Dokl. Akad. Nauk. SSSR **120**, 963–966 (1958) (Russian).
87. MCCARTHY C.A., "The nilpotent part of a spectral operator", Pacific J. Math. **9**, 1223–1231 (1959).

88. McCarthy, C.A., "Commuting Boolean algebras of projections", Pacific J. Math. **11**, 295–307 (1961).

89. McGarvey, D., "Operators commuting translation by one. I. Representations theorems", J. Math. Anal. Appl. **4**, 366–410 (1962).

90. Moyal, J.E., "The theory of spectral and scalar algebras" (to be published).

91. Naimark, M.A., *Normed rings* (Nordhoff, Groningen, 1959).

92. Naimark, M.A., "On commuting unitary operators in spaces with indefinite metric", Acta Sci. Math. **24** 177–190 (1963).

93. Naimark, M.A., "Kommutative symmetrische Operatorenalgebren in Pontryaginschen Räumen Π_k." Math. Annalen **162**, 147–171 (1965).

94. Paley, R. and Wiener, N., *Fourier transforms in the complex domain* (New York, 1934).

95. Pedersen, N.W., "The resolutions of the identity for sums and products of commuting spectral operators", Math. Scand. **11**, 123–130 (1962).

96. Putnam, C.R., "On the spectra of commutators", Proc. Amer. Math. Soc. **5**, 929–931 (1954).

97. Ringrose, J.R., "On well-bounded operators, I", J. Austral. Math. Soc. **1**, 334–343 (1960).

98. Ringrose, J.R., "Super diagonal forms for compact linear operators", Proc. London Math. Soc. **12**, 367–384 (1962).

99. Ringrose, J.R., "On the triangular representation of integral operators", Proc. London Math. Soc. **12**, 385–399 (1962).

100. Ringrose, J.R., "On well-bounded operators, II", Proc. London Math. Soc. **13**, 613–638 (1963).

101. Rofe-Beketov, F.S., "Expansion in eigenfunctions of infinite systems of differential equations in the non-self-adjoint and self-adjoint cases", Mat. Sb. **51** (93), 293–342 (1960) (Russian).

102. Rosemblum, M., "On a theorem of Fuglede and Putnam", J. London Math. Soc. **33**, 376–377 (1958).

103. Rudin, W., *Fourier analysis on groups* (New York, 1962).

104. Sahnovič, L.A., "The reduction of non-self-adjoint operators to triangular form", Izv. Vysš. Ucebn. Zaved. Matematica **1** (8), 180–186 (1959) (Russian).

105. Sahnovič, L.A., "A study of the 'triangular form' of non-self-adjoint operators", Izv. Vysš. Ucebn. Zaved. Matematica **4** (11), 141–149 (1959) (Russian).

106. Schaefer, H.H., "A new class of spectral operators", Bull. Am. Math. Soc. **67**, 154–155 (1961).

107. Schaefer, H.H., "Spectral measures in locally convex algebras", Acta Math. **107**, 125–173 (1962).

108. Schaefer, H.H. and Walsh, B.J., "Spectral operators in spaces of distributions", Bull. Am. Math. Soc. **68**, 509–511 (1962).

109. Schwartz, J.T., "Perturbation of spectral operators and applications, I", Pacific J. Math. **4**, 415–458 (1954).

110. Schwartz, J.T., "Two perturbation formulae", Comm. Pure Appl. Math. **8**, 371–376 (1955).

111. SCHWARTZ, J. T., "Some non-self-adjoint operators", Comm. Pure Appl. Math. **13**, 609–639 (1960).
112. SCHWARTZ, J. T., "Subdiagonalization of operators in Hilbert space with compact imaginary part", Comm. Pure Appl. Math. **15**, 159–172 (1962).
113. SCHWARTZ, L., "Théorie des distributions à valeurs vectorielles, I", Ann. Inst. Fourier (Grenoble) **7**, 1–141 (1957).
114. SIMPSON, J. E., "Nilpotency and spectral operators", Pacific J. Math. **14**, 665–672 (1964).
115. SINE, R. C., "Spectral decomposition of class of operators", Pacific J. Math. **14**, 333–362 (1964).
116. SMART, D. R., "Conditionally convergent expansions", J. Austral. Math. Soc. **1**, 319–333 (1960).
117. STAMPFLI, J. G., "Roots of spectral operators", Proc. Am. Math. Soc. **13**, 796–798 (1962).
118. SZ.-NAGY, B. and FOIAŞ, C., "Sur les contractions de l'espace de Hilbert, VIII. Fonctions caractéristiques. Modèles fonctionnels", Acta Sci. Math. (Szeged) **25**, 38–71 (1964).
119. SZ.-NAGY, B. and FOIAŞ, C., "Quasi-similitude des opérateurs et sous-espaces invariants", C.R. Acad. Sci. Paris **261**, 3938–3940 (1965).
120. SZ.-NAGY, B. and FOIAŞ, C., "Décomposition spectrale des contractions presque unitaires", C.R. Acad. Sci. Paris **262**, 440–442 (1966).
121. TILLMANN, H. G., "Vector-valued distributions and the spectral theorem for self-adjoint operators in Hilbert spaces", Bull. Am. Math. Soc. **69**, 67–71 (1963).
122. TILLMANN, H. G., "Eine Erweiterung des Funktionalkalkuls für lineare Operatoren", Math. Ann. **151**, 424–430 (1963).
123. WAELBROECK, L., "Le calcul symbolique lié à la croissance de la resolvante", Rend. Sem. Math. Univ. Milano **34**, 51–72 (1964).
124. WALSH, B. J., "Structure of spectral measures on locally convex spaces", Trans. Am. Math. Soc. **120** 295–326 (1965).
125. WALSH, J. L., *Interpolation and approximation by rational functions in the complex domain* (Amer. Math. Soc. Colloq. Publ., Providence, 1960), Second Edition, Vol. 20.
126. VASILESCU, F. H., "Spectral algebras of a generalized scalar operator", Rev. Roum. Math. Pures Appl. **10**, 1241–1243 (1966).
127. WERMER, J., "The existence of invariant subspaces", Duke Math. J. **19**, 615–622 (1952).
128. WERMER, J., "On a class of normed rings", Ark. Mat. **2**, **6**, 537–551 (1954).
129. WERMER, J., "Commuting spectral measures on Hilbert spaces", Pacific J. Math. **4**, 355–361 (1954).
130. WOLF, F., "Operators in Banach space which admit a generalized spectral decomposition", Nederl. Akad. Wetensk. Indag. Math. **19**, 302–311 (1957).
131. BERNSTEIN, A. R. and ROBINSON, A., "Solution of an invariant subspace problem of K. T. Smith and P. R. Halmos", Pacific J. Math. **16**, 421–432 (1966).
132. HALMOS, P. R., "Invariant subspaces of polynomially compact operators", Pacific J. Math. **16**, 433–438 (1966).

133. RIESZ, F. and SZ.-NAGY B., *Leçon d'analyse fonctionnelle* (Akadémiai Kiado, Budapest, 1952).
134. SIROKOV, F.V., "Proof of a conjecture of Kaplanski", Uspehi. Mat. Nauk. **11**, 4 (70), 167–168 (1956).
135. SZ.-NAGY, B., "On uniformly bounded linear transformations in Hilbert space", Acta Sci. Math. (Szeged) **11**, 152–157 (1947).
136. LJUBIC, YU.I. and MATZAEV, V.I., "On the spectral theory of linear operators in Banach space", Dokl. Akad. Nauk SSSR **131**, 21–23 (1960) (Russian).
137. LJUBIC, YU.I. and MATZAEV, V.I., "On operators with decomposable spectrum", Mat. Sbornik **56** (98), 433–468 (1962) (Russian).
138. COLOJOARĂ, I. and FOIAŞ, C., "The Riesz-Dunford functional calculus with decomposable operators", Rev. Roumaine Math. Pures Appl. **12**, 627–641 (1967).
139. VASILESCU, P.H., "On an asymptotic behaviour of operators", Rev. Roumaine Math. Pures Appl. **12**, 353–358 (1967).
140. APOSTOL, C., "Remarks on the perturbation and a topology of operators", J. Funct. Anal. (to be published).
141. VASILESCU, P.H., "Spectral distance of two operators", Rev. Roumaine Math. Pures Appl. **12**, 733–736 (1967).
142. VASILESCU, P.H., "Asymptotic properties of the commutators of decomposable operators", J. Math. Anal. App. (to be published).
143. APOSTOL, C., "Roots of decomposable operator-valued analytic functions", Rev. Roumaine Math. Pures Appl. **13**, 433 438 (1968).
144. APOSTOL, C., "Sur les opérateurs scalaires généralisés", Bull. Sci. Math. **91**, 57–61 (1967).
145. APOSTOL, C., "Theorie spectrală şi calcul functional", Studii Cercetari. Mat. **20**, 635-668 (1968).
146. COLOJOARĂ, I. and FOIAŞ, C., "Spectral distribution of finite multiplicity", Rev. Roumaine Mat. Pures Appl. **12**, 1039–1042 (1967).
147. APOSTOL, C., "Spectral decompositions and functional calculus", Revue Roumaine Math. Pures Appl. (to be published).
148. APOSTOL, C., "A theorem on invariant subspaces", Bull. Acad. Polon. Sci. **16**, 181 183 (1968).
149. B. SZ.-NAGY and FOIAŞ, C., "Echelles continues de sous-espaces invariants", Acta Sci. Math. (Szeged) **28**, 213–220 (1967).

Index

Appendix Added in Proof

a. If T does not have the single-valued extension property, then, defining $\sigma_T(x)$ as in 1.1.1, it may occur that $\sigma_T(x) = \emptyset$ and $\neq 0$. This is for instance the case for the operator considered in Example 1.1.7 (see Ref.138).

b. For $T_1, T_2 \in \mathbf{B}(\mathscr{X})$, set

$$\varrho\,(T_1, T_2) = \overline{\lim_{n\to\infty}}\, \|(T_1 - T_2)^{[n]}\|^{1/n}.$$

Then, if $\varrho\,(T_n, T) \to 0$ (where $T, T_n \in \mathbf{B}(\mathscr{X})$, $n = 1, 2, \ldots$) and if the T_n have the single-valued extension property, T has also this property (see Ref. 139); moreover, if the T_n are decomposable and if $\varrho\,(T, T_n) \to 0$, then T is also decomposable (see Ref. 140). Finally, if T_1, T_2 are decomposable,

$$\varrho\,(T_1, T_2) = \sup_{\substack{x\in\mathscr{X}\\ x\neq 0}}\ \sup_{\lambda\in\sigma_{T_1}(x)}\ \inf_{\mu\in\sigma_{T_2}(x)} |\lambda - \mu| \quad \text{(see Ref. 141)}.$$

Using this formula, Vasilescu[141] constructed two decomposable operators T_1, T_2 such that $\varrho\,(T_1, T_2) \neq \varrho\,(T_2, T_1)$.

c. If $T_1 \overset{a}{\sim} T_2$, then for every analytic function $f: G \to C$, where $G\,[\supset \sigma(T_1) = \sigma(T_2)]$ is open, we have

$$f(T_2) = \sum_{n=0}^{\infty} \frac{(T_2 - T_1)^{[n]}}{n!} f^{(n)}(T_1) = \sum_{n=0}^{\infty} (-1)^n f^{(n)}(T_2)\, \frac{(T_1 - T_2)^{[n]}}{n!}.$$

This perturbation formula is due to C. Apostol[140] and reduces to a formula by J. Schwartz[110] if $T_1T_2 = T_2T_1$.

d. If $S \in \mathbf{B}(\mathscr{X})$ and $T \in \mathbf{B}(\mathscr{Y})$ are decomposable, then the commutator $C\,(T, S)$ has the single-valued extension property. One can show that $\sigma_{C(T,S)}(A)$ is, for an operator $A \in \mathbf{B}\,(\mathscr{X}, \mathscr{Y})$, the smallest compact set K such that

$$A\mathscr{X}_S\,(F) \subset \mathscr{Y}_T\,(F + K) \text{ for all closed } F \subset C,$$

where
$$F + K = \{\lambda + \mu \mid \lambda \in F, \mu \in K\}.$$

This constitutes the definitive generalization of § 2.2; for an intermediate generalization see Ref. 142.

e. C. Apostol proved (see Ref. 143) the following important complement to 2.1.10–2.1.12: Let f be as in Corollary 1.1.11, nonconstant on any component of G. Then if $f(T)$ is decomposable, so is T.

f. Decomposable operators admit a characterization very similar to that of the spectral operators in Dunford's sense (see the Appendix to the Introduction). Indeed let us say that $T \in \mathbf{B}(\mathscr{X})$ admits a spectral decomposition if, for every closed set $F \subset C$, there corresponds a (linear closed) subspace $\mathscr{X}(F)$ of $\mathscr{X}$ such that

$$\mathscr{X}(F_1 \cap F_2) = \mathscr{X}(F_1) \cap \mathscr{X}(F_2), \tag{1}$$

$$\mathscr{X} = \mathscr{X}(F_1) + \cdots + \mathscr{X}(F_n) \quad \text{if} \quad C = \sum_{j=1}^{n} \operatorname{Int} F_j, \tag{2}$$

$$\mathscr{X}(\varnothing) = \{0\}, \qquad \mathscr{X}(C) = \mathscr{X}, \tag{3}$$

and

$$T\mathscr{X}(F) \subset \mathscr{X}(F), \tag{i}$$

$$\sigma(T \mid \mathscr{X}(F)) \subset F. \tag{ii}$$

It is obvious that if T is decomposable, then T has a spectral decomposition in the above sense.

C. Apostol conjectured and C. Foiaş proved that if T has a such spectral decomposition, then T is decomposable. Moreover,

$$\mathscr{X}_T(F) = \bigcap_{\substack{G \supset F \\ G \text{ open}}} \mathscr{X}(\overline{G}).$$

g. We recall that, as it follows from 4.4.6, the conditions $\mathbf{V}_{\bar\lambda}\mathbf{U}_\lambda = \mathbf{U}_\lambda\mathbf{V}_{\bar\lambda}$ and $(\mathbf{V}_{\bar\lambda} - \mathbf{U}_{\bar\lambda})^{[n]} = 0 = (\mathbf{U}_{\bar\lambda} - \mathbf{V}_{\bar\lambda})^{[n]}$ are necessary for $\mathbf{V}$ to be another spectral destribution of $S = \mathbf{U}_\lambda$. As it is shown in Ref. 144, these conditions are also sufficient for the existence of $\mathbf{V}$. Moreover, C. Apostol[145] has given a formula relating $\mathbf{V}$ and $\mathbf{U}$.

h. In connection with § 4.2, we say that a spectral distribution $\mathbf{U}$ is of multiplicity 1 if every quasinilpotent operator Q commuting with $\mathbf{U}_\varphi$ $(\varphi \in C^\infty)$ is 0. The conclusions of Theorem 4.2.6 hold for $S = \mathbf{U}_\lambda$ if we replace the condition that S be of multiplicity 1 (see Definition 4.2.5) by the weaker condition that $\mathbf{U}$ be of multiplicity 1 (see Ref. 146).

i. In connection with Secs. 7.1–7.4 of Chap. 4 we want to mention recent results of C. Apostol (see Refs. 143 and 147), of which two illustrations follow:

(i) If $f: G \to C$ is analytic in $G \supset \sigma(T)$, $f'(\lambda) \neq 0$ for $\lambda \in \sigma(T)$, and if $f(T)$ is a (complete) regular generalized (spectral) scalar operator, so is also T.

(ii) If $f(T)$ is a scalar operator and the condition $f'(\lambda) \neq 0$ for $\lambda \in \sigma(T)$ is replaced by the weaker condition that f be nonconstant on the components of G, then T is an $\mathfrak{A}$-scalar operator.

j. In his one-hour address to the International Congress of Mathematicians (held in Moscow, 1966), M. G. Krein announced, along with many others, some new facts which are related to §§ 2, 3 and 5 of Chap. 5, namely:

(i) The operators considered in Theorem 5.3.2 are S-operators in the Ljubic-Mačaev's sense.

(ii) If $T \in \mathbf{B}(\mathscr{H})$, where $\mathscr{H}$ is a Hilbert space, and if $\sigma(T) \subset C_1$ and $1 - T^*T$ belongs to the Mačaev's ideal S_ω of compact operators $\left[K \in S_\omega\right.$ if for $|K| = (K^*K)^{1/2}$ we have $\left.\sum_{n=1}^{\infty} \mu_n(|K|)/n < \infty\right]$, then T verifies the Beurling condition in Theorem 5.3.2. This last result constitutes a great improvement with respect to our § 5.5 since S_ω is much richer than $\bigcup_{0<p<\infty} \mathscr{C}_p$.

k. Theorem 5.6.13 of J. Feldman was generalized to Banach spaces by C. Apostol[148] who also gave a slight generalization of this fact using a very simple argument which reduces the new theorem to the classical one of Aronszajn-Smith.[2]

The problem of the existence of nontrivial invariant subspaces for operators in Hilbert space has not yet been solved, so that we don't know yet if every operator in a Hilbert space has the property (Triang$_0$) (see Definition 5.6.10). In § 5.6 one of the main purposes was to obtain operators having the property (Triang$_2$) (see Definition 5.6.5), by adding orthogonally normal parts to the operators having (Triang$_0$). However this last restriction is not necessary. Indeed, as it was proved by B. Sz.-Nagy and C. Foiaş,[149] for every operator T of a Hilbert space there exists a normal operator N such that $T \oplus N$ has the property (Triang$_2$).

l. A part of problem (g) in § 6.5 was recently solved by C. Apostol,[147] who proved the following facts: (i) The application

$$f \to \int_M f(A(m))\, d\mathbf{E}(m), \qquad [f \in C^\infty(C)]$$

does not yielded always a spectral distribution. (ii) If $M = C$ and $A(m)$ is analytic in m, then A is always an $\mathfrak{A}$-scalar operator for a suitable topologically admissible algebra; under more restrictive conditions one can already infer that A is a generalized scalar operator.